Z-80 Microprocessor

Programming & Interfacing

Book 1

by
**Elizabeth A. Nichols, Joseph C. Nichols,
and Peter R. Rony**

Howard W. Sams & Co., Inc.
4300 WEST 62ND ST. INDIANAPOLIS, INDIANA 46268 USA

International Standard Book Number: 0-672-21609-4
Library of Congress Catalog Card Number: 79-63822

Printed in the United States of America.

Preface

The microelectronics revolution is here, and gaining momentum. It all began 30 years ago with the development of the transistor. The transistor, a physically small, low-power amplifier, replaced the large, power-hungry vacuum tubes of the first generation computers. Due to a natural synergism between transistors and digital logic, their small size and low cost, transistors have become the basic building blocks for computer circuits. Transistors combine to form gates; gates combine to form flip flops, counters, adders, and other logic functions; and these, in turn, combine to form the memory, control, arithmetic, and logic units which make up the central processing unit (cpu) of a computer. Thus, the number of transistors in a logic circuit has become a reasonable measure of its functional complexity. In 1959, the first integrated circuits consisting of small groups of planar transistors were developed on thin wafers of silicon or germanium. This began the era of Small Scale Integration (SSI) in which 12 or fewer gates could be incorporated into a single integrated circuit (IC). Since 1959, the number of transistors in advanced ICs has been at least doubling every year. Today, circuits containing 262,144 elements are available and the technology is still far from its theoretical limits. The Z-80 CPU and support chips, introduced by Zilog in 1976, represents the state-of-the-art in 8-bit microprocessors. Zilog is currently developing a successor to the Z-80 line, the Z-8000 series of cpu and support chips. However, the Z-8000 will be a 16-bit cpu with computational capacity comparable to mid-range mini-computers, a significant jump in capability. And this is only the beginning. The real revolution will be manifest in the exponential proliferation of products and services dependent on microelectronics.

This book is one of two volumes on Z-80 microprocessor programming and interfacing. Book 1 is on Z-80 software—assembly and machine language programming. Book 2 covers interfacing digital circuits with the Z-80 CPU, PIO, and CTC chips. These books are laboratory oriented texts that are designed to give an integrated approach to microcomputer programming and interfacing. The strong emphasis is on learning through experimentation. Each topic introduced is reinforced with laboratory work that shows not only how ideas succeed, but also where they fail, and what the pitfalls are.

Book 1 requires no background in computer science, programming, or digital electronics. Book 2 however, assumes familiarity with the topics covered in Book 1. In both books, topics are presented in the order that the authors feel is most conducive to learning in a self-study environment. Answers are provided for all the exercises, and every attempt is made to anticipate questions and logical extensions to the experiments.

To enhance the laboratory orientation in the books, the experiments use a sophisticated Z-80–based single-board microcomputer manufactured by SGS-ATES, called the Nanocomputer. The Nanocomputer is an excellent educational computer because it is simple for a novice to use, but incorporates enough options, flexibility, expandability, and sophistication to keep the interest of the most experienced user. For more information on the Nanocomputer, contact SGS-ATES Semiconductor Corp., 240 Bear Hill Road, Waltham, MA 02154.

The authors are indebted to many members of the staff at SGS-ATES in Milano, Italy: R. Baldoni, A. Cattania, B. Facchi, F. Luraschi, C. Wallace, and especially A. Watts whose many ideas and technical expertise on the Nanocomputer tremendously improved these books. Also we wish to thank C. Edson and U. Broggi of SGS-ATES in the USA who greatly expedited progress by acting as liasons between the US and Italian efforts on this project. Finally, much credit is due to J. Titus and D. Larsen of the Blacksburg Group for their efforts in coordinating with Howard W. Sams & Co., Inc. to bring about the publication of these books.

ELIZABETH A. NICHOLS
JOSEPH C. NICHOLS
PETER R. RONY

Contents

CHAPTER 1

DIGITAL CODES 9
Objectives — Languages, Communications, and Information — Binary Coding — Bit — Digital Codes — Binary Code — Hexadecimal (HEX) Code — A Note on Notation — Demonstrations — Demonstration No. 1 — Review

CHAPTER 2

AN INTRODUCTION TO MICROCOMPUTER PROGRAMMING . . 21
Objectives — What Is a Computer? — What Is a Microcomputer? — What Is a Computer Program? — Instructions — Mnemonics — Instructions — Machine Language — A Simple Program — Memory — Memory Address — Range of Memory Locations — Hi and Lo Memory Addresses — Demonstration No. 1 — Review

CHAPTER 3

SOME Z-80 MICROPROCESSOR CPU INSTRUCTIONS 33
Objectives — What Is a Computer Program? — Instructions and Operations — Multibyte Instructions — Types of Information Stored in Memory — Operation Code — Data Byte — Device Code — Hi and Lo Address Bytes — Displacement Byte — What Is a Register? — General-Purpose Registers — Accumulator — Some Z-80 Instructions — Instruction Byte Nomenclature — Review

CHAPTER 4

THE NANOCOMPUTER (NBZ80) AND THE SUPER NANO-COMPUTER (NBZ80S) 47
Objectives — The Nanocomputer — Central Processing Unit (CPU) — Rules for Setting up Experiments — Experiment Instructions Format — A Word of Caution — Introduction to the Experiments — Experiment No. 1 — Experiment No. 2 — Experiment No. 3 — Experiment No. 4 — Experiment No. 5

CHAPTER 5

SOME SIMPLE Z-80 MICROCOMPUTER PROGRAMS 79
Objectives — Review of Several Z-80 Instructions — Programming
Languages and Listings — Assembly Language Programming — Introduction to the Experiments — Experiment No. 1 — Experiment
No. 2 — Experiment No. 3 — Experiment No. 4 — Experiment No.
5 — Review

CHAPTER 6

REGISTERS, MEMORY, AND DATA TRANSFER 99
Objectives — Z-80 Instruction Set — Z-80 Addressing Modes — Single Register Load Instructions: Register Addressing Mode LD d,s —
Load Immediate to Register — Register Indirect Load With Accumulator LD A, (rp); LD (rp), A — Load Immediate Extended Pair
LD rp <B3><B2> — Load Extended Pair LD rp, (addr); LD
(addr), rp — Increment Register — Decrement Register — Jump
if not Zero JP NZ, <B3><B2> — Block Data Transfers LDD,
LDI, LDDR, LDIR — Introduction to the Experiments — Experiment No. 1 — Experiment No. 2 — Experiment No. 3 — Experiment No. 4 — Experiment No. 5 — Experiment No. 6

CHAPTER 7

Z-80 ADDRESSING MODES 139
Objectives — What Is an Addressing Mode? — Two's Complement
Binary Representation — Two's Complement Addition and Subtraction — The Z-80 Address Modes — Register Addressing — Immediate Addressing — Immediate Extended Addressing — Register Indirect Addressing — Extended Addressing — Modified Page Zero
Addressing — Implied Addressing — Bit Addressing — Indexed
Addressing — Relative Addressing — The Instruction Group Tables
— The 16-Bit Load Group — Block Transfer and Exchanges — Introduction to the Experiments and Exercises — Review — Experiment No. 1 — Experiment No. 2 — Experiment No. 3

CHAPTER 8

JUMPS, CALLS, AND RETURNS 175
Objectives — Program Control Transfers — Unconditional JUMP
Instructions — Flags and Conditional Jumps — Calls and Returns
— Introduction to the Experiments — Experiment No. 1 — Experiment No. 2 — Experiment No. 3 — Experiment No. 4 — Experiment No. 5

CHAPTER 9

LOGICAL INSTRUCTIONS 205
What Is a Logical Instruction? — Boolean Algebra — Multibit Operations — NOT — De Morgan's Theorem — Z-80 Logical Instruction Group — Complement Accumulator: CPL — AND With Accumulator: AND — Exclusive-OR With Accumulator: XOR — OR With
Accumulator: OR — Logical Instructions and External Device Monitoring — Introduction to the Experiments — Experiment No. 1 —
Experiment No. 2 — Review

CHAPTER 10

Bit Manipulation, ROTATE and SHIFT Instructions . . 223
   Objectives — Bit, Set, Test and Reset Process — ROTATE and
   SHIFT Instruction Group — ROTATE Instructions — SHIFT In-
   structions — Introduction to the Experiments — Experiment No. 1
   — Experiment No. 2 — Experiment No. 3

CHAPTER 11

Arithmetic and Block Search Instruction 243
   Objectives — 8-Bit Arithmetic Group — DAA Instruction — 16-Bit
   Arithmetic Instructions — CP and Block Search Instructions: CPI,
   CPD, CPIR, and CPDR — Introduction to the Experiments —
   Experiment No. 1 — Experiment No. 2 — Experiment No. 3 —
   Experiment No. 4

APPENDIX A

Summary of Z-80 Op Codes and Execution Times . . . 267

APPENDIX B

Z-80 CPU Instructions Sorted by Mnemonics 279

APPENDIX C

Z-80 CPU Instructions Sorted by Op Code 283

APPENDIX D

Computation of Execution Times 287

APPENDIX E

Precautions While Handling MOS Devices 291

APPENDIX F

Master Symbol Table 293

APPENDIX G

References 295

Index 297

CHAPTER 1

Digital Codes

INTRODUCTION

Before you begin to program your microcomputer, it is necessary that you understand how to convert 8-bit binary numbers into hexadecimal code, and vice versa, as well as know certain basic facts about digital codes.

OBJECTIVES

At the completion of this chapter, you will be able to do the following:

- Discuss what is meant by the term *communication*.
- Define *bit*.
- Define *binary code*.
- Define *digital code*.
- Define *hexadecimal code*.
- Convert an 8-bit binary number into a two-digit hexadecimal number.
- Convert a two-digit hexadecimal number into a binary number.
- Distinguish between the binary, hexadecimal, and decimal counting systems.
- List several different digital codes.
- List several different two-state devices.
- Provide one example where the quantity, bits per second, is a measure of information flow.

LANGUAGES, COMMUNICATIONS, AND INFORMATION

One of the most important characteristics that any biological organism (higher order animals) possesses is the ability to communicate with other organisms of the same species. The ability to communicate, which gives many animal organisms a definite survival advantage—in the Darwinian sense of the term—is found in most multicellular creatures, starting with insects and progressing to man. With insects, there exist several modes of communication, including the dance of the bee and forms of chemical communication through remarkable chemical agents called *pheromones*. Man can communicate with the aid of his five senses, as illustrated by handicapped individuals who have lost one or more of their senses but are, nevertheless, highly communicative with those remaining.

Assuming that an individual wishes to communicate with another through the sense of hearing and the use of speech, it is clear that there must be some general agreement concerning how a spoken sound will be interpreted by the individual who hears it. Over the centuries, different regions around the world have each developed their own consensus regarding the meaning of specific sounds and their transcription onto paper. We call such a consensus a *language* or, perhaps, a *foreign language*. Thousands of different languages exist, although only a relatively modest number of them are in widespread use. The popularity of a specific language may wax and wane over the course of several hundred years. Latin, once a dominant language in Europe, is now considered to be a "dead" language, however, it clearly has influenced most of the European languages in very profound ways.

Communication can be defined as the imparting, conveying, or exchanging of ideas, knowledge, information, etc. (whether by speech, writing, or signs).[1]* It is one of the most important and characteristic activities of mankind. As pointed out by James Martin in his excellent book, *Telecommunications and the Computer,*[3] the capacity of major telecommunication links, as measured by a quantity called *bits per second,* has paralleled the advance of civilization over the past one hundred years. The capacity of such links has changed from a rate of 1 bit/second in 1840 to 50,000,000 bits/second in 1970, i.e., a doubling every 5.08 years. Martin has also pointed out that the sum total of human knowledge changed very slowly prior to the relatively recent beginnings of scientific thought. By 1800, it has been estimated that the sum total was doubling every 50 years; by 1950, doubling every 10 years; and that by 1970, it will be doubling every 5 years.

A *language,* which can be defined as the whole body of words and of methods of combination of words used by a nation, people, or race,[1] is just one form of communication. Egyptian hieroglyphics, choreographic scores, mathematical symbols and equations, Ameri-

---

* See Appendix G for all references.

can Indian smoke signals, the sign language employed by the deaf, and the Morse code are other forms of communication used by man.

BINARY CODING

The "information explosion" would have inundated mankind, at least in the more advanced countries, had it not been for the use of *Two-State Coding* to represent all kinds of information, such as the ten decimal numerals (0 through 9), the twenty-six letters of the English alphabet (A through Z), operations, symbols, motions, and the like. We call such two-state coding *Off-On* or *binary coding.* Binary coding can be represented or manifested by any type of two-state device, such as an on or off light, an open or closed switch, a punched or nonpunched computer card, a "north" or "south" magnetized magnetic core or region of magnetic tape or disc; two different voltage levels, two different current levels, two different frequencies; the words YES and NO; or the abstract symbols 0 (off) and 1 (on). The importance of binary coding resides in the fact that it is possible to construct devices that will change state very quickly, in times as fast as 5 nanoseconds (0.000000005 second). Such a device could, in principle, manipulate, transmit, or receive information at the rate of 200 million bits per second. Thirty-two such devices, operating simultaneously, could manipulate 6.4 billion bits per second. This is the basic capability that has permitted society to store, manipulate, and communicate enormous quantities of information.

BIT

The elementary unit of information is called the *bit,* which is an abbreviation for **BI**nary digi**T**. You can think of a bit as being a light bulb that can be lit (on) or unlit (off) at any given time. Thus, a bit can be pictured as a light bulb that is ON or a light bulb that is OFF. Rather than drawing pictures of light bulbs, we can represent each bulb that is in the lit state by the symbol 1 and each bulb in the unlit state by the symbol 0.

So, a bit is equal to one binary decision, or the designation of one of two possible and equally likely values or states (such as 0 or 1).

Information is typically represented by a series of bits. Thus,

1 0 0 0

represents decimal 8 in binary code. The series of bits,

1 1 0 0 0 0 0 1

represents the letter A in 8-bit ASCII code. We shall discuss these two codes shortly.

DIGITAL CODES

A *digital code* is defined as a system of symbols that represent data values and make up a special language that a computer or a digital circuit can understand and use.[3] Digital codes can be considered to be the digital "languages" that permit information to be stored, manipulated, and communicated. Just as there are numerous spoken languages, there also exists a variety of digital codes. Such codes can be subdivided into several important categories:

Category 1. Codes employed by electronic circuitry to perform various digital operations. Example: binary code.

Category 2. Codes employed to convert the decimal numbers 0 through 9 into digital form. Examples: binary code, binary coded decimal (bcd), and gray code.

Category 3. Codes employed to convert decimal numbers, the 26-letter English alphabet, symbols, and operations into digital form. Examples: ASCII code, EBCDIC code, and Baudot code.

Category 4. Instruction codes employed by large computers, minicomputers, and microcomputers that cause the computers to perform a prescribed sequence of operations. Examples: IBM 370 instruction code, PDP 8/E instruction code, Z-80 instruction code.

In this series of modules, we shall pay particular attention to four codes: binary code, binary coded decimal (bcd), ASCII code, and the instruction code for the Z-80 microprocessor chip.

BINARY CODE

The simplest digital code is a two-state, or binary, code that consists of a 0 (off) and a 1 (on) state. We call these two states *logic 0* and *logic 1*. In binary code, decimal 0 is represented by a logic 0 and decimal 1 by a logic 1. This should be quite clear. How, on the other hand, are higher decimal numbers, such as 3, 17, 568, etc., represented using binary code? The answer is that we use a series of bits to build a *binary counting system* that is formed on a *base,* or *radix,* of two. For example, the binary number 11101_2, where the subscript (2) represents the binary counting system, is equivalent to

$$11101_{(2)} = (1 \times 2^{**}4) + (1 \times 2^{**}3) + (1 \times 2^{**}2) + (0 \times 2^{**}1) + (1 \times 2^{**}0) = 29_{(10)}$$

where you should keep in mind that $A^{**}B$ is equivalent to A^B. Therefore,

$$2^{**}4 = 16 \text{ in decimal notation} = 16_{10}$$
$$2^{**}3 = 8 \text{ in decimal notation} = 8_{10}$$
$$2^{**}2 = 4 \text{ in decimal notation} = 4_{10}$$

$$2^{**}1 = 2 \text{ in decimal notation} = 2_{10}$$
$$2^{**}0 = 1 \text{ in decimal notation} = 1_{10}$$

Therefore,

$$11101 (2) = 16 (10) + 8 (10) + 4 (10) + 0 + 1 (10) = 29 (10)$$

where the subscript (10) associated with these numbers represents the decimal counting system, a system that is formed on a base, or radix, of 10. A brief table follows that allows you to convert simple decimal numbers into binary numbers.

Decimal Number	Binary Number
0	0000
1	0001
2	0010
3	0011
4	0100
5	0101
6	0110
7	0111
8	1000
9	1001
10	1010
11	1011
12	1100
13	1101
14	1110
15	1111
16	10000

Thus, a series of four binary digits, or bits, can represent any of sixteen different decimal numbers ranging from zero to fifteen. Decimal numbers larger than fifteen require additional bits, as shown in the following table:

Decimal Number	Binary Number
0	0
1	1
2	10
3	11
4	100
7	111
8	1000
15	1111
16	10000
31	11111
32	100000
63	111111
64	1000000
127	1111111
128	10000000
255	11111111
256	100000000

511	111111111
512	1000000000
1023	1111111111
1024	10000000000
2047	11111111111
2048	100000000000
4095	111111111111
4096	1000000000000
8191	1111111111111
8192	10000000000000
16,383	11111111111111
16,384	100000000000000
32,767	111111111111111
32,768	1000000000000000
65,535	1111111111111111

Therefore, an 8-bit binary number can encode two hundred and fifty-six different decimal numbers, ranging from 0 to 255_{10}, or two hundred and fifty-six different "things," no matter what they may be (instructions, devices, pulses, etc.). The Z-80 is a microprocessor chip that has a 16-bit memory address and an 8-bit I/O device word. This means that it can directly address 65,536 different memory locations and can generate at least 256 different I/O pulses or device addresses.

HEXADECIMAL (HEX) CODE

It can be difficult to remember binary numbers that contain many bits. For example, can you remember the following 8-bit binary number,

10011101

after having looked at it for only one second? Quick, cover it up or look away! Consider also the problem of remembering a list of such 8-bit numbers:

11011010
11100101
01101001
10101011

You probably will conclude that there must be a better way to remember 8-bit binary numbers. We are using 8-bit numbers here because you will encounter them frequently when you begin to program the 8-bit Z-80 microcomputer.

One approach to remembering multi-bit binary numbers is the use of *hexadecimal code*. The term *hex* is simply an abbreviation for the word *hexadecimal*. Hexadecimal code refers to the *hexadecimal counting system,* a system that is formed on a base, or radix, of 16. The hexadecimal counting system consists of sixteen different symbols: 0,1,2,3,4,5,6,7,8,9,A,B,C,D,E, and F. Just as we did with decimal numbers, it is possible to convert hexadecimal numbers into binary numbers:

Decimal Number	Hex Number	Binary Number	
0	0		0000
1	1		0001
2	2		0010
3	3		0011
4	4		0100
5	5		0101
6	6		0110
7	7		0111
8	8		1000
9	9		1001
10	A		1010
11	B		1011
12	C		1100
13	D		1101
14	E		1110
15	F		1111
16	10	0001	0000
17	11	0001	0001
18	12	0001	0010
19	13	0001	0011
20	14	0001	0100
21	15	0001	0101
22	16	0001	0110
23	17	0001	0111
24	18	0001	1000
32	20	0010	0000
40	28	0010	1000
48	30	0011	0000
56	38	0011	1000
63	3F	0011	1111

We have grouped the 8-bit binary numbers into two groups of four bits each to help you understand how the hexadecimal number to binary number conversion was made. While the space between each 4-bit group does not affect the value of the number, it does make the binary number easier to read and has become a standard convention.

We now address the question of how to convert an 8-bit binary number into hex code. The procedure to accomplish this conversion requires three steps:

1. Write down the full 8-bit binary number.
2. Split this 8-bit binary number into two groups with four binary digits in each group.
3. Substitute the equivalent hex digit

    0,1,2,3,4,5,6,7,8,9,A,B,C,D,E,F

for each group of four bits.

Having done this you will have converted an 8-bit binary number into a two-digit hex code. Each group of four binary digits is converted independently of the other.

As an example, consider the 8-bit binary number,

$$1\ 0\ 0\ 1\ 1\ 1\ 0\ 1$$

First, split this binary number into two groups of four binary digits each

$$1001\ 1101$$

Finally, substitute the equivalent hex digit for each of these two groups.

$$9\ D$$

This is the correct answer, 9D (16), where the subscript (16) means "relative to" the hexadecimal counting system. Some additional hex numbers and their corresponding 8-bit binary numbers are listed below:

Decimal Number	Binary Number	Hex Number
64	0100 0000	40
72	0100 1000	48
73	0100 1001	49
74	0100 1010	4A
96	0110 0000	60
120	0111 1000	78
127	0111 1111	7F
128	1000 0000	80
160	1010 0000	A0
184	1011 1000	B8
191	1011 1111	BF
248	1111 1000	F8
255	1111 1111	FF

A NOTE ON NOTATION

It may have occurred to you that dealing with all of these different methods of number representation—binary, hex, and decimal—that there is a possibility for some confusion. For example, the number 10 can be a decimal or a hex or a binary number. To remedy this problem, whenever there is any possibility for ambiguity, all hexadecimal numbers will be followed by the letter H, e.g., 10H, all decimal numbers will be followed by a period or decimal point, e.g., 10., and all binary numbers will appear without any special notation, e.g., 10 or 0110.

DEMONSTRATIONS

In the first three chapters we have included a collection of exercises that we have called demonstrations. These demonstrations are designed to encourage you to operate the Nanocomputer immediately, even though you may not completely understand the Nanocomputer at this time. It is important that you work through these demonstrations even though you may feel at times that you are only pushing buttons and not understanding what is happening.

DEMONSTRATION NO. 1

Step 1

Referring to the Nanocomputer Instruction Manual, apply power to your Nanocomputer. Press the RESET key. Several seven-segment display digits should become lit. If not, press RESET again. If repeated depressions of the RESET key do not "bring up" your Nanocomputer, you have a problem.

Step 2

Notice that the Nanocomputer keyboard has two keys with arrows on them. Press one of these keys several times and observe what happens.
We observed three things. First, we observed that the red selector lamp cycles among eleven different possible positions. We also observed that the red lamp can be moved one step at a time by quickly touching and releasing the key; alternatively, the red lamp can be made to cycle automatically by holding down the key and then releasing the key when the selector lamp reaches the desired location.

Finally, we observed that the digits appearing on the red digit displays changed according to the position of the red selector lamp.

Step 3

Press the other key that is labeled with an arrow and observe what happens.

We observed that the red selector lamp cycled among the eleven different possible positions in the opposite direction from that observed in STEP 1.

Step 4

Position the selector lamp at the position labeled MEM. Notice what appears on the four leftmost red digit displays.

We observed 0000.

Step 5

Press the key labeled INC several times and notice what happens. We observed the following sequence of digits appearing on the left-most red digit display:

0000	0001	0002	0003	0004	0005	0006	0007	0008	0009
000A	000b	000C	000d	000E	000F	0010	0011	0012	0013

and so on.

Notice that the hexadecimal digit sequence 0,1,2,3,4,5,6,7,8,9,A, b,C,d,E,F is displayed, right justified, in each group of four digits. Notice also that the hexadecimal digits A,C,E, and F appear as capital letters, but that the hexadecimal digits b and d appear as lower case letters. This is simply an artifact of the seven-segment display that is being used to represent the letter, and henceforth will be represented by B and D, respectively. The four place hexadecimal digits 0000 through 000F represent the decimal digits 0 through 15, the hex digit 0010 represents the decimal digit 16, 0011 represents 17., and so on. Thus, we have a hexadecimal display. The conclusion is that the Nanocomputer is going to talk to us using the hexadecimal representation of numbers so it makes sense that we will talk to the Nanocomputer using the same hexadecimal (hex) representation.

Step 6

Press the button labeled RESET. Notice that the selector lamp has moved. Move the selector lamp back to the location labeled MEM. We now have 0000 displayed once again, so that subsequent pushing of the INC key will cause the Nanocomputer to begin displaying successive hex digits. What is the largest hex number that the Nanocomputer will be able to display using only these four hex digits? What is the decimal equivalent of this number?

Answer: The largest hex number that the Nanocomputer can display is FFFF. The decimal equivalent of this number is 65,535.

REVIEW

The following questions will help you review digital codes.

1. What is a digital code?
2. List several different types of digital codes.
3. How many bits are there in the following binary numbers?
   a. 11010011
   b. 1000000000000011
   c. 1001
4. To what decimal numbers do the following binary numbers correspond?
   a. 11101
   b. 11111111

    c. 1111111111111111
    d. 1001
    e. 11010011
    f. 10011

5. To what hexadecimal numbers do the following binary numbers correspond?
    a. 11010011
    b. 00111110
    c. 01110110
    d. 00111100
    e. 11111111
    f. 00110010
    g. 11000011
    h. 00000010
    i. 110

6. To what binary numbers do the following hexadecimal numbers correspond?
    a. D3H
    b. FFH
    c. 32H
    d. 3EH
    e. 76H
    f. 02H
    g. 5H
    h. 3CH
    i. 00H

7. What is meant by the following subscripts?
    a. (16)
    b. (10)
    c. (2)

8. Define the following terms.
    a. hexadecimal counting system
    b. bit
    c. binary code
    d. communication
    e. language

9. Are the following numbers binary, hex, or decimal?
    a. 1111
    b. 1101.
    c. 1100H

ANSWERS

1. A digital code is a system of symbols that represent data values and make up a special language that a computer or a digital circuit can understand.
2. Binary code. Binary coded decimal. Gray code. ASCII code. EBCDIC code. Baudot code. IBM 370 instruction code. Z-80 instruction code.
3. a. Eight
    b. Sixteen
    c. Four
4. a. 29.
    b. 255.
    c. 65,535.
    d. 9.
    e. 211.
    f. 19.

5. a. D3H
   b. 3EH
   c. 76H
   d. 3CH
   e. FFH
   f. 32H
   g. C3H
   h. 02H
   i. 06H
6. a. 11010011
   b. 11111111
   c. 00110010
   d. 00111110
   e. 01110110
   f. 00000010
   g. 101
   h. 00111100
   i. 00000000
7. a. Refers to the hexadecimal counting system
   b. Refers to the decimal counting system
   c. Refers to the binary counting system
8. a. A counting system that is based on a base, or radix of 16
   b. An elementary unit of information that is equal to one binary decision, or the designation of one of two possible and equally likely values or states of anything used to store or convey information.
   c. A code in which each code element is one of two different states, which are commonly known as logic 0 and logic 1.
   d. The imparting, conveying, or exchanging of ideas, knowledge, information, etc., (whether by speech, writing, or signs).
   e. The whole body of words and of methods of combination of words used by a nation, people, or race.
9. a. binary
   b. decimal
   c. hexadecimal

CHAPTER 2

An Introduction to Microcomputer Programming

In the chapters that follow, you will perform two different kinds of experiments: (a) experiments that require only microcomputer programming, and (b) experiments that require both microcomputer programming and *interfacing,* i.e., the wiring of circuits that connect the microcomputer to some kind of external device. Since a common denominator of all experiments is programming, we would first like to introduce you to the basic principles of programming and the characteristics of the *programming language* that you will use in this text: the instruction set for the Z-80 microprocessor chip. Along the way, we shall define a variety of important terms, including *computer, mnemonic language, machine language, microcomputer,* and many others. This introduction to programming will occupy twelve chapters. We prefer to give you new programming instructions in groups of five to ten, rather than all of them at once.

OBJECTIVES

At the end of this chapter, you will be able to do the following:

- Define *digital computer.*
- Define *microcomputer.*
- Distinguish between microcomputer instructions written in binary code, hex code, or mnemonic code.
- Distinguish between mnemonic representations and machine language.
- Define *byte.*

- Convert a 16-bit memory address into HI and LO address bytes.
- Convert 8-bit binary-coded instructions into hex-coded instructions, and vice versa.
- Distinguish between read/write memory and read-only memory.
- Define *memory*.
- Define *computer program*.
- State the range of memory locations, in binary or hex code, for your microcomputer.
- Identify 8-bit bytes in a list of binary numbers.

WHAT IS A COMPUTER?

There are many different types of computers in the world—DIGITAL COMPUTERS, ANALOG COMPUTERS, FLUIDIC COMPUTERS, MECHANICAL COMPUTERS. In this book, you will be concerned only with DIGITAL COMPUTERS, which comprise probably 99% of all of the computers in use today. A digital computer can be defined as follows:

Digital computer—An electronic device that is capable of accepting, storing, and arithmetically manipulating information, which includes both data and the controlling program. The information is handled in the form of coded binary digits (0 and 1) that are represented by dual voltage levels.[4]

—Any device, usually electronic, capable of accepting information, comparing, adding, subtracting, multiplying, dividing, and integrating this information, which is in the form of coded binary digits (0 and 1), and then supplying the results of these processes in acceptable form. The major elements of a digital computer usually include memory, control, arithmetic, logical, and input and output facilities.[2]

It should be emphasized that a digital computer manipulates *binary information,* of the kind that we discussed in Chapter 1. The binary information is usually in the form of *digital codes:* instruction codes; codes used to represent decimal numbers in digital form; codes employed by electronic circuitry to perform various digital operations; and codes used to represent in digital form the alphabet, decimal numbers, symbols, and other operations.

WHAT IS A MICROCOMPUTER?

A *microcomputer* is a fully operational digital computer that is based on a *microprocessor chip.* A *microprocessor* is a single *integrated-circuit chip* that possesses at least 75% of the computing and data manipulation power of a digital computer. It usually cannot function without the aid of support chips and memory. An *integrated-circuit chip* is an electronic device in which both active (i.e., transistors) and passive (i.e., resistors) elements are contained within a single package. In digital electronics, the term chiefly applies to circuits containing semiconductor elements.[2] The microprocessor chip is a product of advanced technology in the semiconductor industry, basically the capability that manufacturers now have to fabricate thousands of transistors on a single silicon chip no larger than 60 to 80 square millimeters.

WHAT IS A COMPUTER PROGRAM?

A *computer program* can be defined as a series of instructions or statements prepared in a form acceptable to the computer, the purpose of which is to achieve a certain result.[2] This definition does not imply what the desired result may be. For example, you may simply be interested in rearranging input digital data into a more convenient form, which is either stored or provided as output. With microcomputers, you will be increasingly interested in writing microcomputer programs that control the operation of a device or machine. In a home clothes washer, you may wish to control the amount of water used, the temperature of the water at different washing cycles, the number and kinds of cycles used to wash a particular type of fabric, and the time duration of each cycle. All this can be done with a properly written computer program.

INSTRUCTIONS

A computer *instruction* can be defined as a set of characters that define an operation. Either alone, or with other information, an instruction causes a digital computer to perform the operation or manipulate the indicated quantities.

A *character* is one symbol of a set of elementary symbols, such as those corresponding to typewriter keys. Symbols usually include the decimal digits 0 through 9, the letters A through Z, punctuation marks, dollar signs, commas, operation symbols, and any other single symbols that a computer may read, store, or write.[5] In computer programming, it is not uncommon for one to use the entire typewriter keyboard, including symbols such as @, #, $, %, &, *, (,), /, and possibly others.

Computer instructions may be expressed in a variety of forms. They may be expressed as binary numbers,

11010011
00111110

hex numbers,

                        D3H
                        3EH

mnemonic code,

                    OUT 3EH
                    LD A,02H

full words,

        OUTPUT ACCUMULATOR DATA TO DEVICE #3E (HEX)
        LOAD DATA 02 HEX INTO REGISTER A

or full mathematical expressions,

$$X = A**2 + B*y + C$$

In this book, we will express instructions at the level of binary numbers, hex numbers, and mnemonic representations.

MNEMONICS

Mnemonic is a term that describes something used to assist the human memory. In view of this definition, we have the following:

mnemonic code—Computer instructions written in a form the programmer can easily remember, but which must be converted into machine language later by a computer or by the user.[2]

mnemonic language—A programming language that is based on easily remembered symbols and that can be assembled into machine language by a computer.[2]

mnemonic operation—Computer instructions that are written in a meaningful notation, for example, ADD, LD, and OUT.[2]

INSTRUCTIONS

In this series of chapters, we shall occasionally employ the mnemonic codes for the instructions that you will use when you program the microcomputer. The mnemonic codes will be those suggested by the ZILOG Corporation for its Z-80 microprocessor instruction set, which contains 158 different machine instruction types. With time, you should be able to readily convert from machine language (i.e., binary code) to mnemonic code, and vice versa.

MACHINE LANGUAGE

The modern electronic digital computer is capable of performing manipulations using binary electronic signals, typically two voltage levels (+5 volts and ground potential) that represent the logic states

1 and 0, respectively. Thus, each computer instruction is written as a series of 1s and 0s that specifically characterize that instruction and no other. Such a binary representation of a computer instruction is called *machine language* or *machine code*. For example, the machine language instruction 00000111 rotates the contents of the accumulator within the Z-80 microprocessor chip one bit to the left. The instruction, 00001111, rotates the contents of the accumulator one bit to the right.

In this series of chapters, you will be drilled in the use of machine language instructions for the Z-80 microprocessor. The instructions will be given to you in HEX CODE in order that you may remember them easier. Some hex instruction codes that you will soon use in simple microcomputer programming experiments include:

C3H	Unconditional jump instruction
76H	Halt instruction
3CH	Increment contents of accumulator by 1
3EH	Load accumulator immediate instruction

All of the new phrases that have been used in this section—unconditional jump, load, halt, increment, etc.—will be discussed shortly.

A SIMPLE PROGRAM

Let us examine the following simple Z-80 program.

00H	No operation
3EH	Load the contents of the next program byte into the accumulator
FFH	Data byte
76H	Halt

It contains three instructions and one data byte. In this case, the program has been written in hex code, which you have studied in Chapter 1. This very same program also could have been written in binary code, as shown below.

00000000	No operation
00111110	Load the contents of the next program byte into the accumulator
11111111	Data byte
01110110	Halt

Alternatively, it could have been written in mnemonic code and later converted to machine code with the aid of a special program called an *assembler*. Thus, we have the following mnemonic program:

NOP	No operation
LD A,FFH	Load the data byte FF into the accumulator
HALT	Halt

Note that the mnemonic code program is mainly words or word abbreviations, such as NOP, HALT, and LD.

How does the microcomputer execute this program? It does so step by step, with the first instruction, NOP, being the first executed. The following sequence of operations occurs:

1. The microcomputer executes the NOP instruction, which causes the computer to "pause" for one *instruction cycle*. The computer then advances to the next instruction. There is an important use for the NOP instruction, which you will see in a later program.
2. As the microcomputer executes the LD instruction, which has the 3E hex code, it looks at the next memory location to determine what value to load into the accumulator.
3. The microcomputer goes to the next memory location, where it finds an FF. It takes this value and stores it in the accumulator of the microcomputer.
4. The microcomputer executes the final instruction, HALT. This causes the computer to stop.

The above program may seem straightforward, or it may not. What is *memory*? What is a *byte*? How does one distinguish between an *instruction* and a *data byte*? Where is the accumulator? All of these are very reasonable questions, some of which you may have asked yourself as you studied the above program.

Let us proceed to answer some of these questions.

BYTE

A *byte* is a group of eight contiguous bits that occupy a single memory location in a Z-80 based microcomputer. By "contiguous," we mean adjacent or neighboring, or one-after-the-other. A byte can be any of the 256 possible different arrangements of eight binary digits each of which is either a 0 or a 1. The only restriction is that a byte contains exactly eight bits. Thus, the binary number,

$$0\ 1\ 1\ 0\ 1\ 0\ 0\ 1$$

is a byte, whereas the binary number,

$$1\ 0\ 1\ 0\ 0\ 1$$

is not a byte since it contains only six bits. The term, byte, has become popular because many digital computers have word lengths that are multiples of eight bits. To easily reference bits within a byte, the bits are numbered from 0 through 7:

$$D7\quad D6\quad D5\quad D4\quad D3\quad D2\quad D1\quad D0$$

The "D" (probably short for Data) is sometimes not present. The *most significant bit* (MSB) is D7. The *least significant bit* (LSB) is D0.

In general, a *word* is the number of bits that a computer can manipulate simultaneously. If the number of bits in a *word* is eight, we usually employ the term byte rather than *word*. In any case, the Z-80 has an 8-bit *word* length. The word length for a PDP 8 minicomputer is twelve, which means that the PDP 8 minicomputer manipulates twelve bits at a time when it is executing a program. The PDP 11 minicomputer has a word length of sixteen bits, and large computers generally have word lengths of 32 bits, 36 bits or 60 bits.

MEMORY

Memory can be defined as any device that can store logic 1 and logic 0 bits in such a manner that a single bit or group of bits can be accessed and retrieved.[6] There are many different types of memory that satisfy this requirement; in your microcomputer, however, you have only two different kinds of memory:

read/write memory—A semiconductor memory into which logic 0 and logic 1 states can be written (stored) and read out again (retrieved).[6] These are also called *random access memories* (RAM).

read-only memory—A semiconductor memory from which digital data can be repeatedly read out, but cannot be written into as in the case for read/write memory.[6] Abbreviated ROM.

Actually, the read-only memory in your microcomputer may be a special kind of memory called an *erasable programmable read-only memory,* or EPROM. We shall talk about EPROMs in a subsequent chapter.

The important point here is that your memory consists of semiconductor devices. They are fast and relatively inexpensive, have no mechanical parts, and do not take up much room on your printed-circuit board. They are one reason why computer technology has advanced as fast as it has.

How much memory do you have? The simplest Nanocomputer that you can use contains 4096 bytes of read/write memory and 2048 bytes of read-only memory. The program which allows you to enter data on the keyboard and displays information on the seven-segment displays is loaded into the 2048 bytes of read-only memory. We will refer to this program as the Nanocomputer operating system.

Since a byte contains eight bits, this means that you have at least a total of 49,152 bits of memory in your microcomputer. This is sufficient for all programming and interfacing experiments that you will encounter throughout this book.

On the second level Nanocomputer you are able to increase the number of bytes of read/write memory to 16,384 and increase the number of bytes of read-only memory to 8192. A Nanocomputer with this memory capacity has a total of 24,576 bytes of memory. It is known as a 24K microcomputer, where the "K" represents roughly one thousand (exactly 1024) different memory locations. A 4K microcomputer would contain 4096 bytes of memory. A 64K microcomputer would contain 65,536 bytes of memory.

MEMORY ADDRESS

Memory address is defined as the storage location of a memory word. Note that we said word, not byte. For some computers, a word may contain 32 bits, so each different memory location will contain 32 bits. For the Z-80 microcomputer, each memory location contains a single byte, i.e., eight bits.

With the standard Nanocomputer that you can use, there are 6144 different memory locations. These memory locations are subdivided into two groups, which can be described as follows:

- Memory group 1: The first group of 4096 (4K) memory locations, each containing eight bits. This is the read/write memory that you will normally use when you program your microcomputer.
- Memory group 2: The second group of 2048 (2K) memory locations, each containing eight bits. This memory region is occupied by read-only memory, or perhaps by erasable programmable read-only memory, which contains the Nanocomputer operating system that makes your microcomputer operate. YOU CANNOT CHANGE THE CONTENTS OF THIS MEMORY GROUP.

RANGE OF MEMORY LOCATIONS

The Z-80 microprocessor chip is quite remarkable, it can address up to 65,536 (64K) different memory locations, each containing eight bits. The chip contains a 16-bit memory address word. If you perform a simple calculation, you will conclude that 2 raised to the 16th power (2**16) does indeed equal 65,536.

As indicated above, your Nanocomputer may have only 6144 (6K) memory locations available on the basic card. You might ask, which locations among the possible 65,536 locations are they? Our answer: the first 4K locations together with the last 2K locations.

Stated in another way, the possible range of usable memory addresses for the standard Nanocomputer is:

```
0000000000000000 (BASE 2)  to  0000111111111111 (BASE 2) R/W Memory
1111100000000000 (BASE 2)  to  1111111111111111 (BASE 2) ROM
```

This is a cumbersome notation, one that is very difficult to remember. There is an easier way to identify memory locations and the range of your microcomputer. This is discussed in the next section.

HI AND LO MEMORY ADDRESSES

It is difficult to remember a 16-bit memory address, considerably more so than an 8-bit instruction code or data byte. The Z-80 microprocessor chip treats a 16-bit memory address as two 8-bit memory address bytes, an 8-bit HI byte and an 8-bit LO byte. These are defined as follows:

HI address byte—The eight most significant (or left-most) bits in the 16-bit memory address word for the Z-80 microprocessor chip. Abbreviated H or HI.

LO address byte—The eight least significant (or right-most) bits in the 16-bit memory address word for the Z-80 microprocessor chip. Abbreviated L or LO.

Therefore, the possible range of read/write memory locations for your microcomputer is

$$HI = 00000000 \text{ (2)} \qquad HI = 00001111 \text{ (2)}$$
$$\text{to}$$
$$LO = 00000000 \text{ (2)} \qquad LO = 11111111 \text{ (2)}$$

Recall that you learned how to convert an 8-bit binary number into a 2-digit hex number. Applied to the above HI and LO memory addresses, you should obtain the following range of read/write memory locations:

$$HI = 00 \text{ (16)} \qquad HI = 0F \text{ (16)}$$
$$\text{to}$$
$$LO = 00 \text{ (16)} \qquad LO = FF \text{ (16)}$$

Keep in mind the following rule: To specify a memory location, you must specify both the HI address byte and the LO address byte, which together comprise a memory address word of 16 bits.

DEMONSTRATION NO. 1

At each step in this demonstration, you should have the selector lamp located at the MEM position. Notice in Fig. 2-1 that there are four hex digits displayed on the left-hand side of the red digit displays,

ADDRESS   DATA

Fig. 2-1. Memory location demonstration.

and that there are two hex digits displayed on the right-hand side. The four hex digits displayed on the left represent the address of a memory location. The two hex digits displayed on the right represent the contents of the memory location whose address is displayed on the left. You could think of memory as being a collection of boxes. Each box has a label permanently printed on it. These labels are actually hexadecimal numbers starting with 0000,0001,0002,0003, and so on. Inside each box you can put exactly one byte of information in the form of exactly two hex digits. Using the Nanocomputer keyboard you can examine individual memory locations and change the contents of a given memory location.

Step 1

Set the selector lamp on MEM. We observed that the memory address displayed in the left-most four hex digits, called the *address display,* was 0000. The contents of memory location 0000, displayed in the right-most two hex digits, called the *data display,* was 00.

Let us change the contents of 0000H from 00H to 23H. Push the hex key labeled 2, then push the hex key labeled 3, and finally, push the key labeled ST. ST is a shorthand notation for the word STORE. By pressing ST, you will STORE 23H in location 0000H. Notice that now the address has automatically increased to 0001. So you are now "looking" at memory location 0001H. Store 24H in this location.

Step 2

Now examine memory locations 0000H and 0001H to verify that you have actually stored 23H and 24H in them, respectively. Press 0,0,0,0 in sequence on the keyboard followed by the key labeled LA. LA is shorthand for LOAD ADDRESS. You are loading the hex address 0000 into the address display. Now you should observe that 23 is displayed on the data display as the contents of memory location 0000H. Press the key labeled INC. Notice that the memory address is incremented by one and that the contents of memory location 0001H are indeed 24H. You now should be able to determine the contents of any memory location and to change the contents of any READ/WRITE memory location to any value that you desire.

Step 3

You will look at the contents now of a memory location in ROM (Read-Only Memory) and attempt to write into Read-Only Memory. Look at the contents of FC00H (press F,C,0,0 in order and then press LA). We observed that the contents of FC00H was 18H. Attempt to store the hex value FF at this memory location (press F,F and then press the ST key). Now examine the contents of FC00H again. We observed that the contents of FC00H had not been changed, and are still 18H. Thus we have NOT been able to *write* into read-only memory.

REVIEW

1. Identify the following instructions as to whether they are in binary code, hex code, or mnemonic code.
   - a. HALT
   - b. 11010011
   - c. 3E
   - d. LD
   - e. INC
   - f. 00111100
   - g. 76
2. Write the following binary instructions in hex code.
   - a. 11010011
   - b. 01110110
   - c. 00111100
   - d. 00110010
   - e. 00000000
   - f. 11000011
   - g. 11111111
3. Which of the following is a byte?
   - a. 1001
   - b. 011
   - c. 0000001100000011
   - d. 1110001101
   - e. 111000
   - f. 0100110
4. Write the following 16-bit memory addresses as HI and LO hex bytes.
   - a. 0000001111111111
   - b. 0000000011111111
   - c. 0000000111111111
   - d. 0000001011111111
   - e. 0000000000000000
   - f. 0000000100000000
   - g. 0000001000000000
   - h. 0000001100000000
5. Which of the following instructions are in machine language?
   - a. NOP
   - b. HALT
   - c. LD
   - d. INC
   - e. 3EH
   - f. 76H
   - g. 11010011
   - h. 00H
   - i. 00111100
6. In terms of the HI and LO memory address bytes, write the memory range of the following memory groups in the Z-80 microcomputer.
   - a. The first 4K bytes of memory (read/write)
   - b. The first 16K bytes of memory (read/write)
   - c. The last 4K bytes of memory (read only)
   - d. The last 8K bytes of memory (read only)

7. **Define the following terms.**
   a. byte
   b. memory address
   c. mnemonic code

ANSWERS

1. a. mnemonic code
   b. binary code
   c. hex code
   d. mnemonic code
   e. mnemonic code
   f. binary code
   g. hex code
2. a. D3
   b. 76
   c. 3C
   d. 32
   e. 00
   f. C3
   g. FF
3. None of the examples is a byte. A byte must contain exactly eight bits.
4. a. HI=03   LO=FF
   b. HI=00   LO=FF
   c. HI=01   LO=FF
   d. HI=02   LO=FF
   e. HI=00   LO=00
   f. HI=01   LO=00
   g. HI=02   LO=00
   h. HI=03   LO=00
5. Examples g and i are in machine language.
6. a. The Range is HI=00 and LO=00 to HI=0F and LO=FF
   b. The Range is HI=00 and LO=00 to HI=3F and LO=FF
   c. The Range is HI=F0 and LO=00 to HI=FF and LO=FF
   d. The Range is HI=E0 and LO=00 to HI=FF and LO=FF
7. a. A group of eight contiguous bits that occupy a single memory location in a Z-80 microcomputer.
   b. The storage location of a memory word.
   c. Computer instructions written in a form that the programmer can easily remember, but which must be converted into machine language later to be in computer readable form.

CHAPTER 3

Some Z-80 Microprocessor CPU Instructions

In this chapter, we shall define several important terms, including *operation, data byte, address byte,* and *device code.* We will also introduce you to several simple Z-80 microprocessor instructions that you will use in the programs provided in Chapter 5. Our objective is to gradually introduce you to the entire Z-80 instruction set and to provide programs that permit you to see how some basic instructions are used.

OBJECTIVES

At the end of this chapter, you will be able to do the following:

- Define *computer program.*
- Define *operation.*
- Provide simple representations for single-byte, two-byte, three-byte and four-byte instructions.
- Explain the differences between the following kinds of program bytes: operation code, data byte, device code, HI address byte, LO address byte, and displacement byte.
- Define *register.*
- List the two sets of six general-purpose registers, and the six special-purpose registers in the Z-80 microprocessor chip.
- List which of the general-purpose registers are used as register pairs.
- Define *accumulator.*
- Define *increment.*

- Explain the operation of five common Z-80 microcomputer instructions: NOP, HALT, INC A, LD A,data, and JP address.
- Define the *immediate addressing mode*.
- For a 2.5-MHz Z-80 microcomputer, list the execution times of the following microcomputer instructions: NOP, HALT, INC A, LD A,data, and JP address.

WHAT IS A COMPUTER PROGRAM?

A *computer program* can be defined as a sequence of instructions that, taken as a group, allow the computer to perform a sequence of operations to accomplish a desired task. What is the task? It could be anything within the capability of the computer, associated external input-output devices, and memory.

Programs are stored in memory as a sequence of 0's and 1's (bits) that the computer can read, interpret, and execute in sequence, one at a time. For the Z-80, these bits are stored in 8-bit groups called bytes. A single instruction may occupy one, two, three, or four consecutive bytes of memory. The Z-80 executes a program by reading an instruction, interpreting the bit patterns, and then performing the tasks necessary to complete the operation defined by the instruction. Consecutive memory locations are read until an instruction is reached that tells the computer to halt or jump to another memory location for the next instruction.

Programs do not include just instruction bytes. Data bytes must also be included in programs to provide needed information. For example, a program designed to add two numbers must include the numbers to be added (data bytes) as well as the instructions to perform the addition operation (instruction bytes). Other types of bytes that make up a program include address bytes, device code bytes, and displacement bytes. These are discussed later in this chapter.

The minimum Nanocomputer configuration provides 4K bytes of read/write memory for user program storage. This is sufficient to store highly complex programs. Two very critical terms in our definition of computer programs are "instruction" and "operation." Now let us investigate their meaning further.

INSTRUCTIONS AND OPERATIONS

An *instruction* is a set of characters that defines an operation, alone or together with other information, and which together causes the computer to perform the operation. An *operation* is defined as a specific action which a computer performs whenever an instruction calls for it (e.g., division, addition, subtraction, ORing, etc.). The number of different operations that a computer can perform and the speed with which it can perform such operations provide a measure of how "powerful" the computer is. The operations that the Z-80 microprocessor chip can perform can be subdivided into the following groups:

> Data transfer group
> Arithmetic and Logic group
> Rotate and Shift group
> Bit Manipulation group
> Jump, Call, and Return group
> I/O and machine control group.

MULTIBYTE INSTRUCTIONS

Many instructions within the Z-80 instruction set require only a single byte, but others require two, three, or even four successive bytes before they can be executed. We call these latter instructions *multibyte instructions*. A few definitions are in order:

single byte instruction—An instruction consisting of eight contiguous bits that occupy a single memory location.
two-, three- or four-byte instruction—An instruction consisting of information that occupies two, three, or four successive memory locations.

The number of bytes required for an instruction is closely related to the complexity of the instruction and the information that it requires. The Z-80-instruction set was designed as an extension of the instruction set for a microprocessor, the 8080, manufactured by Intel Corporation. To maintain consistency between the two instruction sets, certain compromises in the definition of the new Z-80 instructions were necessary. This has resulted in making the structure of the Z-80 instructions a bit more complicated than that of the 8080. However, this sacrifice more than compensated by the fact that almost any program written for an 8080 microprocessor can be executed on a Z-80 microprocessor without any changes. The 8080 microprocessor is historically a very important microprocessor chip, for which a lot of software already exists. Hence, this "upward compatibility" is especially beneficial.

Simple representations for one-byte, two-byte, three-byte, and four-byte Z-80 instructions are given in the following paragraphs. Note that in all but one four-byte instruction type, the first one or two bytes are operation codes which specify what the instruction does, and the last bytes are information needed to carry out the instruction. We shall discuss this in great detail when we introduce specific instructions. The instruction formats are presented here merely as a preview of things to come. Since operation codes follow each other sequentially in memory at numbered addresses, we write them down in vertical columns like a table, unlike the page you are reading which is written horizontally.

Single-byte instructions require only on operation code and no auxiliary information.

OPERATION CODE

Two-byte instructions have four forms:

OPERATION CODE
OPERATION CODE

OPERATION CODE
Data byte

OPERATION CODE
Device code

OPERATION CODE
Displacement byte

We shall explain shortly what is meant by the terms *data byte, device code,* and *displacement byte.*

Three-byte instructions have three forms:

OPERATION CODE
Data byte
Data byte

OPERATION CODE
LO address byte
HI address byte

OPERATION CODE
OPERATION CODE
Displacement byte

We have previously discussed the concepts of LO and HI memory address bytes.

Four-byte instructions have four forms:

OPERATION CODE
OPERATION CODE
Data byte
Data byte

OPERATION CODE
OPERATION CODE
LO address byte
HI address byte

OPERATION CODE
OPERATION CODE
Displacement byte
Data byte

OPERATION CODE
OPERATION CODE
Displacement byte
OPERATION CODE

As you may well guess, the last two four-byte instruction types represent fairly complicated instructions. Several examples of these instruction types are discussed in detail later.

TYPES OF INFORMATION STORED IN MEMORY

The memory in a Z-80 microcomputer consists of a sequence of successive 8-bit locations. Everything that the microcomputer does with respect to the memory is done eight bits at a time. There exist six different kinds of information that can be stored in memory:

8-bit operation codes
8-bit data bytes
8-bit device codes
8-bit LO address bytes
8-bit HI address bytes
8-bit displacement bytes

Therefore, in a Z-80 program, we simultaneously store instruction codes, data bytes, device codes, address bytes, and displacement bytes in the same memory. All of these kinds of information can exist side by side. It is reasonable to inquire how the microcomputer is able to distinguish among them.

The basic answer is that the order in which the information appears dictates what type of information it is. Computer programming is a precision activity: ONE programming mistake and your program will not operate correctly. A microcomputer program starts at a chosen memory address and then proceeds operation by operation to a final memory address. The operation codes always tell you what to expect in the program, i.e., whether the next memory byte is a data byte, address byte, device code byte, another operation code, or a displacement byte.

OPERATION CODE

The first byte of a Z-80 instruction is always an *operation code*. Note that some instruction types begin with two operation code bytes. These instructions are extensions of the old 8080 instruction set. If the first byte of an instruction is CB, DD, ED, or FD, then the second byte must also be an operation code. The operation code byte(s) define the specific action that the Z-80 microprocessor chip will perform. Specific actions include data transfer, arithmetic operations, logical operations, branch instructions, stack operations, I/O operations, and machine control operations. If you desire to know what the microcomputer will do next, the operation code(s) of the following instruction will tell you. Synonyms for operation code are *op code* and *instruction code*.

DATA BYTE

Data byte is defined as the 8-bit binary number that the Z-80 micro-processor chip will use in an arithmetic or logical operation or to store in memory. The eight bits can be in any kind of digital code: binary code, binary coded decimal, ASCII code, etc. When we use the term data byte, we mean that the eight bits are not an operation code, memory address, device code, or displacement byte. When you do microcomputer programming, you will find it very convenient to include data in your program where and when you need it, rather than having to refer to a remote memory location for the eight or sixteen bits of data that you need.

DEVICE CODE

Device code, for a Z-80 based microcomputer, is the identifier for the specific input or output device with which you desire to exchange eight bits of information and a device select pulse. We shall talk about the details of how this is done later. The important point is that the device code is an 8-bit code, which means that you can address two to the eighth power, $(2**8)$, or 256 different output devices. On your microcomputer, output device codes 04 and 07 are reserved for the Nanocomputer operating system.

As you proceed through this text, we encourage you to study carefully what is meant by device code and *device select pulse,* and how to use the latter to force input-output devices to operate in synchronization with your microcomputer program.

HI AND LO ADDRESS BYTES

We would like to remind you again that the *HI address byte* is the eight most significant bits, or highest value bits, and the *LO address byte* is the eight least significant bits, or lowest value bits, in the 16-bit Z-80 microprocessor memory address word. Since the Z-80 is an 8-bit microprocessor chip, which obtains data or instructions from memory eight bits at a time, it has no choice but to handle the 16-bit memory address information as a pair of 8-bit address bytes.

DISPLACEMENT BYTE

Displacement bytes appear in instructions which use *Indexed Addressing.* Indexed Addressing is a technique for defining a two-byte memory address by adding a *Displacement* to a 16-bit number which resides in a special location on the microprocessor chip called an *Index Register.* A *Displacement* is a *signed two's complement number.*

We will not attempt to define signed two's complement now. Suffice it to say that it is a method of representing binary numbers which facilitates manipulation of negative numbers. This will be carefully explained later.

Do not feel overwhelmed if many of the above terms appear unfamiliar. A complete understanding of all these terms will come only from experience in using instructions to program your Z-80.

WHAT IS A REGISTER?

A *register* is a short-term storage circuit the capacity of which is usually one computer word. Single registers in the Z-80 microprocessor chip store a single byte, i.e., eight contiguous bits. A variety of registers exist within the Z-80 chip, some of which you use to store digital information and others which are used by the chip itself as it performs instructions. In general, we can subdivide the registers of the chip into two different sets: those that you can address from a program and those that you cannot address from a program. The program-addressable registers include:

- two sets of 8-bit *general-purpose registers* addressed singly or in pairs,

Set 1:	Set 2:
B register	B′ register
C register	C′ register
D register	D′ register
E register	E′ register
H register	H′ register
L register	L′ register

Set 2 is referred to as the alternate register set (ARS).

- an 8-bit ACCUMULATOR for each set, also known as registers A and A′.
- an 8-bit FLAG register for each set, also known as registers F and F′.
- the 16-bit STACK POINTER register (SP).
- the 16-bit PROGRAM COUNTER REGISTER (PC).
- two 16-bit INDEX REGISTERS (IX) and (IY).
- the 8-bit INTERRUPT PAGE ADDRESS register (I).
- the 8-bit MEMORY REFRESH register (R).

These are the only registers with which you can directly exchange information with the aid of a suitably written microcomputer program.

GENERAL-PURPOSE REGISTERS

The two sets of six general-purpose registers—B, C, D, E, H, and L, and B′, C′, D′, E′, H′, and L′,—temporarily store single bytes of information. Since they are located within the Z-80 microprocessor chip, the exchange of information from one general-purpose register to another can be very fast. The exchange of information between any of these general-purpose registers and the accumulator is also fast. These registers can be used singly or in pairs. For Set 1, the three 16-bit register pairs are:

- the 16-bit general-purpose register consisting of the B register and the C register. When used for memory addressing, the B register corresponds to the HI memory address and the C register to the LO memory address.
- the 16-bit general-purpose register consisting of the D register and the E register. When used for memory addressing, the D register corresponds to the HI memory address and the E register to the LO memory address.
- the 16-bit memory address register and general-purpose register consisting of the H register and the L register. When used for memory addressing, the H register corresponds to the HI memory address and the L register corresponds to the LO memory address.

The registers are similarly paired for set 2.

ACCUMULATOR

The *accumulator* is an 8-bit register within the Z-80 microprocessor chip in which the result of most arithmetic and logical operations are placed. In the case of the Z-80 microprocessor chip, the accumulator register is located within the chip and contains a single byte of memory storage capacity, i.e., eight bits. Pay particular attention to what you can do to the contents of the accumulator. For example, you can add, subtract, or compare data with the contents of the accumulator. You can increment or decrement its contents by one. You can exchange the contents of the accumulator with a memory location, or with input-output devices. You can rotate the bits in the accumulator either to the left or to the right. You can perform logical operations on the accumulator, including AND, OR, and exclusive-OR. You may not understand some of these terms at the moment. Be patient, we shall get to all of them. The other registers within the Z-80 microprocessor chip will be discussed in more detail later.

SOME Z-80 INSTRUCTIONS

In Chapter 5, you will begin to test microcomputer programs. The programs that you will try will contain some single-byte, two-byte, and three-byte instructions, including the following:

00	NOP	No operation	
3C	INC A	Increment contents of accumulator by 1	
76	HALT	Halt the microcomputer	
3E <data>	LD A,data	Move the immediately following data byte <data> to the accumulator	
32 LO HI	LD (addr),A	Store the contents of the accumulator in the memory location addressed by the following two bytes (addr) in this three-byte instruction.	
C3 LO HI	JP addr	Unconditional jump to the memory address given in the following two bytes in this three-byte instruction.	

Please note that the above list contains instructions with only single-byte operation codes, i.e., the first byte in each instruction. The hex operation code appears in the first column next to its associated mnemonic.

From this point forward, all operation codes, device codes, data bytes, memory address bytes or displacement bytes will be written in hex code. And all mnemonics containing addresses or data will carry the hex digits followed by the character "H."

An important notational convention is illustrated in the two instructions:

LD (addr), A
JP addr

In the LD instruction, "addr" is enclosed in parentheses, while the parentheses are absent in the JP instruction. A 16-bit address enclosed by parentheses represents the data byte residing at location addr. For example, the instruction

LD (0001H) , A

is executed by placing the one byte of data in the accumulator into the address specified by 0001. The "(   )" are read "the address specified by." The address "addr" in the JP instruction refers to the address of the next instruction to be executed by the computer. Here, program control is being transferred, as opposed to data in the LD instruction. Hence, a 16-bit address appearing without parentheses is a reference to the location itself, whereas the appearance of parentheses implies that the reference is to the *contents* of that location. This is a subtle distinction that will become more natural later.

INSTRUCTION BYTE NOMENCLATURE

The Intel Corporation literature describing 8080 microcomputer mnemonics employs the following useful abbreviations or symbols for the first, second, and third bytes in multibyte instructions:

<B1>	First byte in an instruction
<B2>	Second byte in an instruction
<B3>	Third byte in an instruction

We shall extend this notation to facilitate our description of the Z-80 mnemonics. For example, the three-byte JP and LD instructions can be written in the following manner:

JP <B3> <B2>
LD (<B3> <B2>), A

Similarly, the two-byte LD instruction can be written as

LD A, <B2>

No-Operation: NOP

The simplest Z-80 instruction is the no-operation instruction, NOP, which has the instruction code 00.

0 0 0 0 0 0 0 0

No operation is performed. You can use this instruction whenever you want to provide space in your program so that you can add instruction bytes at a later time. In a later chapter, you will learn that your micro-computer operates at about 2.5 MHz, or 2.5 million states per second. ALL MICROCOMPUTER INSTRUCTIONS TAKE TIME TO EXECUTE. Though no operation is performed, i.e., the condition of the registers and memory is not changed, the NOP instruction nevertheless requires four states, or a total time of 1.6 microseconds, for execution. The execution time depends on the speed of the micro-computer. If the Z-80 operated at 4 MHz, or 4,000,000 states per second, the NOP instruction would require an execution time of 1 microsecond. Z-80A microprocessors can operate at 4 MHz, with some special selected chips operating a bit faster than this.

We shall discuss precisely what is meant by a state in a subsequent unit.

Halt: HALT

Another simple Z-80 instruction is the halt instruction, HALT, which has instruction code 76,

0 1 1 1 0 1 1 0

As soon as this instruction is executed, the microcomputer comes to a halt. It is frequently used to permit the microcomputer to "wait" for an INTERRUPT from an external device. In a computer, an *interrupt* is a break in the normal flow of a routine such that the flow can be resumed from that point at a later time. The HALT instruction requires seven states, or a total time of 2.8 microseconds, for execution.

Increment Accumulator: INC A

The term, *increment,* can be defined as follows:

increment—To increase the value of a binary word, typically, to increase the value by 1.

The increment instruction, INC A, which has an operation code of 3C,

$$0\ 0\ 1\ 1\ 1\ 1\ 0\ 0$$

increases the contents of the accumulator register by 1. The INC A instruction requires five states, or a total time of 2.0 microseconds, for execution.

Load Immediate to Accumulator: LD A, data

Immediate refers to the fact that the data byte is contained within the multibyte instruction. In immediate instructions, an 8-bit data byte or two 8-bit data bytes are acquired via a multibyte instruction that contains the data byte(s) as byte(s) <B2> or <B3> and possibly <B3> or <B4>. The load-immediate-to-accumulator instruction is a 2-byte instruction that has an operation code of 3E, and mnemonics, LD A, <B2>.

$$0\ 0\ 1\ 1\ 1\ 1\ 1\ 0$$
data   byte

The second byte of the instruction is the 8-bit data byte that is to be loaded into the accumulator register. The entire 2-byte instruction requires seven states, or 2.8 microseconds, for execution. You will find this to be a convenient way to alter the contents of the accumulator. It is a very popular instruction.

Load Accumulator Direct: LD (addr), A

The load accumulator direct instruction, LD (<B3><B2>), A is a 3-byte instruction that has an operation code of 32. It permits you to place the contents of the accumulator directly into a memory location, M, address by the second and third bytes in the instruction. The second byte is the LO address byte and the third byte is the HI address byte.

$$0\ 0\ 1\ 1\ 0\ 0\ 1\ 0$$
LO address byte
HI address byte

When the instruction is executed, the program does not change the contents of the accumulator; it simply copies the accumulator byte into the contents of the indicated memory location. This instruction is executed in 13 states, or 5.2 microseconds for a microcomputer running at 2.5 MHz.

Unconditional Jump: JP addr

The unconditional jump instruction, JP <B3> <B2>, is a 3-byte instruction that has an operation code of C3. The second byte of the instruction is the LO memory address byte, and the third byte is the HI memory address byte,

1 1 0 0 0 0 1 1
LO address byte
HI address byte

When the instruction is executed, the program jumps to the 16-bit memory address given by the HI and LO address bytes. We call this type of instruction a *Branch Instruction*. It permits you to stop the normal sequential program execution and jump somewhere else in memory, at which point you resume program execution. The branch instructions are very powerful. They permit you to write program *loops,* groups of instructions that are executed repeatedly. In this manner, you are able to substantially reduce program complexity. The unconditional jump instruction requires ten states for execution, or 4.0 microseconds. During this period of time, the entire 3-byte instruction is executed.

REVIEW

1. What is the difference between an operation code, data byte, device code, address byte, and displacement byte?
2. Provide the mnemonic code for the following 8-bit binary operation codes.
   a. 01110110
   b. 00111110
   c. 11000011
   d. 00110010
   e. 00111100
   f. 00000000
3. Write the two-digit hex operation code for the following Z-80 instructions.
   a. HLT
   b. JP <B2> <B3>
   c. LD (<B2> <B3>), A
   d. NOP
   e. INC A
   f. LD A, <B2>
4. In a multibyte Z-80 instruction, can the operation code be either the second or third or fourth byte of the instruction?
5. For a microcomputer operating at 2.5 MHz how much time is required to execute the following instructions?
   a. JP
   b. LD A, <B2>
   c. INC A
6. List the six general-purpose registers and the six special-purpose registers in the Z-80 microprocessor chip. Indicate which of the general-purpose registers are used as register pairs. What do we mean by ARS?

1. The operation code is the 8-bit, 16-bit, or 24-bit code for the specific action that the Z-80 microprocessor will perform. A data byte is an 8-bit binary number that the Z-80 will use in an arithmetic or logical operation, or store in memory. A device code is the specific input or output device identification with which a Z-80 microprocessor will exchange eight bits of information. An address byte is either the eight most significant or eight least significant bits in the 16-bit Z-80 memory address word. A displacement byte is an 8-bit signed two's complement number that is used for indexed addressing.
2. a. HLT
   b. LD A, <B2>
   c. JP <B2> <B3>
   d. LD (<B2> <B3>), A
   e. INC A
   f. NOP
3. a. 76
   b. C3
   c. 32
   d. 00
   e. 3C
   f. 3E
4. In a multibyte instruction, the first, second, and fourth bytes may be operation codes. The first byte, which is always an operation code byte determines the significance of the second byte. If the second byte is an operation code, it determines the significance of the remaining byte(s), if any.
5. a. 4.0 microseconds
   b. 2.8 microseconds
   c. 1.6 microseconds
6. The six general-purpose registers are B, C, D, E, H, and L.
   The six special-purpose registers are SP, PC, IX, IY, I, and R
   The general-purpose registers are paired into three 16-bit registers as follows: BC, DE, and HL.
   By ARS we mean the alternate register set, a second set of general-purpose registers, flags, and accumulator: A', B', C', D', E', F', H', and L'.

CHAPTER 4

The Nanocomputer (NBZ80) and the Super Nanocomputer (NBZ80S)

In the chapters that follow, you will set up experiments that demonstrate the important concepts of microcomputer programming and interfacing. To perform these experiments, you will use the Nanocomputer (a Z-80-based microcomputer), and later some integrated-circuit chips, some extra breadboarding sockets, wire, and other electronic components. This chapter will cover some of these items and prepare you to use them properly as you perform the experiments. The Z-80 Nanocomputer is manufactured by SGS-ATES Componenti Electronici SpA headquartered at Via C. Olivetti 2-20041 Agrate Brianza-Italy.

OBJECTIVES

By the end of this chapter you will be able to do the following:

- List the power requirements of the Nanocomputer.
- State the function of each of the 30 keys on the Nanocomputer keyboard.
- Explain the significance of each of the 14 lights on the Nanocomputer keyboard.
- Identify and define the significance of the 8 seven-segment displays on the Nanocomputer keyboard.
- State the clock frequency and time duration of a single state for the Nanocomputer.

- Load and execute a simple microcomputer program.
- State which solderless terminals are connected together electrically on a solderless breadboard.
- Explain the difference between read/write memory and programmable read-only memory.
- Give the location of read/write and read-only memory in the Nanocomputer and name the starting address of the operating system in read-only memory.

THE NANOCOMPUTER

Purpose

The Nanocomputer shown in Fig. 4-1 is a small Z-80–based microcomputer with 4K of read/write memory and 2K of PROM/ROM memory. There are two versions of the Nanocomputer:

(1) The NBZ80—an open board microcomputer with a data entry and display station, which we usually refer to as the Nanocomputer keyboard.
(2) The NBZ80S—an NBZ80 board encased in a desk cabinet including an experiment breadboard and power supply. The "S" is for super.

Both Nanocomputers are designed for educational and training use in Z-80 CPU interfacing and programming. Both can be used independently as stand-alone microcomputers, or be integrated into complex systems consisting of other microcomputers and/or larger computers. The next chapters will give you experience in microprocessor software development and later chapters on interfacing will introduce you to practical experiments with the Nanocomputer. You will perform three types of experiments:

(1) Experiments that require programming the Nanocomputer and use only the NBZ80 Nanocomputer and NPZ80 power supply,
(2) Experiments that involve construction of digital circuits and require a breadboard (NEZ80), power supply, and a few digital components, and
(3) Experiments that involve both programming and digital interface circuit construction and require the Super Nanocomputer (NBZ80S).

Description

The Nanocomputer is a self-contained, single board Z-80–based microcomputer with a SGS-ATES Z-80 CPU and PIO, memory, and a 30-key data entry/display station keyboard. The keyboard allows the user to load programs into the microcomputer memory, select specific memory locations for reading and writing of memory, execute

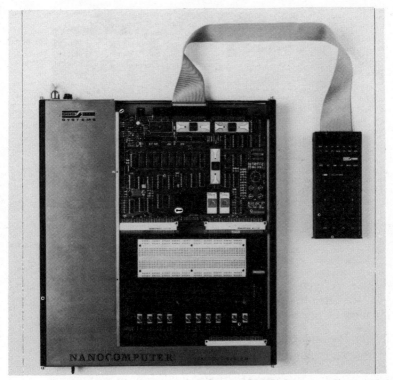

Fig. 4-1. NBZ80 Nanocomputer with keyboard and NPZ80 power supply.

programs at full speed, slow speed, or one step at a time, reset the microcomputer to an initial state, and many more functions. We shall describe all of these functions in detail.

Several diagrams and photographs of the Nanocomputer are shown on the following pages. As shown in Figs. 4-2 and 4-3, the following functional regions or blocks can be identified on a Nanocomputer printed-circuit board:

- CPU
- RAM memory
- ROM or EPROM memory
- 4 Parallel I/O Ports (2 PIO integrated circuits)
- 2 Serial I/O Ports (serial terminal and cassette tape interface)
- Bus Drivers
- Clock and Baud Rate Generator

It is not necessary for you to understand these functional blocks when you first operate the Nanocomputer. Initially, you will be concerned with learning to use the keyboard and read and interpret the

SERIAL INTERFACE

RAM

CLOCK and AUDIO GENERATOR

PIO PORTS

CPU

EPROM

Courtesy SGS-ATES Componenti: Electronici SpA

Fig. 4-2. Nanocomputer p-c board layout.

display. As you develop expertise in microcomputer programming, you will begin to develop a more detailed understanding of the actual circuitry of the Nanocomputer.

Power Requirements

The Nanocomputer requires a power supply of:

$$+5V \quad \pm 5\% \text{ at } 800 \text{ mA}$$
$$-5V \quad \pm 5\% \text{ at } 200 \text{ mA}$$
$$+12V \pm 10\% \text{ at } 100 \text{ mA}$$
$$-12V \pm 10\% \text{ at } 100 \text{ mA}.$$

Such a supply is included in the cabinet of the NBZ80S. For the NBZ80, SGS-ATES manufactures a suitable power supply (NPZ80) which can be purchased separately.

Nanocomputer Keyboard

The Nanocomputer keyboard is connected to the printed-circuit board via a 40-wire cable. The Nanocomputer keyboard is shown in Fig. 4-4. The following is an exhaustive description, for your reference, of the function of each key. Do not attempt to memorize these descriptions, but rather, skim the material first and then depend on the experiments at the end of this and subsequent chapters to teach you the keyboard functions.

0 through F—These keys enter a hexadecimal digit in the right-most position of the four-digit data display. As digits are entered on the right, the remaining three digits are shifted left with the left-most digit being lost.

Fig. 4-3. NBZ80 open board microcomputer.

Left Arrow (←) and Right Arrow (→)—These keys are used to select (light) one of the 14 lights just below the data and address displays. All lights except ARS, BRK, and ERR may be lit by shifting
the selected (lit) lamp left or right. Note that holding either of these
keys in a depressed position causes repeated shifts in the selector light.
Also note that a shift past the last lamp in either direction causes a
new cycle to begin.

Let us discuss the significance of the displays produced by choosing
different selector positions. For positions IR, AF, BC, DE, and HL,
four hex digits appear in the data display (the right-most four digits).
This represents two bytes of data. The left two digits depict the contents of the I, A, B, D, or H register, while the right two digits depict
the contents of the R, F, C, E, or L register depending on the position
of the selector light. For positions IX, IY, SP, PC, and MEM, the four
hex digits in the address display (on the left) represent the contents
of the selected 16-bit register while the two hex digits in the data display give the contents of the memory location pointed to by the address register.

For the I/O position, the address display contains a one-byte device
code and the data display contains the contents of the device at that
port.

ST—ST is an abbreviation for STore. Its precise function depends
on the position of the selector lamp. If the selector lamp is in position

Fig. 4-4. NBZ80 keyboard.

Courtesy SGS-ATES Componenti: Electronici SpA

IR, AF, BC, DE, or HL, the hex digits occupying the right-most positions (i.e. the low order byte) in the data display are *stored* in register R, F, C, E, or L, respectively. If the selector lamp is in position IX, IY, SP, or PC, the four digits (two bytes) in the data display are *stored* in the IX, IY, SP, or PC 16-bit registers.

If the MEM selector lamp is lit, the right-most two hex digits (one byte) are stored in the address appearing in the address display, and the address display is then increased (auto-incremented) to point to the next sequential memory location.

Finally, if the I/O selector lamp is lit, the right-most two hex digits (one byte) are output to the output port selected by the address display which is then auto-incremented.

LA—LA is an abbreviation for Load Address. When the BRK lamp is unlit (i.e., when the Nanocomputer is not in *Breakpoint Mode*), the LA key may be used only when the selector lamp is in position MEM or I/O. In any other selector position, use of the LA key will result in the red ERR error lamp being lit to indicate that an illegal operation has been attempted. When the BRK lamp is lit, the

LA key has a different use. We shall defer further discussion of the Breakpoint Mode use of LA until the paragraphs on the BRK key.

With the Nanocomputer NOT in Breakpoint Mode:

If the selector lamp is in position MEM, LA causes the following to occur:

a) The four hex digits just entered and appearing in the data display are entered into the address display, and

b) The contents of the memory location pointed to by the address display are displayed in the data display.

If the selector lamp is in position I/O, LA causes the following to occur:

a) The two digit device code just entered and appearing in the data display is entered into the address display, and

b) the contents of the I/O port of the address display are displayed in the data display.

2ND—2ND refers to the second or high order byte in the register pairs IR, AF, BC, DE, and HL, namely I, A, B, D, and H. To store a byte (two hex digits) in these registers the procedure is:

STEP 1. Position the selector lamp to the desired register pair (IR, AF, BC, DE, HL)

STEP 2. Enter two hex digits in the data display

STEP 3. Press the 2ND key

STEP 4. Press the ST key

The result is that the contents of the register pair are redisplayed in the data display with the high order byte changed accordingly. The low order byte is unchanged. Note that if more than two hex digits are entered in STEP 2 above, the right-most two (i.e., the last two digits entered) are the ones stored.

The 2nd key has no effect when the selector lamp is positioned at IX, IY, SP, PC, MEM, or I/O since these "registers" are not PAIRS of 8-bit registers, as are IR, AF, BC, DE, and HL.

SS—SS stands for *Single Step.* This is a very useful feature of the Nanocomputer operating system in which programs may be executed one step at a time. After each step, the contents of various registers may be examined, thus giving the user a powerful debugging aid in the program development process.

We shall also make use of the single-step feature to illustrate some of the details of how the Z-80 microprocessor works, something which can only be seen when the Z-80 is operating in "slow motion."

An interesting fact about the single-step feature on the Nanocomputer is that it is implemented in software. Most single-step features are implemented in hardware. We shall talk more on this fascinating subject later.

One uses the ss key by loading a program, placing its start address into the PC register, and then pressing the ss key. Each time the ss key is pressed, a single instruction is executed. Between successive depressions of the ss key, the user may position the selector lamp anywhere to choose information for display. The single-step execution of a program may also begin after a breakpoint. (See BRK for information on breakpoints.)

Note that holding the ss key in a depressed position causes the program to continue stepping slowly until pressure is released.

INC—INC is an abbreviation for *INCrement*. This key has two functions. First, when the Nanocomputer is not in Breakpoint mode and the selector lamp is in position MEM or I/O, it causes the memory location or device code in the address display to be increased by one, thus displaying successive memory locations or I/O ports and their contents. In any other selector position, use of the INC key causes the ERR lamp to light up, indicating an illegal operation.

The second use of the INC key occurs when the Nanocomputer is in Breakpoint mode. The exact use of the INC key in Breakpoint mode is described below in the paragraphs on the BRK key.

ARS—ARS stands for *Alternate Register Set*. This key causes the two sets of registers A, B, C, D, E, F, H, L, and A′, B′, C′, D′, E′, F′, H′, L′ to be exchanged.

By pressing the ARS key once with the selector lamp in position AF, you cause registers A′ and F′ to be displayed in the data display. The results are similar for positions BC, DE, and HL of the selector lamp. There is no change in the display for the other positions of the selector lamp.

When the alternate register set is being displayed, the ARS lamp is lit. Note that pressing the ARS key alternately turns the ARS lamp on and off.

GO—This key has two functions. The first function is to initiate or resume execution of a microcomputer program. The other function is to remove breakpoints, which will be discussed in the paragraphs describing the BRK key. In order to initiate execution of a microcomputer program, one must specify the starting address of the program. This can be accomplished in either of two ways:

1. Load the PC (Program Counter) with the starting address, then press GO to begin execution.
2. Enter the starting address in the data display and immediately press GO.

In either case, program execution will proceed until the program either halts, returns control to the Nanocomputer operations system, or encounters a breakpoint. To resume execution after a breakpoint, merely press GO again.

BRK—BRK is an abbreviation for *breakpoint*. This key is a switch that places the Nanocomputer in and out of the Breakpoint Mode. When in the Breakpoint Mode, the BRK selector lamp is lit; otherwise it is unlit. Thus, alternate depressions of the BRK cause the lamp to turn on and off.

Let us discuss what a breakpoint is and what it means for your Nanocomputer to be in the Breakpoint Mode. A breakpoint is a break in program execution. You define a breakpoint by specifying a program instruction where execution should stop. You may then examine the registers and memory before continuing program execution. Execution may be resumed in single-step mode (using the SS key) or at full speed (pressing the GO key again). You specify a breakpoint by giving an address (two bytes or four hex digits). This address MUST point to the first byte of a multibyte instruction. It is important to note that the instruction beginning at the breakpoint address is NOT executed when the breakpoint is encountered. This instruction will be executed only when program execution resumes.

You may define up to eight breakpoint addresses at one time. These addresses are numbered 0 through 7. This numbering is only for ease of reference and does not imply anything about the order in which breakpoints must be entered. For example, breakpoint 0 may occur later in the execution of a program than breakpoint 5. The following sequence of steps describes how to define breakpoints as well as the particular functions of the BRK, INC, and LA keys in this process of program execution.

Step 1: Press the BRK key to enter Breakpoint Mode. The Nano-computer is now ready to accept breakpoint definitions.

Step 2: A single digit 0 should appear in the data display. Pressing the INC key causes this number to be increased by one up to 7 and then back to 0 again. This digit indicates the current breakpoint number.

Step 3: Define the breakpoint address for the desired breakpoint number by first displaying the correct single digit, and then typing in a four-digit address followed by the LA key. The resultant display should be such that

a) The first four digits are the address you entered.
b) There is a blank space followed by three digits.
c) The first digit of the three-digit group is the breakpoint number.
d) The second and third digits of the three-digit group are the contents of the breakpoint address, i.e., the first byte of the breakpoint instruction.

Step 4: Successive breakpoints may be defined by INCrementing to the desired breakpoint number, entering an address, and pressing LA. Any currently defined breakpoint may be changed using the same procedure.

Step 5: Press the BRK key again to exit from the Breakpoint Mode.

To remove a breakpoint, enter Breakpoint Mode, INCrement to the breakpoint you wish to delete, then press GO. The resultant display should contain only the breakpoint number.

LD and DP—If your Nanocomputer is equipped with a tape cassette recorder/player interface, you may use tape cassettes as a mass storage medium. That is, you may dump to tape programs or data which are stored in memory (the DP key); or you may load from tape programs or data which have been previously saved (the LD key).

Since the contents of read/write memory are always destroyed when the power to the Nanocomputer is turned off, a mass storage medium such as cassette tape greatly facilitates returning memory to a desirable state after power-up. In fact, when you perform the programming experiments in this and subsequent chapters, we strongly recommend that you dump the longer programs to tape after keying them in. In this way, should it become necessary to reload the program, you won't have to re-key each byte . . . you can just hit the LD key!

It is important to mention also that the LD and DP keys can be used in conjunction with devices other than cassette tape recorder/players. Any ASCII serial device can send or receive data to/from the Nanocomputer. That is, the LD and DP commands can be used for output to paper-tape punches, printers, crts, etc., and for input from paper-tape readers, crts, etc. You merely inform the Nanocomputer, via the TTY/CASS switch on the keyboard, whether it is accessing a serial digital teletype (TTY) or an audio cassette recorder/player (CASS). We will specifically discuss audio cassette I/O in more detail later.

Let us now discuss how to use the RCZ80 audio cassette-tape recorder/player. Then we will fully describe the load and dump operations.

The RCZ80 audio cassette-tape recorder/player is supplied by SGS-ATES for interfacing with the Nanocomputer. However, any standard recorder/player can be used. The discussion below applies specifically to the RCZ80 unit, though, with only slight modification, can apply equally to units manufactured by others. For these we refer you to the unit operation manual.

To set up the recorder/player for operation:

- select the proper operating voltage (110/120 or 220/240 vac) using the switch on the back of the recorder/player case

- connect the AC mains
- turn the volume control to maximum volume (10)
- with the power off to the Nanocomputer, connect the cassette cable: The 7-pin round connector plugs into the mating outlet on the side of the recorder/player, and the 8-pin flat connector plugs into the J3 connector of the NBZ80 board (upper left).
- position the TTY/CASS switch on the Nanocomputer keyboard to CASS.

The DP Operation

The DP key is used to initiate a cassette write operation. The procedure for recording the contents of a contiguous block of Nanocomputer memory (RAM, ROM, or EPROM) is as follows:

1. Apply power to the Nanocomputer.
2. Position the tape to the initial recording position (use the FAST FORWARD (>>) and REWIND (<<) keys).
3. Position the selector lamp on the Nanocomputer keyboard to MEM.
4. On the Nanocomputer keyboard, enter the first address of the block of memory you wish to dump (up to four hex digits), then press the LA key.
5. On the Nanocomputer keyboard, enter the length of the block of memory you wish to dump (up to four hex digits). The keyboard display should now show the start address on the left and the block length on the right.
6. On the Nanocomputer keyboard, press the DP key. The keyboard display will go dark. The cassette write operation has been initiated.
7. Confirm that the TTY/CASS switch is in the CASS position. Simultaneously press the red RECORD key and the FORWARD key (>). The tape will not start to move yet.
8. Press the GO key. The tape will start to move slowly. After about 20 seconds of continuous tone (written as a header), the Nanocomputer will start to record data on the tape cassette.
9. When the cassette write operation terminates, the cassette will stop automatically. Our experience is that it takes 20-25 seconds to write 256 bytes, so do not become alarmed if the write operation seems to take longer than you expect. After the cassette stops, hit the recorder STOP key to acknowledge the end of the write operation.
10. Press any key on the Nanocomputer keyboard to restart normal operation. Also, at this point, you can rewind the tape and remove it from the recorder/player, if you wish.

The LD Operation

The LD key is used to load programs and/or data previously recorded on a cassette into memory. The start address and number of bytes have been stored on the tape along with the program and data bytes, so it is not necessary to specify them again. Here is the sequence of steps for a cassette read operation:

1. Apply power to the Nanocomputer.
2. Position the tape to the initial reading position (use the FAST FORWARD (>>) and REWIND (<<) keys).
3. Double check the TTY/CASS switch on the Nanocomputer keyboard to ensure that it is in the CASS position.
4. Press the LD key. The Nanocomputer display should go dark. The load operation has now been initiated.
5. Press the FORWARD key (>) and listen for the high pitched sound of data.
6. The cassette will stop when the cassette read operation is terminated. Also, you should hear an unmistakable sound which we will not attempt to describe here.
7. When the cassette has stopped, press the RECORDER STOP key to acknowledge the end of the read operation.
8. If the ERR light on the Nanocomputer keyboard is on, a checksum error (error in data transmission) has occurred. Try to read the tape again. If the ERR light comes on again, the cassette is defective or incorrectly written.
9. If the load was successful, the ERR light will be off.
10. Press any key on the Nanocomputer keyboard to restart normal operation.

NOTE 1:

At the termination of both load and dump operations, the tape cassette motion is disabled until acknowledgement is received and normal operation resumed by pressing any key on the Nanocomputer keyboard. This end sequence of steps is quite important, so always adhere to it closely.

NOTE 2:

The speed of serial I/O during cassette tape reads and writes is programmable. When the Nanocomputer is powered up or reset (the RESET key is pressed), the speed is set to 600 baud or 60 characters per second, where each character consists of 10 bits (2 start bits, 7 bit ASCII code, and 1 stop bit). By changing the content of memory locations BAUDRT and BAUDRT +1, serial I/O speeds of 110 and 300 baud can be obtained. The following table gives the correspondence between the content of locations BAUDRT and BAUDRT + 1 and the serial I/O speeds.

(BAUDRT)	(BAUDRT + 1)	BAUD Rate
9A	00	600
35	01	300
55	03	110

The absolute address associated with the label BAUDRT can be obtained from the Master Symbol Table in Appendix F.

NOTE 3:

The format of the bytes recorded on tape is as follows:

- Each memory byte is translated into two ASCII characters, one ASCII character for each hex nibble (half byte). For example, the binary memory byte 00101010 is translated into an ASCII 2 and an ASCII A.
- Memory bytes are grouped eight to a record.
- Each record has the format:

Characters	Contents
1	Carriage return
2	Line feed
3	Colon
4–5	Record length
6–7	Record memory start address, HI byte
8–9	Record memory start address, LO byte
10–11	Not used
12–N	Data memory bytes of 2 ASCII characters per byte (number dependent on record length field in characters 4–5)
(N + 1)–(N + 2)	Checksum

NOTE 4:

The Nanocomputer is capable of reading a cassette tape recorded by another SGS-ATES product called the CLZ80 Z-80–based microcomputer, if the tape was created using the MO-Z Monitor/ Debug or ASS-Z Assembler software. This is accomplished by loading the memory location INMODE (see the Master Symbol Table in Appendix F for the absolute address) with any byte not equal to 00 (hex), and then following the usual Nanocomputer tape load procedure. Note that tapes created by the Nanocomputer may not be read by a CLZ80 operating under the MO-Z Monitor/ Debug or ASS-Z Assembler software.

BREAK—The BREAK key may be thought of as a "panic button." Pressing the BREAK key causes a nonmaskable interrupt of the CPU (NMI) which, in turn, causes immediate termination of the program currently executing. Control is returned to the Nano-computer operating system with the selector lamp in position PC. The address display points to the last instruction executed and the other registers are preserved as they were after the last executed program instruction.

RESET—The function of the RESET key is to restore the Nano-computer to its initial state. Execution of the operating system is restarted at the beginning. Thus, all the registers are reset and all pre-existing breakpoint addresses are erased.

CASS/TTY Switch—For Nanocomputers with both audio cassette recorder/players and serial teletype terminal devices interfaced to them, this switch selects one of the two device types for serial I/O.

This concludes our discussion of the Z-80-based Nanocomputer keyboard.

CENTRAL PROCESSING UNIT (CPU)

The Nanocomputer is a Z-80-based microcomputer system. The Z-80 40-pin dual-in-line package (DIP) chip was originally designed and produced by Zilog Corporation in 1976. The Z-80 microprocessor chip is now manufactured in Europe by SGS-ATES headquartered in Italy.

Clock

The quartz crystal found in the lower left-hand corner of the Nanocomputer pc board has a frequency of 2.4576 MHz. Associated with the crystal is a clock generator and driver chip which outputs a clock frequency of 2.4576 MHz. This 2.4576-MHz clock frequency drives the Z-80 microprocessor chip through each of the computing steps it performs. The maximum frequency that can be applied to Z-80A chips is 4 MHz. Unfortunately, at this frequency, PROM devices such as the 2708 or 2716 EPROMs are not fast enough. It is for this reason that SGS-ATES has chosen the standard Z-80 CPU operating at approximately 2.5 MHz. Note that at 2.5 MHz a single state, or clock cycle, has a duration of 400 nanoseconds, or 0.4 microsecond.

Memory

The memory of the Nanocomputer is composed of dynamic read/write memory and read-only memory. The dynamic RAM available on the Nanocomputer is 4K bytes but can be expanded to 16K bytes. The read/write memory is addressed in the first 4K region: locations 0000H through 0FFFH. The ROM on the Nanocomputer is 2K bytes expandable to 8K bytes. The ROM is addressed in the last 2K to 8K region, depending on ROM size.

I/O Ports

The Nanocomputer provides for both parallel and serial I/O. Two Z80-PIO chips implement parallel I/O, while serial device and digital/audio interface circuitry implement serial I/O. While one PIO chip is used for the display and keyboard interfaces, the other PIO chip is available to the user for his/her own use. The serial device drive circuits may be used to interface the Nanocomputer with most serial terminals at a data rate of 110 baud; and the digital/audio interface circuitry is for driving a tape cassette recorder/player.

Breadboard Description

For many experiments that you will perform with your Nanocomputer you will be required to construct electrical circuits using a breadboard, wire, integrated-circuit chips, and other electrical components. Here we give a brief description of a breadboard; however, we shall cover this topic more thoroughly later.

The breadboard is designed to accommodate the many experiments that you will perform in subsequent books. Integrated-circuit chips, resistors, capacitors, wires, and additional digital devices all connect to or tie in directly to the breadboard.

Top and bottom views of the breadboard are shown in Figs. 4-5 and 4-6. The breadboard contains 128 sets of 5 electrically connected solderless terminals and 2 sets of 64 straddle both sides of a narrow

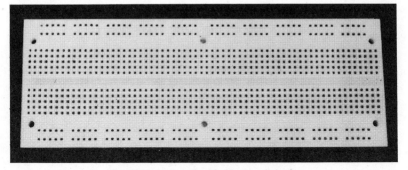

Fig. 4-5. Top view of solderless breadboard.

center groove. In addition, there are 8 sets of 25 electrically connected solderless terminals along the edges of the breadboard. The term, solderless, is used here because you make electrical connections between electronic components without the need for solder or a soldering iron.

The center groups of five electrically connected terminals accommodate integrated-circuit "chips" and permit up to four additional connections to be made at each pin for the smaller 14-pin and 16-pin

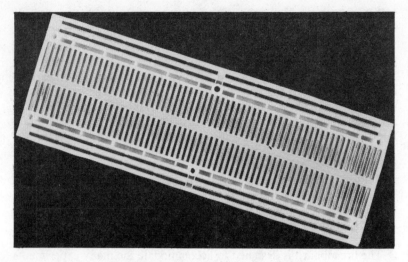

Fig. 4-6. Bottom view of solderless breadboard.

chips. The groups of 25 electrically connected terminals at the edges of the breadboard are tied to either +5 volts or to ground. They provide power both to the integrated-circuit chips and to auxiliary breadboarding station functions, which will be described in another chapter.

RULES FOR SETTING UP EXPERIMENTS

In the following chapters, you will use the Nanocomputer to perform experiments that demonstrate concepts of microcomputer programming and interfacing. Before you set up any experiment, we recommend that you observe the following ground rules:

1. Plan your experiment beforehand. Know what types of results you are expected to observe.
2. Clear the breadboarding socket of all unnecessary wires and components from previous experiments.
3. IMPORTANT: Before you do any breadboarding, disconnect the +5-volt wire connection to the outer bus strip on the breadboarding socket. Note that we have not asked you to disconnect power to the entire microcomputer, since by doing so you will erase all read/write memory.
4. With the +5-volt wire connection on the breadboard disconnected, carefully wire the interface circuit to the microcomputer. Wire power connections to individual integrated-circuit chips before you make any other connections.

5. Pay careful attention to the location of the various chips on the breadboarding socket. The judicious location of these devices can frequently minimize the jungle of wire connections that is inherent in any digital circuit of modest complexity.
6. Check the wired circuit to make certain that it is correct. PAY PARTICULAR ATTENTION TO THE POWER CONNECTIONS TO THE INTEGRATED CIRCUIT CHIPS. If they are wrong, you will burn out your chip and perhaps erase the read/write memory. Use a finger placed on the top surface of a chip to determine how hot it is; if it is hot, you have done something wrong.
7. Apply +5 volts of power to the bus strips when everything has been checked. You can now apply the "touch" test to determine if any chip becomes excessively warm.
8. Once you have finished with the experiment, do not disconnect the circuit. Instead, check the following experiment to determine whether or not it employs the same circuit.
9. Disconnect the main power to the microcomputer when you are finished for the day. If you have a cassette recorder interfaced to your Nanocomputer, you can store your programs before disconnecting the power, a practice which we highly recommend, since disconnecting the power erases read/write memory.

EXPERIMENT INSTRUCTIONS FORMAT

The instructions for each experiment are presented in the following format.

Purpose

The material presented under this heading states the purpose of the experiment. It would be useful for you to have this intended purpose in mind as you conduct the experiment.

Pin Configurations of Integrated-Circuit Chips

Pin configurations, shown with the permission of SGS-ATES, are given under this heading for all of the integrated-circuit chips used in the experiment. Note that all the experiments use SGS-ATES low-power Schottky TTL chips. If the circuit is identical to that given in the immediately preceding experiment, the pin configurations may be omitted.

Schematic Diagram of Circuit

You will be provided with a schematic diagram of the completed circuit that you will wire in the experiment. You should analyze this diagram in an effort to understand the circuit before you proceed further with the experiment. Check the pin numbers of all connections to integrated-circuit chips. KEEP IN MIND THAT THE POWER CONNECTIONS TO GATES HAVE BEEN OMITTED. Pay special attention to all +5-volt and ground power connections; your wired circuit will not operate at all if any of them are omitted.

Program

You will be provided with the microcomputer program that you should load into memory at the indicated memory addresses.

Steps

Under the heading of each sequential step, i.e., Step 1, Step 2, etc., are detailed instructions concerning how you should perform that portion of the experiment. Questions also are asked during the experiment. You should answer the questions at the time that you are performing the experiment. After you have written your answer, determine whether the correct answer is provided in the text immediately following the questions. If such is the case, or if the two answers disagree, make certain that you understand the discrepancy (and correct your answer, if possible) before you continue further with the experiment.

Questions

Questions will frequently be provided that probe (a) your understanding of the experiment that you have just finished, (b) your ability to anticipate future experiments or problems, (c) your ability to correlate textual material with experimentally determined information, and, using this information, formulate answers to questions covering material to which you have not been previously exposed. The number of questions provided will depend on the nature of the experiment, how far you are in the book, the phase of the moon, and the fatigue of the authors. In many chapters, the questions will be consolidated in a Review section at the end of the chapter. Answers are provided for each Review section.

A WORD OF CAUTION

For the novice microcomputer programmers who are using this text, we would like to make one point perfectly clear:

IT IS IMPOSSIBLE TO DAMAGE A MICROCOMPUTER BY IMPROPER PROGRAMMING

You may erase the contents of read/write memory, but you cannot destroy or damage the microcomputer system if you make errors in a program and then attempt to execute it. Therefore, relax and have fun with your microcomputer. Make mistakes in programming. Learn from them.

You can damage the Nanocomputer system if you:

- Apply power to it incorrectly.
- Allow metallic materials to accidentally short any wire interconnections on the printed-circuit board.
- Make improper wire connections in an interface. Pay specific attention to the input of data to the data bus; INPUT ALL DATA WITH THE AID OF THREE-STATE BUFFERS.
- Drop it.
- Operate it in an excessively warm or corrosive environment.
- Tinker with it without knowing what you are doing.

Most laboratory instruments are housed in metal or heavy-duty plastic and offer, to a reasonable extent, protection for the electronics from the careless user. The Nanocomputer (NBZ80) is exposed, so that you can observe how it is constructed and how it operates; however, it is vulnerable as a result of this exposure. We believe that it is important that you not be intimidated by your microcomputer, and that it not be hidden from you with an opaque chassis.

Remember, if you are only doing microcomputer programming, you cannot damage the microcomputer. If you are both programming and interfacing the microcomputer, you will have to be careful. In certain cases, you can damage a Z-80 chip by poor programming if you use an interface circuit incorrectly.

We do ask you to be careful.

INTRODUCTION TO THE EXPERIMENTS

The following experiments are designed to demonstrate the operation of the various keys on the Nanocomputer keyboard. To conduct these experiments you will require:

1 Nanocomputer (NBZ80 or NBZ80S) that is in good working order
1 Nanocomputer keyboard and software PROM/ROM (supplied with the Nanocomputer)
1 power supply for your NBZ80 (the NBZ80S has its own supply)

The experiments that you will perform may be summarized as follows:

Experiment No.	Comments
1	Demonstrates the operation of the 0 through F numeric keys, the LEFT-ARROW key, and the

RIGHT-ARROW key on the Nanocomputer keyboard.

2   Demonstrates the function of the ST and 2ND keys in loading registers with data.

3   Demonstrates the loading of information present in the DATA DISPLAY into a specific memory location in read/write memory. The function of the INC key is also demonstrated as an excellent way to display the contents of successive memory locations.

4   Demonstrates the loading and execution of a very simple microprocessor program in single step mode (SS key). Also demonstrates the functions of the GO and RESET keys.

5   Demonstrates two Nanocomputer utility routines which are resident in read-only memory: RAM test and Keyboard/Display test.

EXPERIMENT NO. 1

Purpose

The purpose of this experiment is to test the operation of the numeric keys, the LEFT-ARROW key, and the RIGHT-ARROW key on the Nanocomputer keyboard.

Step 1

Apply power to the Nanocomputer and press the RESET key. You should observe four hex digits in the address display, two hex digits in the data display, and the selector lamp should be in position PC. In our case, the address display read 0000 and the data display read 00.

Step 2

Press the 0 key. What do you observe in the data register?

We observed a 0 right justified with three leading blanks in the data register. If this did not happen to you, then you have a problem with your Nanocomputer. You should check it out before proceeding. (See the write-up in Experiment No. 6 of this chapter of the memory and keyboard/display self-diagnostic tests.)

Step 3

Press the 1 key and then the 2 key. The 0 should have shifted left two digits to make room for the 1 and 2. Thus the data display should contain a blank followed by 012. Enter 3, then 4. What do you observe now?

We observed that 0 was shifted off the display to make room for the digit 4. The data display has four digits illuminated: 1234.

Step 4

Continue entering digits. Each time a digit is entered, the four-digit data display is shifted left with the left-most digit disappearing. What has happened to the address display? the selector lamp?

The address display and selector lamp remain unchanged.

Step 5

Now press the RIGHT-ARROW (→) key once. What do you observe?

We observed several changes. First both the address and data displays changed to read 0000 and 00 respectively. Your Nanocomputer may not have produced those exact readings, but a change should have occurred. Also, the selector lamp is now moved over to position MEM. You also should have observed this. The significance of this display is that memory location 0000 contains the data byte 00.

Step 6

Press the LEFT-ARROW (←) key. Your very first display should be restored. Ours was 0000 00. This means that the 16-bit PC register contains 0000 and the content of memory location 0000 is 00.

Step 7

How can you position the selector lamp at AF?

There are two ways to do this, one way using the LEFT-ARROW (←) key and one way using the RIGHT-ARROW (→) key. With either key, merely press it down and hold it until the desired position is reached. The lamp marches along one step at a time, lighting each selector lamp until it reaches AF.

Step 8

What do you observe in the address and data displays with the selector in position AF?

We observed a blank address display (you should also) and a data display with the four hex digits 0000. This represents the contents of the AF register pair, i.e., the accumulator contains 00 and the flags contain 00. Your data display may have contained four different hex digits.

Step 9

Continue to choose different selector positions. What can you say about the address and data displays for positions IR, AF, BC, DE, HL? How about positions IX, IY, SP, PC, and MEM? How about the I/O position?

We observed that positions IR, AF, BC, DE, and HL produce a blank address display and a four-digit data display signifying the contents of the selected register pair. Positions IX, IY, SP, PC, and MEM yield a four-digit address display and a two-digit data display. For positions IX, IY, SP, and PC, the address display gives the contents of the selected 16-bit register, while the data display gives the contents of the memory location addressed by the register. The significance of the displays for position MEM is given in Step 5.

In the I/O position, two digits appear right justified in the address and data displays. The address display contains a device code, while the data display represents the one byte of information currently at that device. We will spend considerable time discussing I/O and device codes in later chapters.

EXPERIMENT NO. 2

Purpose

The purpose of this experiment is to demonstrate the function of the ST and 2ND keys in loading registers with data.

Step 1

Move the selector lamp to position BC, enter hex digits 11 into the data display, and press the ST key. What did you observe?

You should see that the data display, which represents the contents of the BC register pair, has 11 as its right-most digits. In other words, you have stored a byte (11 hex or 00010001 binary) in the C register of the Z-80 CPU!

Step 2

Now try entering 22 into the data display, then press the 2ND key followed by the ST key. What does the data display read now? Which Z-80 register was changed this time?

It should read 2211. You just stored a byte in the high order register, i.e., register B, of the register pair BC.

Step 3

How would you store the bytes 2103 in register pair HL?

Answer: Press the following keys in sequence.

1. RIGHT-ARROW (→), until the selector lamp is in position HL
2. 2
3. 1
4. 2ND
5. ST, to store high order byte 21 in H
6. 0
7. 3
8. ST, to store low order byte 03 in L

Is there any other way to accomplish the same thing?

The answer is yes; the key used to position the selector lamp could have been the LEFT-ARROW (←) key and the low order byte (03) could have been stored in L before the high order byte (21) was stored in H. Hence, with the Nanocomputer and its flexible set of keyboard operations, there are many ways to perform simple tasks, such as register loading.

Step 4

Try loading some other registers with data. In particular, try one of the non-pairs like IX, IY, SP, or PC. Notice that if you enter two hex digits and press ST the 16-bit register is loaded with 00 on the left and the byte (two digits) you entered on the right. Now try entering four hex digits, say ABCD, and press STORE. What happens? Can you explain this?

We observe that ABCD appears in the address display indicating that the 16-bit register has been loaded with two new bytes (namely AB and CD). The explanation for the "leading zeros" when only two digits (one byte) are stored, is as follows: Four digits (two bytes) ALWAYS are stored with the selector lamp at IX, IY, SP, or HL. The Nanocomputer fills in two zeros on the left if you only enter two digits. What happens if you enter one digit and press ST? Three digits and press ST? This is called *left zero filling*. It saves typing leading zeros.

EXPERIMENT NO. 3

Purpose

The purpose of this experiment is to demonstrate the loading of data into memory locations and the use of the INC key to display the contents of successive memory locations.

Step 1

Since we are working with MEMory locations and their contents, position the selector lamp at MEM. As we have mentioned before, the four digits of the address display give the memory address and the data display gives the contents of that location. Let us look at the contents of location 0100. To do this enter 0100 or 100 via the keyboard, then press LA, the LOAD ADDRESS key. What do you observe?

You should notice that 0100 now appears in the address display. In our case, the data display read 00. That is, in our case location 0100 contained 8 bits all set to 0, or the byte 00. Your data may be different.

Step 2

Try to STore AA in location 0100. Enter AA, then press ST. What happened?

The address display should read 0101 and, in our case, we observed that the data display read 00.

What does this mean? It means that AA was stored at location 0100 and the computer is waiting for you to store a byte at the next location (0101). The current contents of that location (0101) appear in the data display, (ours read 00). Try SToring BB by entering BB and then pressing ST.

Step 3

Let us not trust our Nanocomputer too much. We should check to be certain that 0100 contains AA and 0101 contains BB. How can we do this?

To see the contents of 0100, we need to display 0100 as the address. This requires the LA key. Type 0100 or 100 followed by LA. We hope you see AA in the data display.

Step 4

What about 0101? You could enter the address 0101 (or 101) followed by pressing LA. However, the Nanocomputer also can INCrement a memory location by one, thus saving all the retyping of addresses. Press the INC key once lightly. What do you see?

The address register is increased by one and the data register displays BB. Press INC and hold the key down. As you can see, the memory locations are shown in sequence.

The LA, ST, and INC keys are the major tools that you will use in this book for Z-80 program loading and load verification. You will see in the next experiment just how important these keys are.

Step 5

Reposition the selector lamp to any of the positions IR, AF, BC, DE, HL, IX, IY, SP, or PC, enter 11 and press LA. What do you observe?

The red error lamp is lit! We have led you astray. By using the LA key with the selector lamp positioned anywhere but MEM or I/O, you have attempted an illegal operation. The only situation in which LA can be used is in loading the address display with a MEMory address or an I/O device code.

Note: To extinguish the error lamp, simply start entering the next keyboard instruction.

Step 6

See if you can work out how to load a one-byte device code into the address display, with the contents of the I/O ports appearing automatically in the data display. The procedure is as follows: Position the selector lamp at I/O, enter two hex digits, and press LA.

EXPERIMENT NO. 4

Purpose

The purpose of this experiment is to load and execute a very simple microprocessor program both at full speed and in the single-step mode. The SS, GO, and RESET keys are demonstrated.

Step 1

At the end of this step, we want the Nanocomputer memory locations 0100 through 0105 to appear as follows:

Address	Contents
0100	3E
0101	00
0102	3C
0103	C3
0104	02
0105	01

Toward this end, position the selector lamp at MEM. Enter 0100 or 100 and press LA. The address display should read 0100 signifying that the Nanocomputer is ready to begin loading a program at 0100. The following key-ins will load the program:

3E	press ST
00	press ST
3C	press ST
C3	press ST
02	press ST
01	press ST

Step 2

You must now verify that you have correctly loaded the program. How can you do this?

Use the INC key: first display memory location 0100 (use LA key), then press the INC key to display each successive memory location. Be certain that you have the contents of each memory location correct.

Step 3

Load the PC register with the program starting address, 0100. To accomplish this, recall that you first position the selector lamp at PC, enter 0100 or 100, and then press ST.

Step 4

Position the selector lamp at AF. This signifies to the Nanocomputer that you wish to observe the contents of the AF register pair as the program executes in slow motion. Repeatedly press the ss key. What do you observe?

With every other depression of the ss key, you should notice that the contents of the A register (the accumulator) increase by one. Hold the ss key down. The A register will continue to count up. Your Nanocomputer is executing a program in slow motion!

Step 5

Now press GO. What happened?

All the lamps and displays have gone dark. Did you break the Nanocomputer? NO! It is now executing the program at full speed. You can stop it by pressing the RESET key. How fast was full speed? The accumulator was being incremented over one hundred thousand times each second. Note that immediately after pressing RESET, the displays of the Nanocomputer come on with the selector lamp in position PC. Whenever the Nanocomputer "goes dark" as you just observed, you can get control back by pressing RESET or BREAK. You have just executed your first Z-80 microcomputer program.

EXPERIMENT NO. 5

Purpose

The purpose of this experiment is to investigate two utility routines which SGS-ATES provides along with the Nanocomputer operating system in read-only memory. The two utility routines test read/write memory and the keyboard/display software and hardware.

Step 1

Since the programs which you will execute in this experiment already reside in read-only memory, there is no need to manually load any bytes, as you did above.

Let us first examine the read/write memory test. This test is comprised of two parts. The first part tests read/write memory locations 0FAB through 0FFF. These memory locations are used by the Nanocomputer operating system for storing data such as the bytes to be displayed on the keyboard. Each memory location is tested by writing zeros into it and then reading it to see if the zeros are indeed there. This is certainly not an exhaustive test, but it does ensure some functionality of each location. The test of locations 0FAB through 0FFF occurs automatically when the RESET key is pressed. If no error is detected by the test, the Nanocomputer shows that it is ready by lighting the PC lamp and displaying the contents of the PC register on the left and the contents of the memory location pointed to by the PC register on the right.

Press the RESET key several times. Hopefully you detect no errors!

Step 2 (Optional)

This step is NOT recommended for students without extra 4027 dynamic RAMS, because these chips are very sensitive to static electricity and are easily damaged if removed from their socket or replaced incorrectly.

Before performing Step 2, we urge you to read Appendix III on Precautions While Handling MOS Devices.

Let us now fool the Nanocomputer into thinking it has some faulty memory locations. First, REMOVE ALL POWER TO THE NANOCOMPUTER. This is critical! You may damage the computer, if you leave the power attached. With the power off, and referring to the illustration below, carefully remove RAM memory chip No. 1 from its plastic socket. This is most easily accomplished with a small screwdriver to pry up the chip. *Be very careful to maintain the wire leads on the memory chip as straight as possible.* With the memory chip out of its socket, turn on the Nanocomputer and press the RESET key. What do you observe?

We observed the ERR lamp became lit and the display read

8 – – – – – – –

This unusual output is produced by the memory test routine which detected an error in chip No. 1. The presence of the 8 (all segments lit) corresponds to the errant chip. Similarly, removing the RAM chip No. 3 would produce an 8 in the third position (given that the rest of the chips were all right). As it is very easy to break off pins on semiconductor chips: we do not recommend that you experimentally verify the correspondence between chip position and the position of the 8 in the resultant error display.

REMOVE POWER TO THE NANOCOMPUTER and carefully replace the memory chip. With the RAM chip residing properly in its socket, re-apply power to the Nanocomputer and press the RESET key. You should not encounter any error.

Fig. 4-7. CLZ80 RAM chip numbers and KBD display digit numbers.

Step 3

The second part of the read/write memory test tests user RAM (Fig. 4-7), locations 0000 through 0FAA. For each memory location, the following bytes are alternately loaded into and then read from it:

$$
\begin{array}{cccccccc}
0 & 0 & 0 & 0 & 0 & 0 & 0 & 1 \\
0 & 0 & 0 & 0 & 0 & 0 & 1 & 0 \\
0 & 0 & 0 & 0 & 0 & 1 & 0 & 0 \\
0 & 0 & 0 & 0 & 1 & 0 & 0 & 0 \\
 & & & \cdot & \cdot & \cdot & & \\
0 & 1 & 0 & 0 & 0 & 0 & 0 & 0 \\
1 & 0 & 0 & 0 & 0 & 0 & 0 & 0 \\
\end{array}
$$

This procedure is called "rotating a one bit through memory" and is a common technique used in memory testing. This memory test can be executed by typing the following sequence of keys:

1. Be sure the selector lamp is at position PC (use the RIGHT- and left-arrow keys)
2. Enter the address associated with the label MEMTUT (see the Master Symbol Table in Appendix F).
3. Press the GO key

You have just executed the program residing at memory location MEMTUT, which, of course, is the memory test program. The displays should all be dark as the computer busily rotates bits through memory. This will go on virtually forever. The display will light only if one of two events occurs:

1. You press the RESET or BREAK key, which terminates the test and causes a return to normal operating status with the selector lamp at the PC position.
2. The memory test detects a faulty memory location. In this case, the display will show the following:

> Error byte address in the left-most four digits
> The data byte written in the next two digits
> The data byte read in the next two digits

Naturally, the test failed because the last two pairs of digits were unequal.

Step 4

The keyboard/display test checks out all but two of the keys (BREAK and RESET) and all of the LEDs on the Nanocomputer keyboard/display unit. The program begins at location CONTST (see the Master Symbol Table in Appendix F. Thus, to execute it:

1. Position the selector lamp at PC.
2. Enter the address associated with the label CONTST.
3. Press the GO key.

What do you observe?

We observed the BRK and IR LEDs were lit. Also, one of the segments on each of the eight seven-segment displays was lit. For convenience and ease of reference, the segments are lettered as shown in Fig. 4-8 and the following list.

A correspondence between key row (numbered from bottom to top) and lit LEDs and segments follows.

Key Row	LED Lit	Segment Lit
1	AF, I/O	b
2	BC, MEM	c
3	PC, DE	d
4	SP, HL	e
5	ERR, IX	f
6	IY, ARS	g
7	BRK, IR	a

The BREAK and RESET keys cannot be tested, since pressing each will terminate the test. Verify the above correspondence by pressing

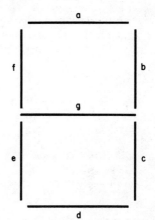

Fig. 4-8. Seven-segment display numbering scheme.

several keys in each horizontal row of keys on the Nanocomputer keyboard.

CHAPTER 5

Some Simple Z-80 Microcomputer Programs

In this chapter, you will load and execute several simple micro-computer programs that employ the Z-80 instructions discussed in Chapter 3.

OBJECTIVES

At the completion of this chapter, you will be able to do the following:

- Define the terms *binary code, hexadecimal code, assembly code,* and *high level language.*

- Explain the operation of the following Z-80 instructions:

  NOP; INC A; HALT; LD A,<B2>; LD (<B3> <B2>),A; and JP <B3> <B2>.
- Load and execute simple Z-80 microprocessor programs on the Nanocomputer.
- Be able to read and understand Z-80 assembly language program listings which show memory location, object code, source code, and comments.

REVIEW OF SEVERAL Z-80 INSTRUCTIONS

In Chapter 3, we discussed the following Z-80 instructions:

Hex Machine Code	Mnemonic Code	Operation
00	NOP	No operation
3C	INC A	Increment the accumulator by 1
76	HALT	Halt the microcomputer
3E <B2>	LD A,<B2>	Move the immediately following data byte to the accumulator
32 <B2> <B3>	LD (<B3><B2>),A	Store the contents of the accumulator in the memory location addressed by the following two bytes in this 3-byte instruction
C3 <B2> <B3>	JP <B3><B2>	Unconditional jump to the memory address given in the following two bytes of this 3-byte instruction

PROGRAMMING LANGUAGES AND LISTINGS

You read in Chapter 2 that a program is a series of instructions and that instructions come in a variety of forms: binary, hexadecimal, mnemonic code, and full words (high level language). Let us examine these forms more closely.

Binary Code

This is the true language of the Z-80. Eventually, all program instructions must be expressed in this form to be understandable to the Z-80. If humans found this a natural mode of expressing themselves, there would be no need for any other form for presenting instructions to the computer. Each subsequent form, hexadecimal, mnemonic, and high level language, is tailored more and more to the human and less and less to the computer. Obviously, a price is paid for each successive level of convenience to the human, namely time, which is required to perform the translation to bits, and memory space which is required to house a program to perform the translation.

Let us look at a sample program, written in binary code. The following program adds the two numbers in memory locations 0160H and 0161H and stores the sum in location 0162H:

A Binary Code Program Listing

```
0 0 1 1 1 0 1 0
0 1 1 0 0 0 0 0
0 0 0 0 0 0 0 1
0 1 0 0 0 1 1 1
0 0 1 1 1 0 1 0
0 1 1 0 0 0 0 1
0 0 0 0 0 0 0 1
1 0 0 0 0 0 0 0
0 0 1 1 0 0 1 0
0 1 1 0 0 0 1 0
0 0 0 0 0 0 0 1
```

This may look pleasing to your Nanocomputer, but it is hardly natural to you.

Hexadecimal Code

This mode of instruction representation is an improvement over the binary method because it abbreviates each group of 8-bits to two hexadecimal digits. Let us list the preceding program using hexadecimal code:

A Hexadecimal Code Program Listing

```
3A
60
01
47
3A
61
01
80
32
62
01
```

This is certainly an improvement by human standards, but a Z-80 would not be able to interpret this program as it is. A *hexadecimal loader* is required to take the above hexadecimal listing and convert it to the binary code which is understandable to the Z-80. The Nanocomputer operating system contains a hexadecimal loader which senses when a hexadecimal key (0-F) has been depressed and converts the hex code to binary code for storage in read/write memory.

What are the advantages and disadvantages of hex loaders? The advantages are:

1. Greater ease in programmer/machine interface, in that only two digits instead of eight digits per byte must be dealt with.
2. Resultant increase in programmer efficiency, in that errors are more easily detected and corrected.

However the disadvantages are:

1. The hex loader—a program itself—must reside in memory so that hex input can be interpreted (i.e., converted to binary representation) and stored.
2. The conversion process takes time.

In this day and age, programmers are becoming more expensive than computers, so the human factors are in many cases considered to be more important and will, most likely, gain in relative importance.

Mnemonic Code

This form of representing instructions carries us one step further from the computer and closer to the programmer. Mnemonic code uses alphabetic characters to describe instructions. For example LD B,A is the mnemonic code for the hex coded 47 instruction. This instruction causes the contents of the A register to be loaded into the B register. Clearly, the mnemonic representation is more suggestive of this (at least from a human viewpoint). Here is the mnemonic listing for the previous addition program.

A Mnemonic Program Listing or Assembly Listing

```
LD      A, (0160H)
LD      B, A
LD      A, (0161H)
ADD     A, B
LD      (0162H),A
```

(The character "H" following the address indicates that it is in HEX.) Note that:

a. Mnemonics are used to describe operations which the Z-80 is to perform. For example, the "LD" mnemonic is an abbreviation for "LOAD" which is an instruction which moves data from a source to a destination in the general form:

```
LD    "destination",    "source"
```

The first Load instruction loads the A register or accumulator with the contents of memory location 0160H.

b. Names have been assigned to the registers within the Z-80 CPU chip. For example, registers A and B (known usually as 111 and 000 to the Z-80) are mentioned in the preceding program.

A program written using mnemonics is called an *assembly language* program. The assembly language mnemonics used in the above program were developed by the Zilog Corporation when they developed the Z-80 CPU and, as such, are the SGS-ATES recommended mnemonics. However, SGS-ATES certainly cannot force the user to employ these mnemonics and many other companies have developed alternate sets of mnemonics which they feel are better. For the Z-80, the most widespread and universal mnemonic set is by SGS-ATES and Zilog, so we will use their set in this book.

As you might well imagine, the process for translating an assembly language program to binary code is fairly involved. This is true, but the process is so systematic and repetitive that it can be programmed and implemented on the Z-80 itself. The program which inputs an assembly listing (called *source code*) and outputs a binary-coded program (called *object code*) is called an *assembler*. SGS-ATES has written an assembler for the Nanocomputer which is currently available on tape cassette ASS-Z or EPROM FR-Z. To use the assembler, you need an upgraded version of the Nanocomputer, a keyboard with ASCII characters (the alphabet, numbers, and special characters such as period, comma, semicolon, etc.) to input the mnemonics, and an ASCII display device for output, as well as a minimum of 16K bytes of read/write memory and two audio cassette recorder/players. We will not assume that you have such a sophisticated microcomputer configuration. Thus, in this book, we will do our program assembly by hand.

By hand assembly, we mean that the programmer takes the set of mnemonics and translates them one-by-one to hex code. Hex code can then be input to the Nanocomputer whose hex loader makes the final conversion to Z-80 intelligible binary code. The hand assembly process makes extensive use of mnemonic-to-hex cross references. There is an excellent set of cross-references in matrix form with instructions grouped by similar function. These will all be presented in this book.

A hand assembled program listing is given next. Note that the hex code here is called *object code,* and the assembler code is called *source code.* Note also that a semicolon (;) separates each comment from its associated line of source code. The purpose of the semicolon is to notify the assembler that it should ignore all that follows, i.e., that which follows is for human benefit only. Also, assembler listings strictly follow the conventions mentioned earlier about numeric representations: decimal numbers are followed by a period (.), hexadecimal numbers are followed by the character "H," and binary numbers appear without special notation.

Memory Location	Object Code	Source Code		Comments
0150	3A 60 01	LD	A,(0160H)	;A = contents of location 0160
0153	47	LD	B,A	;Load B from A
0154	3A 61 01	LD	A,(0161H)	;A = contents of location 0161
0157	80	ADD	A, B	;Add A and B
0158	32 62 01	LD	(0162H),A	;Store sum in 0162

Thus, you can see that hand-assembly involves translation of the mnemonics plus location of the resultant byte in read/write memory. In the previous case, the program begins at location 0150 and ends at 015A. The comments are, of course, optional but highly desirable. This is the way all programs will be listed in this book.

High Level Languages

The last category of programming languages which we will discuss is called high level languages. High level languages are one more step removed from the computer than assemblers. Typically, high level languages do not require programmers to know anything about registers or memory addresses. Rather, these languages are designed to allow a programmer to concentrate on the problem to be solved, instead of concentrating on the computer. For example, in a high level language such as FORTRAN, the program to add two numbers would appear as follows

$$ANS = X + Y$$

Examples of other high level languages are COBOL, PL/1, ALGOL, SNOBOL, PASCAL, JOVIAL, and many more. Each of these source languages requires large translators called *compilers* to convert programs to binary object code.

A high level language called *BASIC* can be implemented on an upgraded Nanocomputer. The SGS-ATES BASIC is a language oriented to control applications and is available in 8K of PROM/ROM (BAS-Z). As each BASIC language statement is entered, the BASIC translator interprets the statement, converts it to (many) bytes of binary object code and then executes it immediately. This is not like a FORTRAN or COBOL compiler or Z-80 assembler which waits until the entire program is entered before starting the translation. For this reason the BASIC translator is called an *INTER-PRETER*. The BASIC version of our addition program is:

$$LET\ A1 = X + Y$$

High level languages have two major advantages which often outweigh the disadvantages of large compilers or interpreters:

1. Programs are more "procedure oriented" and less computer oriented.
2. Programs written in a high level language for one computer can often run on another computer with little or no change, a property called *portability*. This is almost never possible with either assembly or hex codes, simply because they are too closely related to the machine.

ASSEMBLY LANGUAGE PROGRAMMING

As we mentioned earlier, in this series of chapters we will program in assembly language and hand assemble programs to obtain hex code to load into the Nanocomputer. Besides translating mnemonics to hex codes, hand assembly involves the location of the microcomputer program somewhere in the available read/write memory of your Nanocomputer. Please note the first column in the assembly listing given in the last section. This column, with the heading "Memory Location," indicates the memory address of the first byte in that program line. If more than one byte occupies that line, the next sequential addresses contain those bytes, with the following program line beginning at the next memory location.

Let us now try to execute some simple Z-80 programs on the Nanocomputer.

INTRODUCTION TO THE EXPERIMENTS

The following experiments permit you to execute several simple programs which are described in detail in each experiment. This will give you experience in loading and executing microprocessor programs as well as teach you some rudiments of programming.

The experiments you will perform can be summarized as follows:

Experiment No.	Comments
1	Demonstrates the execution of the NOP, HALT, and LD A,<B2> instructions.
2	Demonstrates the execution of the INC A and JP <B3><B2> instructions in a simple program loop.
3	Demonstrates the execution of a program with a simple loop, and the INC B and INC C instructions.
4	Demonstrates the LD (<B2>,<B3>), A instruction for setting memory contents to a specified value.
5	Demonstrates execution of the addition program used as an example in the section on program languages and listings.

EXPERIMENT NO. 1

Purpose

The purpose of this experiment is to demonstrate the execution of three Z-80 instructions: NOP, HALT, and LD A,<B2>.

Program No. 1

Memory Location	Object Code	Source Code	Comments
0100	3E BB	LD A, BBH	;Load the accumulator with BB
0102	76	HALT	;Halt the microcomputer

Program No. 2

0103	3E BB	LD A, BBH	;Load the accumulator with BB
0105	00	NOP	;No operation
0106	3E FF	LD A, FFH	;Load the accumulator with FF
0108	76	HALT	;Halt

Step 1

Power up the Nanocomputer and press the RESET key a few times to initialize the Z-80 CPU. Position the selector lamp at MEM, enter 0100, and press LA. You are now ready to begin loading a program into memory beginning at location 0100. Enter Program No. 1 by alternately entering object code bytes and pressing the ST key.

Step 2

Recheck to be sure that Program No. 1 has been loaded correctly by repositioning the memory pointer at 0100 (enter 0100 followed by LA) and pressing the INC key.

Step 3

Prior to executing this program, let us pause to reflect on what we expect to happen. Please write in the following space what the contents of the accumulator should be after program execution has finished.

Given your prediction, let us now proceed to find out if it has any merit. First let us check the accumulator to find out its contents now: position the selector lamp at AF. What do the left-most two digits in the data display read?

Step 4

Execute the program starting at 0100: position the selector lamp at position PC, enter 0100, ST, then press GO. What happens?

The Nanocomputer immediately goes dark! The computer is in the HALT state.

Step 5

Revive the Nanocomputer by pressing the BREAK key. The computer immediately "wakes-up" with the selector lamp at position PC showing the contents of the program counter or PC register to be 0103. This is the memory location of the next instruction to be executed. However, because the instruction at location 0102 is HALT (76), the next instruction is not reached.

Step 6

Check the contents of the accumulator to see if your prediction at Step 3 was correct: Move the selector lamp to AF. What do you see as the contents of A?

We hope you see BB. The very first instruction of Program No. 1 instructs the microcomputer to put BB into register A, the accumulator. The next instruction, which halts the microprocessor, has no effect on the A register, so after program execution, the contents of A should be BB.

Step 7

Change the contents of A to 00 (00, 2ND, ST) and then execute Program No. 1 in single-step mode, watching the accumulator: position the selector lamp at PC, enter 0100, press ST, position the selector lamp at AF, and press ss once. What happens?

Immediately the contents of the A register changed from 00 to BB.

Step 8

Press ss again. You will notice that nothing happens. The single-step mechanism does not allow the computer to halt. Thus, in single-step mode, the HALT command has no effect.

Step 9

Load and check Program No. 2 beginning at location 0103. What should be the contents of the A register at the conclusion of executing this program?

Step 10

Execute Program No. 2. Again be sure to revive the Nanocomputer using the BREAK key (do not use RESET as it changes the contents of all of the registers). Check the A register.

We hope that you read FF as its contents. So, what happened is that the original BB was over-written with an FF.

Step 11

Let us execute this program in single-step mode to observe the effect of the NOP instruction at location 0105. Set the PC to 0103 and then position the selector lamp at AF to observe the single-step execution. Press ss: the A register goes immediately to BB. Press ss: Nothing happens. This is the execution of the NOP instruction. If you position the selector lamp at PC you will see that the address display reads 0106 indicating that 0105, the NOP, has just been executed and that the instruction beginning at 0106 is next. Position the selector back at AF and press ss again. The A immediately reads FF showing the effect of the LD A, FFH instruction.

Thus, you can see from the above steps that NOP has merely one effect on a program and this is that it causes the program to do nothing for one step.

EXPERIMENT NO. 2

Purpose

The purpose of this experiment is to demonstrate the execution of the INC A and JP <B3><B2> instructions in a simple program loop.

Program No. 3

Memory Location	Object Code	Source Code	Comments
0109	3E FF	LD A, FFH	;Load the accumulator with FF
010B	3C	INC A	;Increment the accumulator
010C	C3 0B 01	JP 010BH	;Jump to address 010B

Step 1

Note that the INC A instruction is a one-byte instruction which tells the computer to add one to the contents of the accumulator. The JP instruction causes control to be transferred unconditionally to the address given by the two bytes following the C3 op code. Notice that the two address bytes appear with the LO address byte first and the HI address byte second.

Step 2

Load and verify Program No. 3.

Step 3

Let us examine Program No. 3 to anticipate what it will do. Program No. 3 initializes the accumulator to FF and then increments A by 1. The third instruction causes an unconditional branch back to location 010B, i.e., the INC A instruction. So the accumulator is incremented followed by a jump back to the INC A instruction. The effect of all this is that the INC A instruction is executed repeatedly until someone stops the "loop" by turning off the computer, or pressing RESET or BREAK.

Step 4

Now let us execute the program in single-step mode to see what happens to the accumulator (A) and program counter (PC). First let us observe the accumulator, so, after loading the PC with the program start address, 0109, move the selector lamp to the AF position. Recall that the left-most two digits of the data display represent the contents of the A register. Press the ss key once. What happens to the A register?

We observed that its contents immediately became FF.

Step 5

The next instruction says to increment A. What should the contents of A be after the next step?

Press ss once to verify your conjecture. You should observe that the contents of A went to 00. Did you also observe a change in the F register? We will discuss this later.

Step 6

Hold the ss key down for awhile. You should observe the contents of the register incrementing as the INC A instruction is being repeatedly executed.

Step 7

Now position the selector lamp at PC. Hold the ss key down and observe what happens to the contents of the PC register. Write down what you observed:

We observed the PC register alternating between 010B and 010C.

EXPERIMENT NO. 3

Purpose

To demonstrate the execution of a program with a simple loop and the INC B and INC C instructions.

Program No. 4

Memory Location	Object Code	Source Code	Comments
010F	04	INC B	;Increment the B register
0110	C3 20 01	JP 0120H	;Jump to location 0120
0120	C3 30 01	JP 0130H	;Jump to location 0130
0130	04	INC B	;Increment the B register
0131	0C	INC C	;Increment the C register
0132	C3 0F 01	JP 010FH	;Jump to location 010F

Step 1

Let us make a few observations about the listing of Program No. 4.

a. First note that a jump instruction such as JP 0130H translates to the series of three hex bytes:

C3   Jump instruction operation code
30   LO address byte
01   HI address byte

There is always the temptation to translate the instruction with the address bytes in the reverse order. Every programmer seems to fall into that trap at least once. All we can do is keep warning you.

b. Two new instructions, INC B and INC C, appear in this program. They cause the computer to add one to the B and C registers, respectively.

Step 2

Load and verify the Program No. 4. Note that you need only load the bytes specified because no other memory locations between 010F and 0134 are ever used. Loading this program requires that you have an excellent understanding of the LA and ST keys and the subtleties of their usage.

Step 3

When you are convinced that you have loaded Program No. 4 correctly, study the mnemonic program statements very carefully and try to determine exactly what the program is doing.

Let us describe in words, and then with a picture, what this program does.

1. The first step in the program increments the B register, that is, adds 1 to its current contents.
2. The next step is an unconditional branch to location 0120. This means that this step instructs the computer to go to location 0120 for its next instruction.
3. Now the computer reaches 0120 and reads the instruction there. Another unconditional branch! Where do we go this time? 0130.
4. So, here we are at 0130, what now? The program says increment B, so 1 is added to the B register.
5. The next instruction says increment the C register. So, add 1 to C.
6. The next instruction is a branch, so we transfer to location 010F. Notice that 010F is the instruction executed back at 1. Thus we have a cycle going here: Steps 1-6 will be executed repetitively until some outside force interferes.

Let us use the diagram in Fig. 5-1.

The end result of all this incrementing and jumping is that the B register is incremented twice as often as the C register.

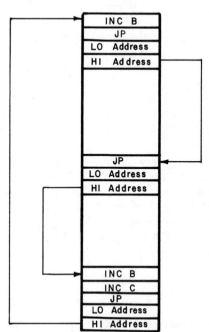

Fig. 5-1.

Step 4

Let us now execute Program No. 4 in single-step mode. We will want to observe what happens to the PC register and the BC register pair during execution. First, load the BC register pair with zeros to initialize both registers (position the selector lamp at BC, enter 00, 2ND, ST to initialize B, and enter 00, ST, to initialize C). Now load the PC register with 010F, and leaving the selector lamp at PC, press ss. How many times will you press ss before the PC reads 0120, 0130, 010F for the second time?

Your answer should be 2, 3, and 6, respectively. Thus, we have a six-step program loop. When will this loop end? Never, unless we stop it by pressing RESET or BREAK.

Step 5

Hold the ss key depressed and watch the recurrent pattern of six PC addresses. Enter these addresses in the following space.

We observe the following PC addresses:

```
010F
0110
0120
0130
0131
0132
```

Step 6

Let us now observe the BC register pair during single-step execution of Program No. 4. We predicted in Step 3, that the B register will be incremented twice for every time that the C register is incremented. Let us see if this is the case. Read the BC pair and write what you see in the following space. (Make sure you are at the beginning of a new cycle, i.e., PC = 010F.)

We observed 04 02. (Depending on how long you held the ss key down in Step 5, your results may be different. However, the first digit should be twice the second, no matter what.) That is, B has been incremented from 00 to 04 while C has been incremented from 00 to 02. This would bear out our conjecture. To make sure, begin pressing ss and write down your observations:

We observed the following:

> During single step 1: B was incremented
> During single step 4: B was incremented again
> During single step 5: C was incremented

Single steps 2, 3, and 6 are occupied with jump instructions.

Step 7

Hold the ss key down for awhile. We observed the following sequence of data displays:

08 04	0C 05	0E 07
09 04	0C 06	0F 07
0A 04	0D 06	10 07
0A 05	0E 06	10 08
0B 05		

Step 8

Let us make one last remark about this program. The first two jump statements can be replaced by a single jump instruction. What is it?

The answer is JP 0130H. The reason is that the first JP always causes a jump to the statement at 0120, itself a jump to 0130.

EXPERIMENT NO. 4

Purpose

The purpose of this experiment is to demonstrate the LD ($<$B3$>$ $<$B2$>$),A instruction for setting memory contents to a specific value.

Program No. 5

Memory Location	Object Code	Source Code	Comments
0136	3E 11	LD A,11H	;Load with 11
0138	32 45 01	LD (0145H),A	;Load memory location 0145 with the contents of A
013B	76	HALT	;Halt

Step 1

The new instruction is the LD (0145H),A instruction at address 0138. This instruction copies the contents of the A-register into memory location 0145. Notice that, like the jump instruction, the address makes up the second and third bytes of this LD instruction with the LO byte preceding the HI byte.

Step 2

Load and verify Program No. 5.

Step 3

Check the current contents of memory location 0145 and write it in the following space.

We observed 00.

Step 4

Execute the above program either at full speed (GO) or single-step speed (SS). If you executed the program at full speed, return control to the Nanocomputer operating system by pressing BREAK to ensure that registers and memory are preserved. Check the accumulator and memory location 0145. What do they contain?

They should both contain 11.

Step 5

Write, load, and execute a program, starting at location 013C to store 22 at memory location 0146. You can test to see if the program works by looking at location 0146 after you have executed the program. We have written an exceptable answer in the following space. Your answer may, of course, differ somewhat from ours.

Answer

Memory Location	Object Code	Source Code	Comments
013C	3E 22	LD A,22H	;Load A with 22H
013E	32 46 01	LD (0146H),A	;Load memory location 0146 from A
0141	76	HALT	;Halt

EXPERIMENT NO. 5

Purpose

The purpose of this experiment is to demonstrate the execution of the addition program used as an example in the section of this chapter on programming languages and listings.

Program No. 6

Memory Location	Object Code	Source Code	Comments
0150	3A 60 01	LD A,(0160H)	;A=contents of location 0160
0153	47	LD B,A	;Load the B register with A
0154	3A 61 01	LD A,(0161H)	;A=contents of location 0161
0157	80	ADD A, B	;Add B to A, store result in A
0158	32 62 01	LD (0162H),A	;Store sum in location 0162
015B	76	HALT	

Step 1

Notice that several new instructions have been introduced in this program. These instructions are listed and explained below. They all will be covered in detail in subsequent units.

Object Code	Mnemonic Code	Operation
3A <B2> <B3>	LD A, (<B3><B2>)	Loads the contents of memory location <B3><B2> into the accumulator.
47	LD B,A	Loads the contents of the accumulator into the B register.
80	ADD A, B	Adds the contents of the B register to the contents of the A register storing the resultant sum in the A register.

Step 2

Load and verify Program No. 6.

Step 3

Let us now test the program by adding 2 and 3. To do this we must store 2 in location 0160 and 3 in location 0161 (we could store 2 in location 0161 and 3 in location 0160, it makes no difference). Thus 02 and 03 (the hex equivalents of 2 and 3, respectively) must be stored accordingly. Now load the PC register with 0150 and press GO.

Step 4

Press BREAK to restore control to the Nanocomputer operating system and then look at the contents of the A register and memory location 0162. What do you see?

We expect to see 05 and that is indeed what we find.

Step 5

Execute the program in single-step mode watching the contents of the A and B registers.

Step 6

Try adding other pairs of numbers. To stay out of trouble, be sure that the two given numbers do not sum to a number greater than FFH or 255. (base 10), the capacity of one 8-bit byte.

Step 7

If you are feeling ambitious, see if you can deduce what happens when the sum does exceed FFH (or 255. base 10).

REVIEW

The following questions will help you review the instructions that you learned in this unit.

1. Explain what each of the following operations does.
    - a. 3E
      - 5B
    - b. C3
      - A5
      - 03
    - c. 3C
    - d. 32
      - E4
      - 1B
    - e. 76
    - f. 00
2. Provide the correct hex code for the following operations by referring to the text of this chapter or to Appendix B.
    - a. Jump to memory address HI=24 and LO=53
    - b. Store the contents of the accumulator in memory location HI=02 and LO=38
    - c. Move the immediate data byte 92 to the accumulator
    - d. Increment the contents of the accumulator
    - e. Halt the microcomputer
    - f. No operation

Answers
1. a. Move the data byte 5B to the accumulator
   b. Jump to memory address HI=03 and LO=A5
   c. Increment contents of accumulator
   d. Store contents of accumulator in memory location HI=1B and LO=E4
   e. Halt the microcomputer
   f. No operation
2. a. C3
      53
      24

b. 32
   38
   02
c. 3E
   92
d. 3C
e. 76
f. 00

CHAPTER 6

Registers, Memory, and Data Transfer

In this chapter, you will learn some of the many ways to transfer data between the Z-80 microprocessor chip and memory, as well as between different locations in memory. You will get your first look at the entire Z-80 instruction set, which should impress you at least with its size and complexity. The JP NZ, INC, and DEC instructions are introduced so that you may create *time delay loops* in your programs.

OBJECTIVES

At the completion of this chapter, you will be able to do the following:

- Understand what *instruction decoding* means
- Cite the 3-bit binary code assigned to each general-purpose register
- Define the term *addressing mode*
- Define: *register addressing*
     immediate addressing
     immediate extended addressing
     register indirect addressing
     extended addressing
- Explain the increment register and decrement register instructions
- Explain the LD instructions for the above addressing modes
- Explain the block transfer instructions

- Write a program that has a time delay loop
- Write programs for various kinds of data transfer

Z-80 INSTRUCTION SET

The complete Z-80 instruction set is given on the following pages in a form similar to that first suggested by R. Baker for the Intel 8080A microcomputer. This form of instruction set description first appeared in *Byte,* a magazine devoted to microcomputer hobbyists. In Chapter 3, you learned that the operation code (op code) is the code for the specific operation that the microprocessor executes. With eight bits of information, or a one-byte op code, it is possible to have 2 to the eighth power or 256 different operation codes; these are shown in Table 6-1. The five binary digits in the left-hand column are the first five binary digits of the 8-bit operation code. The remaining binary digits are shown in columns across the top and are repeated in three other locations in the table. The two-byte and three-byte op-code instructions appear in Tables 6-2 through 6-5.

You will not be asked to memorize this instruction set. Our purpose here is simply to show you the entire set so that you can refer to it as you learn new instructions. For example, in Chapter 3, you learned the following instructions:

Object Code	Source Code
00	NOP
32 <B2> <B3>	LD (<B3><B2>), A
3C	INC A
3E <B2>	LD A, <B2>
76	HALT
C3 <B2> <B3>	JP <B3><B2>

Can you find them in the table? (Hint: these are one-byte op-code instructions.)

The Z-80 instructions presented in Tables 6-1, 6-2, 6-3, 6-4, and 6-5, provide an overview of its capabilities. In particular, one can readily see how the Intel 8080A instruction set forms a basis for the expanded language of the Z-80. All but twelve of the one-byte operation codes are implemented on the 8080A. The new Z-80 one-byte operation-code instructions are the exchange register sets instruction (EXX) and the "relative jump" instructions (JR) which are enclosed in boxes in Table 6-1. The other op codes, which are not used by the 8080A, are CB, DD, ED, and FD. Each of these is always the first byte of a multibyte op-code Z-80 instruction. We will discuss each of these instruction codes later, but first, more about the one-byte op-code instructions.

If you examine the one-byte op codes in Table 6-1, you will notice that the first two bits determine the general class of operation. All of the single-byte load (LD) instructions in Table 6-1 have 01 for their first two bits. All of the arithmetic and logic instructions begin with the binary digits 10. With the exception of the relative jump (JR) instructions (which all begin with 00), the branch instructions—jumps, calls, and returns—have first bits equal to 11. In determining the relationships between individual bits in the op code and the actual operations that are performed, you are *decoding* the operation code. This is essentially what the instruction decoder does electronically within the microprocessor chip.

The above decoding of the first two op-code bits of Z-80 one-byte op-code instructions is just the beginning. If you closely examine the load instructions, with the first two bits equal to 01, you will notice the following:

1. Each instruction moves the contents of one register to another register.
2. Each register has a 3-bit code associated with it.

Register	Binary Code	
B	000	
C	001	
D	010	
E	011	
H	100	
L	101	
(HL)	110	(see note)
A	111	(see note)

Note: Remember that (HL) refers to the memory location addressed by the contents of the HL register pair. The letter A refers to the accumulator register, which we have discussed previously. Strictly speaking, (HL) is not a register, but it is often referred to as one in certain contexts. We will be careful to specify whether or not we wish to include (HL) when we use the word "register."

To see how the three-bit code for registers applies to load instructions, consider this 8-bit byte:

$$0\ 1\ 1\ 1\ 1\ 0\ 1\ 0$$

We can immediately see what this instruction does by decoding its bits as follows:

```
0 1 -----------   LD instruction
    1 1 1 -----   A is destination register
          0 1 0   D is the source register
```

Hence the mnemonic for this instruction is LD A,D (check Table 6-1) which means that the Z-80 puts the contents of the D-register into the accumulator, i.e., the A-register is *loaded* with the contents of the D-register.

Table 6-1. Z-80 One-Byte Operation Codes

	000	001	010	011	100	101	110	111
00 000	NOP	LD BC, <B3><B2>	LD (BC), A	INC BC	INC B	DEC B	LD B, <B2>	RLCA
00 001	EX AF, AF'	ADD HL, BC	LD A, (BC)	DEC BC	INC C	DEC C	LD C, <B2>	RRCA
00 010	DJNZ <B2>	LD DE, <B3><B2>	LD (DE), A	INC DE	INC D	DEC D	LD D, <B2>	RLA
00 011	JR <B2>	ADD HL, DE	LD A, (DE)	DEC DE	INC E	DEC E	LD E, <B2>	RRA
00 100	JR NZ, <B2>	LD HL, <B3><B2>	LD (<B3><B2>), HL	INC HL	INC H	DEC H	LD H, <B2>	DAA
00 101	JR Z, <B2>	ADD HL, HL	LD HL, (<B3><B2>)	DEC HL	INC L	DEC L	LD L, <B2>	CPL
00 110	JR NC, <B2>	LD SP, <B3><B2>	LD (<B3><B2>), A	INC SP	INC (HL)	DEC (HL)	LD (HL), <B2>	SCF
00 111	JR C, <B2>	ADD HL, SP	LD A, (<B3><B2>)	DEC SP	INC A	DEC A	LD A, <B2>	CCF

	000	001	010	011	100	101	110	111
01 000	LD B, B	LD B, C	LD B, D	LD B, E	LD B, H	LD B, L	LD B, (HL)	LD B, A
01 001	LD C, B	LD C, C	LD C, D	LD C, E	LD C, H	LD C, L	LD C, (HL)	LD C, A
01 010	LD D, B	LD D, C	LD D, D	LD D, E	LD D, H	LD D, L	LD D, (HL)	LD D, A
01 011	LD E, B	LD E, C	LD E, D	LD E, E	LD E, H	LD E, L	LD E, (HL)	LD E, A
01 100	LD H, B	LD H,C	LD H, D	LD H, E	LD H, H	LD H, L	LD H, (HL)	LD H, A
01 101	LD L, B	LD L, C	LD L, D	LD L, E	LD L, H	LD L, L	LD L, (HL)	LD L, A
01 110	LD (HL), B	LD (HL), C	LD (HL), D	LD (HL), E	LD (HL),H	LD (HL), L	HALT	LD (HL), A
01 111	LD A, B	LD A, C	LD A, D	LD A, E	LD A, H	LD A, L	LD A, (HL)	LD A, A

	000	001	010	011	100	101	110	111
10 000	ADD A, B	ADD A, C	ADD A, D	ADD A, E	ADD A, H	ADD A, L	ADD A, (HL)	ADD A, A
10 001	ADC A, B	ADC A, C	ADC A, D	ADC A, E	ADC A, H	ADC A, L	ADC A, (HL)	ADC A, A
10 010	SUB B	SUB C	SUB D	SUB E	SUB H	SUB L	SUB (HL)	SUB A
10 011	SBC A, B	SBC A, C	SBC A, D	SBC A, E	SBC A, H	SBC A, L	SBC A, (HL)	SBC A, A
10 100	AND B	AND C	AND D	AND E	AND H	AND L	AND (HL)	AND A
10 101	XOR B	XOR C	XOR D	XOR E	XOR H	XOR L	XOR (HL)	XOR A
10 110	OR B	OR C	OR D	OR E	OR H	OR L	OR (HL)	OR A
10 111	CP B	CP C	CP D	CP E	CP H	CP L	CP (HL)	CP A

	000	001	010	011	100	101	110	111
11 000	RET NZ	POP BC	JP NZ, <B3><B2>	JP <B3><B2>	CALL NZ, <B3><B2>	PUSH BC	ADD A, <B2>	RST 0
11 001	RET Z	RET	JP Z, <B3><B2>	see note 1	CALL Z, <B3><B2>	CALL <B3><B2>	ADC A, <B2>	RST 8
11 010	RET NC	POP DE	JP NC, <B3><B2>	OUT (<B2>), A	CALL NC, <B3><B2>	PUSH DE	SUB <B2>	RST 10H
11 011	RET C	EXX	JP C, <B3><B2>	IN A, (<B2>)	CALL C, <B3><B2>	see note 1	SBC A, <B2>	RST 18H
11 100	RET PO	POP HL	JP PO, <B3><B2>	EX (SP), HL	CALL PO, <B3><B2>	PUSH HL	AND <B2>	RST 20H
11 101	RET PE	JP (HL)	JP PE, <B3><B2>	EX DE, HL	CALL PE, <B3><B2>	see note 1	XOR <B2>	RST 28H
11 110	RET P	POP AF	JP P, <B3><B2>	DI	CALL P, <B3><B2>	PUSH AF	OR <B2>	RST 30H
11 111	RET M	LD SP, HL	JP M, <B3><B2>	EI	CALL M, <B3><B2>	see note 1	CP <B2>	RST 38H

NOTE: Bytes CB, DD, ED, and FD do not appear in the 8080A instruction set. In the Z-80 instruction set, they always appear as the first byte of a multibyte op-code instruction.

Table 6-2. Z-80 Two-Byte Operation Codes: Byte 1 = CB

	000	001	010	011	100	101	110	111
00 000	RLC B	RLC C	RLC D	RLC E	RLC H	RLC L	RLC (HL)	RLC A
00 001	RRC B	RRC C	RRC D	RRC E	RRC H	RRC L	RRC (HL)	RRC A
00 010	RL B	RL C	RL D	RL E	RL H	RL L	RL (HL)	RL A
00 011	RR B	RR C	RR D	RR E	RR H	RR L	RR (HL)	RR A
00 100	SLA B	SLA C	SLA D	SLA E	SLA H	SLA L	SLA (HL)	SLA A
00 101	SRA B	SRA C	SRA D	SRA E	SRA H	SRA L	SRA (HL)	SRA A
00 110								
00 111	SRL B	SRL C	SRL D	SRL E	SRL H	SRL L	SRL (HL)	SRL A
	000	001	010	011	100	101	110	111
01 000	BIT 0,B	BIT 0,C	BIT 0,D	BIT 0,E	BIT 0,H	BIT 0,L	BIT 0,(HL)	BIT 0,A
01 001	BIT 1,B	BIT 1,C	BIT 1,D	BIT 1,E	BIT 1,H	BIT 1,L	BIT 1,(HL)	BIT 1,A
01 010	BIT 2,B	BIT 2,C	BIT 2,D	BIT 2,E	BIT 2,H	BIT 2,L	BIT 2,(HL)	BIT 2,A
01 011	BIT 3,B	BIT 3,C	BIT 3,D	BIT 3,E	BIT 3,H	BIT 3,L	BIT 3,(HL)	BIT 3,A
01 100	BIT 4,B	BIT 4,C	BIT 4,D	BIT 4,E	BIT 4,H	BIT 4,L	BIT 4,(HL)	BIT 4,A
01 101	BIT 5,B	BIT 5,C	BIT 5,D	BIT 5,E	BIT 5,H	BIT 5,L	BIT 5,(HL)	BIT 5,A
01 110	BIT 6,B	BIT 6,C	BIT 6,D	BIT 6,E	BIT 6,H	BIT 6,L	BIT 6,(HL)	BIT 6,A
01 111	BIT 7,B	BIT 7,C	BIT 7,D	BIT 7,E	BIT 7,H	BIT 7,L	BIT 7,(HL)	BIT 7,A

	000	001	010	011	100	101	110	111
10 000	RES, 0,B	RES 0,C	RES 0,D	RES 0,E	RES 0,H	RES 0,L	RES 0,(HL)	RES 0,A
10 001	RES 1,B	RES 1,C	RES 1,D	RES 1,E	RES 1,H	RES 1,L	RES 1,(HL)	RES 1,A
10 010	RES 2,B	RES 2,C	RES 2,D	RES 2,E	RES 2,H	RES 2,L	RES 2,(HL)	RES 2,A
10 011	RES 3,B	RES 3,C	RES 3,D	RES 3,E	RES 3,H	RES 3,L	RES 3,(HL)	RES 3,A
10 100	RES 4,B	RES 4,C	RES 4,D	RES 4,E	RES 4,H	RES 4,L	RES 4,(HL)	RES 4,A
10 101	RES 5,B	RES 5,C	RES 5,D	RES 5,E	RES 5,H	RES 5,L	RES 5,(HL)	RES 5,A
10 110	RES 6,B	RES 6,C	RES 6,D	RES 6,E	RES 6,H	RES 6,L	RES 6,(HL)	RES 6,A
10 111	RES 7,B	RES 7,C	RES 7,D	RES 7,E	RES 7,H	RES 7,L	RES 7,(HL)	RES 7,A
	000	001	010	011	100	101	110	111
11 000	SET 0,B	SET 0,C	SET 0,D	SET 0,E	SET 0,H	SET 0,L	SET 0,(HL)	SET 0,A
11 001	SET 1,B	SET 1,C	SET 1,D	SET 1,E	SET 1,H	SET 1,L	SET 1,(HL)	SET 1,A
11 010	SET 2,B	SET 2,C	SET 2,D	SET 2,E	SET 2,H	SET 2,L	SET 2,(HL)	SET 2,A
11 011	SET 3,B	SET 3,C	SET 3,D	SET 3,E	SET 3,H	SET 3,L	SET 3,(HL)	SET 3,A
11 100	SET 4,B	SET 4,C	SET 4,D	SET 4,E	SET 4,H	SET 4,L	SET 4,(HL)	SET 4,A
11 101	SET 5,B	SET 5,C	SET 5,D	SET 5,E	SET 5,H	SET 5,L	SET 5,(HL)	SET 5,A
11 110	SET 6,B	SET 6,C	SET 6,D	SET 6,E	SET 6,H	SET 6,L	SET 6,(HL)	SET 6,A
11 111	SET 7,B	SET 7,C	SET 7,D	SET 7,E	SET 7,H	SET 7,L	SET 7,(HL)	SET 7,A

NOTE: CB is the first byte of all two-byte op codes for the above instructions. The position of an instruction in the table determines the second byte of the op code.

Table 6-3. Z-80 Two-Byte Operation Codes: First Byte = DD

	000	001	010	011	100	101	110	111
00 000								
00 001		ADD IX,BC						
00 010								
00 011		ADD IX,DE						
00 100		LD IX,<B4><B3>	LD(<B4><B3>),IX	INC IX				
00 101		ADD IX,IX	LD IX,(<B4><B3>)	DEC IX				
00 110					INC (IX+<B3>)	DEC (IX+<B3>)	LD (IX+<B3>),<B4>	
00 111		ADD IX,SP						

	000	001	010	011	100	101	110	111
01 000							LD B,(IX+<B3>)	
01 001							LD C,(IX+<B3>)	
01 010							LD D,(IX+<B3>)	
01 011							LD E,(IX+<B3>)	
01 100							LD H,(IX+<B3>)	
01 101							LD L,(IX+<B3>)	
01 110	LD (IX+<B3>),B	LD (IX+<B3>),C	LD (IX+<B3>),D	LD (IX+<B3>),E	LD (IX+<B3>),H	LD (IX+<B3>),L		LD (IX+<B3>),A
01 111							LD A,(IX+<B3>)	

	000	001	010	011	100	101	110	111
10 000							ADD A,(IX+<B3>)	
10 001							ADC A,(IX+<B3>)	
10 010							SUB (IX+<B3>)	
10 011							SBC A,(IX+<B3>)	
10 100							AND (IX+<B3>)	
10 101							XOR (IX+<B3>)	
10 110							OR (IX+<B3>)	
10 111							CP (IX+<B3>)	
	000	001	010	011	100	101	110	111
11 000								
11 001								
11 010								
11 011								
11 100		POP IX		EX (SP),IX		PUSH IX		
11 101		JP (IX)						
11 110								
11 111		LD SP,IX						

NOTE: There are 70 Z-80 instructions with two- and three-byte op codes for the IY register. Their definition is exactly the same as the IX instructions with DD replaced by FD as byte one.

Table 6-4. Z-80 Three-Byte Operation Codes: Byte 1 = DD, Byte 2 = CB

	000	001	010	011	100	101	110	111
00 000							RLC (IX+<B3>)	
00 001							RRC (IX+<B3>)	
00 010							RL (IX+<B3>)	
00 011							RR (IX+<B3>)	
00 100							SLA (IX+<B3>)	
00 101							SRA (IX+<B3>)	
00 110							SRL (IX+<B3>)	
00 111								
	000	001	010	011	100	101	110	111
01 000							BIT 0,(IX+<B3>)	
01 001							BIT 1,(IX+<B3>)	
01 010							BIT 2,(IX+<B3>)	
01 011							BIT 3,(IX+<B3>)	
01 100							BIT 4,(IX+<B3>)	
01 101							BIT 5,(IX+<B3>)	
01 110							BIT 6,(IX+<B3>)	
01 111							BIT 7,(IX+<B3>)	
	000	001	010	011	100	101	110	111
10 000							RES 0,(IX+<B3>)	
10 001							RES 1,(IX+<B3>)	
10 010							RES 2,(IX+<B3>)	
10 011							RES 3,(IX+<B3>)	
10 100							RES 4,(IX+<B3>)	
10 101							RES 5,(IX+<B3>)	
10 110							RES 6,(IX+<B3>)	
10 111							RES 7,(IX+<B3>)	
	000	001	010	011	100	101	110	111
11 000							SET 0,(IX+<B3>)	
11 001							SET 1,(IX+<B3>)	
11 010							SET 2,(IX+<B3>)	
11 011							SET 3,(IX+<B3>)	
11 100							SET 4,(IX+<B3>)	
11 101							SET 5,(IX+<B3>)	
11 110							SET 6,(IX+<B3>)	
11 111							SET 7,(IX+<B3>)	

Table 6-5. Z-80 Two-Byte Operation Codes: Byte 1 = ED

	000	001	010	011	100	101	110	111
01 000	IN B,(C)	OUT (C),B	SBC HL,BC	LD (<B4><B3>),BC	NEG	RETN	IM0	LD I,A
01 001	IN C,(C)	OUT (C),C	ADC HL,BC	LD BC,(<B4><B3>)		RETI		
01 010	IN D,(C)	OUT (C),D	SBC HL,DE	LD (<B4><B3>),DE			IM1	LD A,I
01 011	IN E,(C)	OUT (C),E	ADC HL,DE	LD DE,(<B4><B3>)			IM2	
01 100	IN H,(C)	OUT (C),H	SBC HL,HL					RRD
01 101	IN L,(C)	OUT (C),L	ADC HL,HL					RLD
01 110			SBC HL,SP	LD (<B4><B3>),SP				
01 111	IN A,(C)	OUT (C),A	ADC HL,SP	LD SP,(<B4><B3>)				
	000	001	010	011				
10 000								
10 001								
10 010								
10 011								
10 100	LDI	CPI	INI	OUTI				
10 101	LDD	CPD	IND	OUTD				
10 110	LDIR	CPIR	INIR	OTIR				
10 111	LDDR	CPDR	INDR	OTDR				

The arithmetic and logic instructions (those op codes beginning with 10) illustrate register decoding also. For example, in the set

to
$$
\begin{array}{l}
1\ 0\ 0\ 0\ 0\ \text{-}\ \text{-}\ \text{-} \\
1\ 0\ 1\ 1\ 1\ \text{-}\ \text{-}\ \text{-}
\end{array}
$$

the last three bits correspond to the *register* involved. For the instructions in the sets

to
$$
\begin{array}{l}
0\ 0\ 0\ 0\ 0\ 1\ 0\ 0 \\
0\ 0\ 1\ 1\ 1\ 1\ 0\ 0
\end{array}
$$

and
to
$$
\begin{array}{l}
0\ 0\ 0\ 0\ 0\ 1\ 0\ 1 \\
0\ 0\ 1\ 1\ 1\ 1\ 0\ 1
\end{array}
$$

and
to
$$
\begin{array}{l}
0\ 0\ 0\ 0\ 0\ 1\ 1\ 1 \\
0\ 0\ 1\ 1\ 1\ 1\ 1\ 1,
\end{array}
$$

the third, fourth, and fifth bits (numbering from left to right) represent the register that is involved in the operation.

So far, we have discussed only one-byte operation-code instructions. Tables 6-2 through 6-5 display the instructions with multibyte operation codes. None of the multibyte operation codes are implemented on the Intel 8080A microprocessor. The entire 8080A instruction set is comprised only of one-byte operation codes and, except for the eight marked bytes, appears in Table 6-1. Hence, most of the new instructions for the Z-80 appear in the multibyte operation-code Tables 6-2 through 6-5.

The multibyte operation codes can be divided into four groups based on their first byte—CB, DD, ED, or FD. We shall point out some major properties of each of these groups.

The CB Instructions (Table 6-2)

The two-byte op codes with first byte equal to CB are displayed in Table 6-2. The eight bits derived from the row and column position of the instruction represent the second byte of the op code. For example, the instruction BIT 2,C corresponds to the two-byte op code:

Byte 1 = CB
Byte 2 = 51   (0 1 0 1 0 0 0 1)

The structure of byte 2 is easily discernible from Table 6-2.

First two bits =

    00 - - - - - - a rotate or shift instruction in which the last three bits are the code for the register involved.

    01 - - - - - - a BIT instruction in which the last three bits specify the register and the other three bits specify the bit to be addressed.

    10 - - - - - - a RES instruction in which the last six bits have the same significance as in the BIT instruction.

    11 - - - - - - a SET instruction in which the last six bits have the same significance as in the BIT instruction.

The DD and FD Instructions (Tables 6-3 and 6-4)

Instructions which begin with DD or FD may have two or three byte op codes. Table 6-3 displays the two-byte op-code DD instructions. Notice that they all involve the index register IX. The FD two-byte codes are analogously defined for the IY index register.

All the three-byte op codes implemented on the Z-80 have the following structure:

Byte 1: DD or FD depending on index register (IX or IY)
Byte 2: CB
Byte 3: displacement byte
Byte 4: First two bits indicate rotate or shift, BIT, RES, or SET as in the CB instructions above. The next three bits are always 110. The remaining bits indicate the type of rotate or shift or bit number as in the CB instructions above.

The three-byte DD operation codes are displayed in Table 6-4 with byte four determined by the row and column position of the instruction.

The ED Instructions (Table 6-5)

The instructions which begin with ED all have two-byte op codes. Table 6-5 displays these instructions, with the second byte being determined by the row and column position of the instruction. The patterns that emerge are left as exercises for the interested instruction decoders among the readers.

Z-80 ADDRESSING MODES

Almost all of the Z-80 instructions involve operating on data that can be stored in registers within the CPU chip, in memory, or can be input or output from I/O ports. The term *addressing mode* refers to the method by which this data is accessed by the instruction. Is the data actually part of the instruction? Does the instruction contain a code telling the computer where the data is? Does the instruction contain a pointer to the location in memory where the data is stored? In all, the Z-80 has ten distinct addressing modes. We shall investigate these in detail in this and subsequent chapters.

The variety and power of the Z-80 addressing modes contribute in large measure to the many advantages the chip has over other 8-bit microprocessors, such as the Intel 8080A. Unfortunately, they also add to the complexity of the Z-80 instruction set. However, be assured that the extra time and effort spent learning the addressing modes will be amply repaid in many ways. First, the more ways in which data can be retrieved and manipulated, the easier it is to write efficient programs. Second, the Zilog Corporation has devised an excellent method for cross-referencing Z-80 mnemonics and their associated hexadecimal code which requires that the user know and understand the ten addressing modes. Many more rewards will come to those who persevere in learning the addressing modes, they are too numerous to try to list here. One final bit of advice before plunging into the first set of addressing modes: devote your initial efforts toward understanding what the addressing modes *mean,* rather than memorizing their sometimes fancy, unintuitive names. The memorization of the names can come with experience later. The addressing modes are important, though, and we urge you to spend the time necessary to learn them.

SINGLE REGISTER LOAD INSTRUCTIONS:
REGISTER ADDRESSING MODE
LD d,s

There exist 63 different single register LD instructions in the Z-80 instruction set. Each instruction has the mnemonic LD d,s where

d = destination register
s = source register

The instruction codes range exclusively from 40 to 7F, with the lone exception of 76 which is the HALT instruction. The 8-bit form of the LD instruction is,

0 1 D D D S S S

The values of DDD or SSS are the three bits that correspond to the specific three-bit binary code for the register. Thus:

Register	DDD or SSS Binary Code
B	000
C	001
D	010
E	011
H	100
L	101
(HL)	110
A	111

We are now ready to define the *register* addressing mode:
register addressing—The technique of using groups of bits within the Z-80 instruction code to specify which register(s) are involved.

Some examples of the use of this class of instructions are summarized as follow:

Load register C from register B	LD C,B
Load the accumulator from register C	LD A,C
Load register D from register E	LD D,E
Load the accumulator from register H	LD A,H
Load register L from the accumulator	LD L,A
Load the memory location addressed by the HL register pair from the accumulator	LD (HL),A
Load the accumulator from the memory location addressed by the HL register pair	LD A,(HL)

The transfer of data between a memory location, (HL), and any other register requires additional explanation, and will be discussed in a subsequent section. The LD A,B; LD B,A; LD A,(HL); and LD (HL),A instructions are shown in the illustration of Fig. 6-1. The arrow points in the direction of data transfer.

LOAD IMMEDIATE TO REGISTER
LD r,<B2>

The term *immediate* refers to the addressing mode for which the data to be loaded into register r is actually contained within the multi-byte instruction as byte number two, <B2>. In the load-immediate-to-register instruction, the destination of the data byte is indicated by the bits marked "D,"

```
Byte 1  0 0 D D D 1 1 0
Byte 2  data byte <B2>
```

The values for DDD are the register codes on the preceding page. The mnemonic is LD r, <B2>. The number of states is 7, which corresponds to an execution time of 2.8 microseconds, with the exception of the LD (HL),<B2> instruction, which requires 10 states or 4.0 microseconds. In Fig. 6-1 we depict the eight different load-immedi-

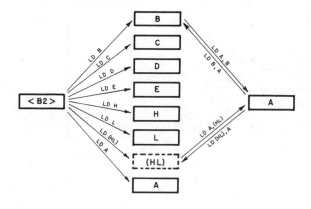

Fig. 6-1.

ate-to-register instructions. Byte <B2> is the second byte in the two-byte instruction; this information is transferred from the program to the designated register.

Note that *all register and data movement within the Z-80 and within the Nanocomputer is in parallel; eight bits of information are transferred at the same time.* Special conditions are involved in the transfer of data to and from the memory location (HL). This topic is discussed below.

REGISTER INDIRECT LOAD WITH ACCUMULATOR
LD A,(rp); LD (rp),A

Register indirect is an addressing mode in which a register pair—BC, DE, or HL—is used to point to a memory address whose contents are either being replaced with or loaded into the accumulator A. For example LD A,(DE) places the 8-bit byte, the memory address of which is contained in the register pair DE, into the accumulator. LD (DE),A stores the contents of the accumulator in the memory location that is addressed by the contents of register pair DE.

The op codes for these instructions are

LD A,(rp):	0 0 r p 1 0 1 0	or	LD A,(HL) 0 1 1 1 1 1 1 0
LD (rp),A:	0 0 r p 0 0 1 0	or	LD (HL),A 0 1 1 1 0 1 1 1

where the register pairs are encoded as follows. Fig. 6-2 shows how register indirect addressing works.

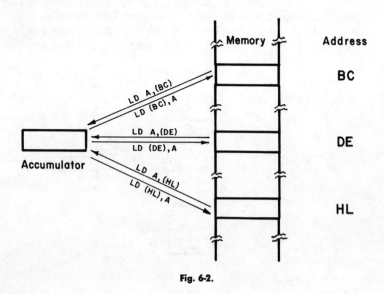

Fig. 6-2.

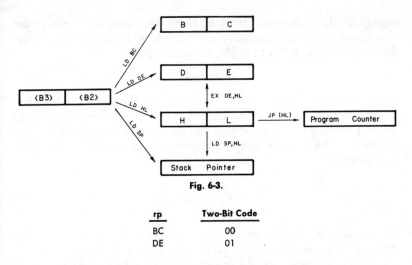

Fig. 6-3.

rp	Two-Bit Code
BC	00
DE	01

LOAD IMMEDIATE EXTENDED TO REGISTER PAIR
LD rp, <B3><B2>

The load immediate extended instructions belong to the so called "16-bit load" group because these instructions cause the transfer of two bytes from the instruction (bytes two and three) into a register pair—BC, DE, HL, or SP. The term *immediate extended* refers to another Z-80 addressing mode in which *extended* means a two-byte transfer, and *immediate* means that the two data bytes are actually part of the instruction. Fig. 6-3 shows several load immediate extended instructions and a pictorial representation of their data transfer properties.

The register pair destination of the data bytes is indicated by the bits marked "rp" in the op code for these instructions:

0 0 r p 0 0 0 1

where the following correspondence exists between register pairs and two-bit codes:

Register Pair	Binary Code
BC	00
DE	01
HL	10
SP	11

LOAD EXTENDED REGISTER PAIR
LD rp,(addr); LD (addr),rp

These instructions use *extended addressing* to move two bytes between memory and a register pair BC, DE, or HL. Extended addressing means that two bytes contained within the instruction point to the first of the two bytes in memory which are to be the source or destination of the transfer. For example, the instruction

LD HL, (0100H)

loads register L with the data byte stored in location 0100 and register H with the data byte stored in location 0101. Note that the *second* register in the pair is loaded with the data from the *lower* of the two addresses. The op code for this instruction is 2A so LD HL,(0100H) translates to

2A   op code
00   LO memory address byte
01   HI memory address byte

The analogous load operations for register pairs BC and DE have two-byte op codes. Rather than list the instructions and their op codes as we have in the past, we will present them later in a more structured format in the 16-bit load group table in the next chapter. The most important idea here is to understand extended addressing.

INCREMENT REGISTER
INC r

To *increment* a register means to increase the contents of the register by 1. The single-byte instruction is simply,

0 0 r 1 0 0

and has a mnemonic of INC r, where r is the identity (A, B, C, etc.) of the register being incremented. With the exception of INC (HL), the increment register instruction requires only five states, or 2.0 microseconds, for execution.

DECREMENT REGISTER
DEC r

To *decrement* a register means to decrease the contents of the register by 1. The single-byte instruction is similar to the increment instruction above,

0 0 r 1 0 1

and has a mnemonic of DEC r. With the exception of DEC (HL), the decrement register instruction requires five states, or 2.0 microseconds, for execution. Both the increment and decrement instructions employ the usual 3-bit binary code for the register.

JUMP IF NOT ZERO
JP NZ,<B3><B2>

This is your first *conditional branch instruction,* which is an instruction that is subject to a condition. In this case, the jump occurs to the memory address given in the second <B2> and third <B3> bytes of the instruction *if the zero flag is at logic 0.* We are not prepared here to talk about flags; for our purposes here, the jump occurs only if the result of a register operation is not zero. If the result of the register operation is zero then the JP NZ instruction is ignored and the program skips over the three instruction bytes to the following instruction. The JP NZ instruction is a three-byte instruction,

1 1 0 0 0 0 1 0
LO address byte <B2>
HI address byte <B3>

that has an execution time of 10 states, or 4.0 microseconds. The instruction is widely used in the creation of time delay loops, an example of which will be given in a program in this chapter.

BLOCK DATA TRANSFERS
LDD, LDI, LDDR, LDIR

So far, we have discussed many ways to transfer data between registers and memory locations one byte at a time. The Z-80 has four very powerful instructions designed to facilitate moving blocks of data from one set of locations in memory to another. Prior to executing any of these four instructions, a Z-80 program must *initialize* the BC, DE, and HL registers as follows:

HL = address of the first source byte
DE = address of the first destination byte
BC = number of bytes to be moved

Execution of the LDI (*load-increment*) instruction causes the following steps to occur:

1. The byte in the memory location addressed by register pair HL is loaded into the location addressed by register pair DE.
2. The contents of register pairs HL and DE are both incremented (by 1).
3. The contents of the register pair BC are decremented (by 1).

Execution of the LDIR (*load-increment-repeat*) instruction causes the following to occur:

1. The byte in the location pointed to by register pair HL is loaded into the location addressed by register pair DE.
2. The contents of register pairs HL and DE are both incremented.

3. The contents of register pair BC are decremented.
4. The value of the register pair BC is checked. If BC is not equal to 0000 then steps 1, 2, 3, and 4 are repeated. If BC is equal to 0000 then execution proceeds to the next instruction in the program.

Execution of the LDD (*load-decrement*) and LDDR (*load-decrement-repeat*) instructions result in very similar sequences of steps. The only difference is that Step 2 *decrements* both HL and DE.

Fig. 6-4 shows the registers and memory locations before and after execution of the LDIR instruction. This instruction is the subject of an experiment which you will perform at the end of this chapter.

INTRODUCTION TO THE EXPERIMENTS

The following experiments are designed to demonstrate what you have learned in Chapter 6 about transferring data between registers and registers, between registers and memory locations, and between memory locations and other memory locations.

The experiments you will perform may be summarized as follows:

Experiment No.	Comments
1	Demonstrates the immediate and register addressing modes.
2	Demonstrates the immediate extended, extended and register indirect addressing modes.
3	Demonstrates the techniques for implementing program loops. Specifically, the JP NZ instruction is used to form a time delay loop.
4	Demonstrates the block move instruction LDDR.
5	Demonstrates the block move instruction LDI. Two new conditional jumps as well as a logical instruction are introduced.
6	Demonstrates the value of the block move instruction by showing how it can save memory and program steps.

EXPERIMENT NO. 1

Purpose

The purpose of this experiment is to demonstrate the immediate and register addressing modes.

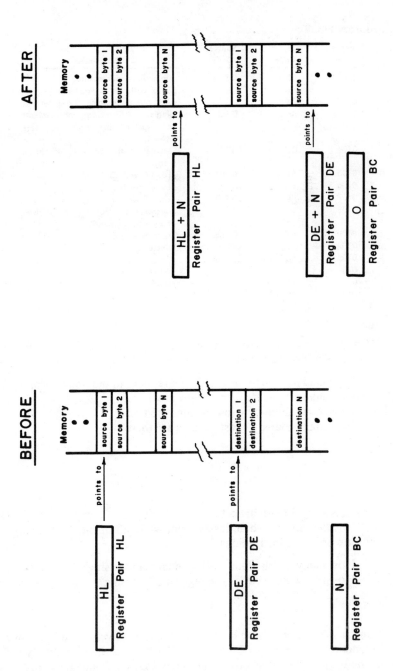

Fig. 6-4.

Program No. 7

Memory Location	Object Code	Source Code	Comments
0100	06 80	LD B,80H	; Immediate addressing: Data byte ; 80 is loaded into register B
0102	04	INC B	; Add one (to increment) register B
0103	48	LD C,B	; Register addressing: the contents ; of register B are loaded into reg- ; ister C
0104	0C	INC C	; Increment the contents of the C ; register
0105	51	LD D,C	; Load D with C
0106	14	INC D	; Increment D
0107	5A	LD E,D	; Load E with D
0108	1D	DEC E	; Decrease the contents of register ; E by 1 (decrement)
0109	63	LD H,E	; Load H with E
010A	25	DEC H	; Decrement H
010B	6C	LD L,H	; Load L with H
010C	2D	DEC L	; Decrement L
010D	7D	LD A,L	; Load A with L
010E	76	HALT	; Halt the microcomputer

Step 1

Load the preceding program into memory starting at location 0100. Verify that it has been loaded correctly.

How many one-byte instructions are there in the above program?
How many two-byte instructions are there?
How many three-byte instructions are there?
How many four-byte instructions are there?

Your answers should have been 13, 1, 0, and 0, respectively. LD B,80H is the only two-byte instruction, while all of the other instructions are one-byte instructions.

How many instructions use immediate addressing?
How many instructions use register addressing?

Your answers should have been 1 and 12, respectively. The LD B,80H instruction uses immediate addressing because the data is actually part of the instruction (byte two). The other LD, INC, and DEC instructions (all one byte long) use register addressing.

Step 2

Analyze the program and predict the value which will be in each register at the conclusion of execution. You can write your predictions in the space provided.

B=_____   C=_____   D=_____   E=_____
H=_____   L=_____   A=_____

Step 3

Verify your predictions by executing the program. If you execute in single-step mode, you can check your prediction for each register as it is changed. If you execute the program at full speed, remember to press BREAK instead of RESET so that the register contents will be saved.

Note: It is particularly interesting to watch the execution in single-step mode because you can watch more than one register at a time. With the selector lamp in position BC you can directly observe the effects of the first four instructions, then move the selector lamp to position DE for the next four instructions, to position HL for the next four instructions, and to position AF for the final instructions.

The registers should now read as follows:

B=81, C=82, D=83, E=82, H=81, L=80, and A=80.

It is essential to be able to predict the contents of the registers that are affected by a program, because then you can detect program bugs if predictions do not match results. We recommend that you work hard to develop this skill.

Step 4

Change the data byte at location 0101 to 01. Predict what the registers B, C, D, E, H, L, and A will contain after executing the changed program.

B=_____   C=_____   D=_____   E=_____
H=_____   L=_____   A=_____

Execute the program in single-step mode, watching the registers as they change. After execution the registers should read

B=02, C=03, D=04, E=03, H=02, L=01, and A=01.

Step 5

Change the data byte at location 0101 to FF. Predict what registers B, C, D, E, H, L, and A will contain now. Check your predictions by executing the program in single-step mode and watching the registers as they change.

B=_____   C=_____   D=_____   E=_____
H=_____   L=_____   A=_____

We observed that B=00, C=01, D=02, E=01, H=00, L=FF, and A=FF. These values are easily explained if you know one fact: addition is cyclic on the Z-80 microcomputer. That is,

> If we increment FF by one we get 00
> If we decrement 00 by one we get FF

Another way of saying this is that the Z-80 adds modulo 256 (base 10) or modulo 100 (base 16). Whenever this happens, i.e., we "pass through zero"; the event is noted by the Z-80 by setting a CARRY FLAG. We will discuss this more in a subsequent chapter.

EXPERIMENT NO. 2

Purpose

The purpose of this experiment is to demonstrate the immediate extended, extended, and register indirect addressing modes.

Program No. 8

Memory Location	Object Code	Source Code	Comments
0110	21 1C 01	LD HL,011CH	; Immediate extended addressing: ; H is loaded with 01 (HI) ; L is loaded with 1C (LO)
0113	36 FF	LD (HL),FFH	; Register indirect addressing: ; The memory location pointed to ; by the contents of HL is ; loaded with FF
0115	2C	INC L	; Increment register L-- so that ; HL is pointing to the next ; sequential memory location
0116	36 EE	LD (HL),EEH	; Register indirect addressing: ; The memory location pointed to ; by the contents of HL is ; loaded with EE
0118	2A 1C 01	LD HL,(011CH)	; Extended addressing: Register ; L is loaded with the contents ; of memory location 011C and ; register H is loaded with the ; contents of memory location ; 011D.
011B	76	HALT	; Halt

Step 1

Load the above program into memory starting at location 0110. Verify that you have loaded the program correctly.

Step 2

Let us closely examine the above program to try to understand what it does. First note that the program involves the H and L registers and two memory locations 011C and 011D. The program basically loads these two locations with FF and EE, respectively, and then moves the contents of the two locations to the HL register pair. This is not a particularly exciting program but it does illustrate several important facts about three kinds of addressing.

Consider the two mnemonic instructions:

```
LD  HL,011CH
LD  HL,(011CH)
```

The only difference is that the second instruction has parentheses surrounding the address. This difference is critical. In the first instruction the 011C represents *two data bytes* to be loaded into H and L; in the second instruction 011C is an *address*. Both of these instructions load 16-bits (or two bytes) of data but the first uses *immediate extended* addressing and the second uses *extended* addressing.

The instructions LD (HL),FFH and LD (HL),EEH are both 8-bit loads because only one byte is involved. The parentheses around HL are critically important here also. They imply that the instructions do not change HL but, rather, change the memory location pointed to by HL.

Step 3

Predict the values in the following registers and memory locations after executing the preceding program:

H=_____   (011C)=_____
L=_____   (011D)=_____

Step 4

Execute the program at full speed and then examine the registers and memory to see if your predictions were correct. We observed H=EE, L=FF, (011C)=FF, (011D)=EE.

EXPERIMENT NO. 3

Purpose

The purpose of this experiment is to demonstrate the techniques for implementing program loops. Specifically, the JP NZ instruction is used to form a time-delay loop.

Program No. 9

Memory Location	Object Code		Source Code	Comments
0120	0E 00		LD C,00H	; Load immediate C with 00
0122	0D	LOOP:	DEC C	; Decrement C
0123	C2 22 01		JP NZ, LOOP	; If C not zero, go back to LOOP
0126	FF		RST 38H	; If C is zero, return control ; to the Nanocomputer operating ; system.

Program No. 10

Memory Location	Object Code		Source Code	Comments
0130	06 00		LD B, 00H	; Load immediate B with 00
0132	0E 00	LOOP1:	LD C, 00H	; Load immediate C with 00
0134	0D	LOOP2:	DEC C	; Decrement C
0135	C2 34 01		JP NZ, LOOP2	; If C not zero, go back to LOOP 2
0138	05		DEC B	; If C is zero, decrement B
0139	C2 32 01		JP NZ, LOOP1	; If B not zero, go back to LOOP 1
013C	FF		RST 38H	; If B is zero, return control ; the Nanocomputer operating ; system.

Step 1

Load and verify Program No. 9.
Load and verify Program No. 10.

Step 2

Let us examine these two programs quite closely to understand exactly what they are doing. First, let us concentrate on Program No. 9. Program No. 9 is a simple delay loop. Note that this program uses *labels*. That is, in the source code, certain statements are assigned names. In Program No. 9, the statement DEC C at location 0122 is assigned the label LOOP. You can tell that LOOP is a label because it is followed by a colon (:) and an instruction. Later on, the JP NZ, LOOP instruction refers to the label as a synonym for the address 0122. That is, the instruction JP NZ, LOOP is equivalent to the instruction JP NZ, 0122H and is converted by the assembler to hex object code C2 22 01. It is important for you to realize that labels, as entities used in source code statements, are always translated to hex object code equivalents so that the Z-80 CPU *NEVER* sees the label.

Note also that Program No. 9 uses the instruction RST 38H which we have not yet defined. This statement essentially tells the Z-80 CPU to return control to the Nanocomputer operating system. Later on, we discuss the RST instructions in detail.

Register C is loaded initially with zeros, then C is decremented repeatedly until C reaches 00 again, whence the loop ends and control is returned to the Nanocomputer operating system. Program No. 9 is called a delay loop because it just performs busy work (decrementing C) for awhile and then stops. The net result is a time delay; note that C starts out and finishes with zeros.

For programs with loops, it is often quite helpful to draw *flow charts* to illustrate the overall program logic. The flow chart for Program No. 9 is given in Fig. 6-5. We will explain the significance of the shape of the "boxes" in the flow chart.

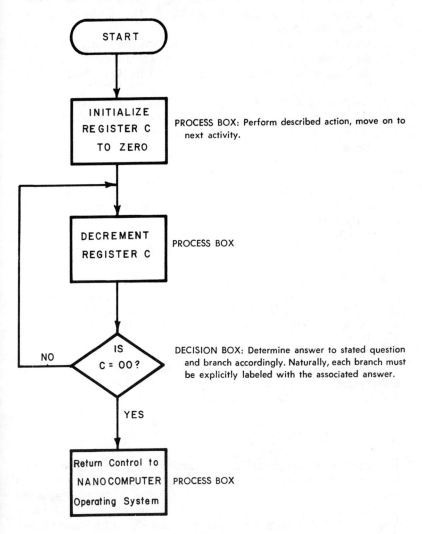

Fig. 6-5.

It is appropriate to make some general remarks about program loops. All program loops can be analyzed as containing the following four components:

1. *Initialization Process*—Counting variables, memory addresses, registers, and other necessary variables are set to desired starting values (e.g., LD C, 00H in Program No. 9).
2. *Process to be Repeated*—This component is made up of the statements which will be executed on each loop. (Note: this component is empty for Program No. 9. This is why it is called a time-delay loop.)
3. *Loop Control Process*—The counting variables and any necessary memory pointers or other values which control how often the loop is repeated are updated (e.g., DEC C in Program No. 9).
4. *Loop Termination Process*—The loop control variables are checked to determine if a termination condition holds. Looping either continues or stops accordingly (e.g., JP NZ,LOOP in Program No. 9).

Step 3

Let us now analyze Program No. 10 in a similar fashion. First, try to draw a flow chart for Program No. 10. Compare yours with ours which appears in Fig. 6-6.

Notice that from the flow chart, the logical structure for Program No. 10 is quite clearly shown: Program No. 10 is a loop within a loop. For each time register B is decremented once, register C is decremented all the way from 00 back to 00 again, i.e., 256 decrements! Please be sure that you understand what is happening here. A full set of decrements on C results in B getting decremented once. Thus, which program do you think forms a longer delay loop. . . No. 9 or No. 10?

We hope that you said No. 10!

Execute Program No. 9 at full speed. What do you observe? Execute Program No. 10 at full speed. What do you observe, and how does it compare with the behavior of Program No. 9?

In both cases, we observed that the Nanocomputer displays went dark for a brief instant and then all of the displays came back on with the selector lamp in position PC. For Program No. 9, the time between pressing GO and the displays becoming lit was instantaneous, while the length of time that elapsed between the same events for Program No. 10 was longer. Perhaps half a second.

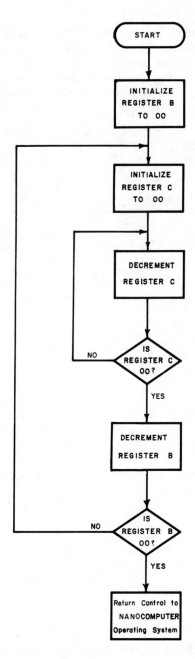

Fig. 6-6.

127

Step 4

Let us investigate how we can make the delay longer between pressing GO and seeing the displays light up. One way is to add another loop, thus making the program a loop within a loop, within a loop. This technique is called forming *nested loops*. In Program No. 10, the loop which decrements register C is *nested* within the loop which decrements register B.

Change Program No. 10 as follows:

Memory Location	Object Code	Source Code	Comments
012E	16 30	LD D, 30H	; Initialize the outer-most ; counter
– – – – – –keep locations 0130-013B the same– – – –these instructions form the – – – – – – – –·inner loops now –
013C	15	DEC D	; Decrement outer-most loop ; counter
013D	C2 30 01	JP NZ, 0130H	; Start the two inner loops again ; if D not zero.
0140	FF	RST 38H	; If D is 0, return control to ; the Nanocomputer operating ; system.

Step 5

Draw a flow diagram of the changed Program No. 10 whose starting address is 012E. Study it thoroughly to understand the function of each of the three loops.

Step 6

Execute the program starting at 012E. You should be expecting a much longer delay between pressing GO and control returning to the Nanocomputer operating system (displays relighting). Wait patiently, the delay is much longer. (If nothing has happened after one minute, something is wrong. Press RESET and double check that your program is loaded correctly.)

Step 7

You can change the time duration of the delay loop by varying the initial value of the D-register. The higher the value, the longer the delay loop. Try different values for the data byte at location 012F to verify this.

EXPERIMENT NO. 4

Purpose

The purpose of this experiment is to demonstrate the block move instruction LDDR.

Program No. 11

Memory Location	Object Code	Source Code	Comments
0150	21 75 01	LD HL,0175H	; Specify the end address ; of the source block of data
0153	11 6F 01	LD DE,016FH	; Specify the end address ; of the destination
0156	01 05 00	LD BC,0005H	; Specify the number of bytes to ; be transferred
0159	ED B8	LDDR	; Move the entire block of bytes
015B	FF	RST 38H	; Transfer control back to the ; Nanocomputer operating ; system.

Step 1

Load the program into memory starting at 0150. Verify that you have loaded it correctly.

Step 2

Examine the program closely to discover exactly what it does. Basically, the program utilizes the LDDR instruction to move five data bytes. The LDDR instruction is one of the many very powerful capabilities of the Z-80 not implemented on the older Intel 8080 microprocessor. The following diagram illustrates how the LDDR instruction performs in the preceding program:

```
LDDR:  (0175) transferred to (016F)
       (0174) transferred to (016E)
       (0173) transferred to (016D)
       (0172) transferred to (016C)
       (0171) transferred to (016B)
```

A total of BC=0005 bytes are moved in the order in which they appear in the diagram.

Step 3

Initialize the contents of memory locations 0171-0175 as follows:

```
(0171) = AA
(0172) = BB
(0173) = CC
(0174) = DD
(0175) = FF
```

Execute the program at full speed; then examine memory locations 016B-016F. Write your observations:

```
(016B) =
(016C) =
(016D) =
(016E) =
(016F) =
```

We observed AA, BB, CC, DD, and EE respectively, in the preceding locations. Thus, the LDDR instruction causes five memory bytes to be transferred. If BC were initialized to 0006 or 0003, then 6 or 3 bytes would have been transferred. Reinitialize the memory bytes 016B-016F to, say 11's, and try BC=0003 and BC=0006 by changing the program (locations 0157 and 0158) accordingly.

Step 4

Let us now zero out the 20 bytes of memory from 0161 through 0175 inclusive by making some changes to the previous program.
1. Change LD DE, 016FH to LD DE, 0174H
2. Change LD BC, 0005H to LD BC, 0014H
3. Store 00 in memory location 0175 using the keyboard

Execute the program starting at 0150. Examine memory locations 0161 through 0175. Are they all zero?

We observed that they were.

Step 5

Let us attempt to explain what we just did. First, here is the source code for the program with the preceding changes incorporated:

```
LD HL, 0175H
LD DE, 0174H
LD BC, 0014H
LDDR
RST 38H
```

Therefore, the sequence of transfers is

```
(0175)---(0174)
(0174)---(0173)
(0173)---(0172)
        . . .
(0162)---(0161)
```

A total of 20 (base 10) or 14 (base 16) bytes were transferred. Loading 00 into memory location 0175 (step 3 above), started a domino effect. The first transfer zeroed out location 0174, then the contents of 0174, zeros, were then transferred to 0173, and so on. . . .

Step 6

Note carefully the values of all three register pairs after program execution:

	Our observations
HL=_____	0161
DE=_____	0160
BC=_____	0000

HL is one less than the address of the last source byte transferred. DE is one less than the address of the last destination byte transferred. BC=0000.

Step 7

What happens if we execute the above program with BC starting out initialized to 0000? There are two possibilities depending on the subtleties of the way in which the Z-80 executes an LDDR instruction. Consider the following two operational scenarios for a Z-80 which has just encountered an LDDR instruction:

Scenario No. 1:
   Step 1—transfer the data byte: (HL) to (DE)
   Step 2—decrement HL, DE, and BC
   Step 3—check if BC=0000. If not, go back to Step 1, else go on to next instruction.

Scenario No. 2:
   Step 1—check if BC=0000. If not, continue to Step 2, else go on to next instruction.
   Step 2—transfer the data byte: (HL) to (DE)
   Step 3—decrement HL, DE, and BC: return to Step 1

If BC initially is not zero, then the two scenarios above produce identical results. What if BC is initialized to zero? Then the two scenarios differ drastically. Scenario No. 1 will attempt to move 64K bytes while Scenario No. 2 will move 0 bytes.

Let us make a simple test to see which scenario the Z-80 follows. Simply change the current program by replacing the 14 in location 0157 with 00. What does this accomplish? The instruction LD BC, 0014 is replaced with the instruction LD BC, 0000.

Step 8

Execute the program (starting at 0150) in single-step mode. First, watch the three register pairs get initialized (3 steps). Now *watch the BC register pair for Step 4.* What did you observe? This observation should settle our question. Which scenario does the Z-80 follow, 1 or 2?

We observed BC become FFFF! Thus the Z-80 decrements *before* checking, so we may conclude that Scenario No. 1 is implemented, not Scenario No. 2. We have just investigated a *boundary condition* of the LDDR instruction. Boundary conditions related to loop control on the first and/or last iteration are always extremely critical. Many program bugs in execution of loops are due to incorrectly implemented boundary conditions.

Let us pursue our preceding observations one more step. We have just initiated a 64K byte block move! We do not even have 64K bytes of memory. But, more importantly, we are heading towards over-writing our program. Consider the following transfers that will take place:

$$(0175)-(0174)$$
$$(0174)-(0173)$$
$$. . .$$
$$(0160)-(015F)$$
$$(015F)-(015E)$$
$$. . .$$
$$(015B)-(015A)$$
$$(015B)-(0159)$$

With the transfer of the contents of memory location 015E to location 015D, we are beginning to alter the program that is currently being executed. The Z-80 is not aware of this yet because it is merrily executing away on the LDDR instruction at locations 0159 and 0160.

Continue your step-by-step execution of the program watching the DE register. When DE=015D you are beginning to over-write (sometimes called "clobber" or "eat-up") your own program. How far do you think you will get? Continue stepping. With each step the DE register descends one byte closer to the LDDR instruction. When does the DE register stop decrementing?

We observed that it stopped at 0159. That is, once the second byte of the LDDR instruction was changed, the program fell apart. So, it hung in there as long as it could! Once the very instruction it was executing was destroyed, it could no longer carry on.

You have just witnessed, under very controlled conditions, a program destroy itself. This, sadly, will not be the last time this happens to you. Just keep in mind that it can happen and try your best to guard against it. Whenever you execute a program which you are trying to debug, prepare for the worst by first copying it out to cassette (if possible) or at least have it well documented, because it may disappear after you hit the GO key!

EXPERIMENT NO. 5

Purpose

The purpose of this experiment is to demonstrate the LDI instruction. Two new conditional jump instructions JP Z and JP PE are introduced. Also the logical instruction OR A is introduced.

Program No. 12

Memory Location	Object Code	Source Code	Comments
0180	21 A0 01	LD HL, 01A0H	; Specify the beginning address ; of the source block of data
0183	11 C0 01	LD DE, 01C0H	; Specify the beginning address ; of the destination block of ; data.
0186	01 10 00	LD BC, 0010H	; Specify the maximum number of ; bytes to be moved.
0189	7E	LOOP: LD A, (HL)	; Load the next source byte to be ; transferred into register A
018A	B7	OR A	; Set the zero flag to logic 1 if ; A is 0.
018B	CA 93 01	JP Z, QUIT	; If A is zero, jump to the end ; of the program
018E	ED A0	LDI	; Transfer the non-zero byte
0190	EA 89 01	JP PE, LOOP	; Jump back to transfer another ; byte if BC is not 0000.
0193	FF	QUIT: RST 38H	; Return control to the Nano- ; computer operating system.

Step 1

Load the preceding program starting at address 0180. Verify that you have loaded it correctly.

Step 2

Let us first describe the new instructions which appear in this program:

Object Code	Mnemonic Code	Operation
B7	OR A	Performs a bit by bit logical OR of the accumulator with itself. The zero flag is set to 1 if A is zero, otherwise the zero flag is set to zero. See the chapter on logical operations for a more complete discussion of this instruction.
CA $<$B2$>$ $<$B3$>$	JP Z, $<$B3$><$B2$>$	Conditional jump:jump to the address given by $<$B3$><$B2$>$ if the zero flag is at logic 1
EA $<$B2$>$ $<$B3$>$	JP PE, $<$B3$><$B2$>$	Conditional jump: jump to the address given by $<$B3$><$B2$>$ if the parity flag is at logic 1

Both of the conditional jumps described are quite similar to the JP NZ instruction. The only difference is the condition which is tested prior to deciding whether or not to jump. These conditions always involve *flags*, which we will discuss in great detail later. For now, we are telling you just what you need to know to understand the preceding program.

Step 3

Let us now examine the program, as a whole, to understand exactly what it is doing. The first three instructions initialize the register pairs HL, DE, and BC in preparation for invoking the LDI instruction. The next two instructions are designed to determine if the next byte to be transferred is 00: the byte (pointed to by HL) is loaded into the accumulator and then "ORed" with itself. The only way the result of this OR operation can be zero is if A itself is zero. Thus, OR A sets the zero flag to logic 1 only if A is zero. The next instruction, the conditional jump JP Z, examines the zero flag, if it is set to logic 1 then A is zero, that is, the next byte to be transferred is 00, so the jump to statement QUIT is executed which returns program control to the Nanocomputer operating system. On the other hand, the conditional jump at location 018B is not executed if the next byte to be transferred is nonzero. Thus, the LDI instruction is executed (i.e., the byte is transferred and HL, DE are incremented while BC is decremented). An often ignored but crucial fact about the LDI and LDD instructions is that as long as BC is NOT ZERO, the parity flag is set to logic 1. Hence, when BC is decremented, a check is made and the parity flag updated accordingly. So, the conditional jump JP PE checks the parity flag. If it is at logic 1, then BC is not zero, so the cycle starts again with a determination if the next byte to be transferred is zero. If the parity flag is at logic 0, all the bytes have been transferred so control is returned to the Nanocomputer operating system, i.e., the JP PE is not executed.

The last paragraph is a very complicated English-language description of a program. You can probably now appreciate the saying "a picture worth 1K words" when you look at the flow chart in Fig. 6-7.

By now, it should be clear that the program transfers a block of memory a maximum of 16 bytes long. The first zero byte in the source block terminates the transfer.

Step 4

Initialize the 16-byte memory block starting at 01A0 to non-zero bytes, say 11. Execute the program in single-step mode watching the register pairs BC, DE, and HL change. What are the final values in these registers after control is returned to the Nanocomputer operating system?

$$HL =$$
$$DE =$$
$$BC =$$

We observed that HL=01B0, DE=01D0, and BC=0000.

Step 5

Initialize the 16-bit memory block starting at 01A0 as follows:

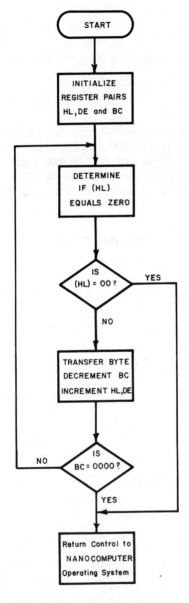

Fig. 6-7.

01A0 = 10
01A1 = 0F
01A2 = 0E
01A3 = 00
01A4 thru 01AF = FF

Execute the program again. Watch the BC register pair and the A register. What happens to the BC register after the A register is loaded with 00? What were the final values of the HL, DE, and BC registers?

You should have observed that the BC register remained constant at 000D. The final values for HL and DE were 01A3 and 01C3, respectively. Just three bytes were transferred, as anticipated.

Note that this program cannot be implemented with the LDIR instruction because some manipulation of the data between transfers is required.

EXPERIMENT NO. 6

Purpose

The purpose of this experiment is to demonstrate the value of the block move instruction by showing how it can save memory and program steps.

Program No. 13: With LDIR

Memory Location	Object Code	Source Code	Comments
01D0	21 00 02	LD HL, 0200H	; Initialize the three block move
01D3	11 01 02	LD DE, 0201H	; register pairs to specify
01D6	01 64 00	LD BC, 0064H	; source, destination, and number ; of bytes.
01D9	ED B0	LDIR	; Move the block of data
01DB	FF	RST 38H	; Transfer control to Nano- ; computer operating system

Program No. 14: Without LDIR

Memory Location	Object Code	Source Code	Comments
01D0	21 00 02	LD HL, 0200H	; Same as above
01D3	11 01 02	LD DE, 0201H	; Same as above
01D6	01 64 00	LD BC, 0064H	; Same as above
01D9	7E	LOOP: LD A, (HL)	; Load source byte to accumulator
01DA	12	LD (DE), A	; Store at destination
01DB	23	INC HL	; Update HL: 16-bit increment
01DC	13	INC DE	; Update DE: 16-bit increment
01DD	0B	DEC BC	; Update BC: 16-bit decrement

01DE	78	LD A, B	; Check to see if BC=0000 - -
01DF	B1	OR C	; this is a trick worth remember-
			; ing. It is discussed in detail in
			; Unit 9.
01E0	C2 D9 01	JP NZ, LOOP	; If BC is not zero, transfer
			; another byte
01E3	FF	RST 38H	; Else return control to the
			; Nanocomputer operating system

Step 1

This experiment is designed to show you the incredible savings the LDIR and other block move instructions can cause for programs which move data. Both programs move a block of 100 consecutive memory bytes. However, Program No. 13 takes 14 memory bytes and 2095 cpu states or $(2095 \times 0.000004) = .00838$ second to execute. Program No. 14 takes 22 memory bytes and 5000 cpu states or $(5000 \times .000004) = .020$ second to execute . . . over twice as long! (We discuss the methodology for obtaining these execution times in detail in the appendix.)

Note that the discrepancy gets more pronounced as the number of bytes to be transferred increases. The reason this comparison is interesting is because the Intel 8080 microprocessor does not have block move instructions. Thus on an 8080, the procedure for moving blocks of data must be that of Program No. 14.

Step 2

Note that there are several new instructions present in Program No. 14. Rather than provide detailed discussion here, we will defer more explanation until later. Our major point here is illustration of the utility and efficiency of the LDIR and other block instructions.

Step 3

Load and execute each of the preceding programs and demonstrate that Program No. 13 performs precisely the same function as Program No. 14.

CHAPTER 7

Z-80 Addressing Modes

This chapter continues with the description of Z-80 addressing modes begun in Chapter 6. In particular, the especially important indexed addressing capability is investigated. As a knowledge of two's complement arithmetic is necessary to understand indexed addressing, we have included a section on this topic. At the end of the chapter we introduce a tabular form for displaying instruction mnemonics and their associated op codes. This method was first suggested by the Zilog Corporation in their Z-80 CPU Technical Manual. We have found it quite useful.

OBJECTIVES

At the completion of this chapter, you will be able to do the following:

- Define the two's complement binary representation for any number.
- Use two's complement arithmetic to perform operations that utilize indexed addressing.
- Explain all of the Z-80 addressing modes and give examples of instructions for each.
- Define the stack and its associated operations—PUSH and POP.
- Explain and use the exchange instructions.
- Understand and use the Zilog instruction tables for the following groups of Z-80 instructions:

8-bit loads

16-bit loads

block transfers
exchanges

WHAT IS AN ADDRESSING MODE?

The notion of addressing mode was introduced in the previous chapter. For the sake of completeness we will give a formal definition here.

addressing mode—The technique by which an instruction refers to data on which it will operate. The Z-80 instructions implement a total of ten addressing modes, with some instructions combining two addressing modes to access the affected data.

In Chapter 6, we described the register, register indirect, immediate, immediate extended, and the extended addressing modes. The other addressing modes are: modified page zero, relative, indexed, implied, and bit addressing. Indexed and relative addressing provide major capabilities for the Z-80 programmer and require a working knowledge of two's complement binary arithmetic, the subject of the next section.

TWO'S COMPLEMENT BINARY REPRESENTATION

In Chapter 1, we defined a digital code as a system of symbols that represent data values in a way useful to computers or other digital circuits. The two's complement representation is a way of encoding integers which is very similar to binary encoding. The difference is that negative as well as positive integers can be encoded using two's complement representation. Moreover, two's complement representation makes addition and subtraction particularly easy for implementation by digital circuits.

In the brief table that follows, we show both positive and negative decimal numbers and their associated 4-bit two's complement representation. We must always specify the number of bits in the two's complement representation (for reasons which will become obvious later).

Decimal Number	4-Bit Two's Complement Representation
7	0 1 1 1
6	0 1 1 0
5	0 1 0 1
4	0 1 0 0
3	0 0 1 1
2	0 0 1 0
1	0 0 0 1
0	0 0 0 0

−1	1 1 1 1
−2	1 1 1 0
−3	1 1 0 1
−4	1 1 0 0
−5	1 0 1 1
−6	1 0 1 0
−7	1 0 0 1
−8	1 0 0 0

We can make several observations:

1. Normal binary representation with four bits allows us to represent the decimal numbers from 0 through 15. Four-bit two's complement encoding encompasses the integers between −8 and +7, half of the codes are positive and half of the codes are negative. Hence, n-bit two's complement encodes the numbers between $-2**(N-1)$ and $+(2**(N-1))-1$.

2. The positive numbers all have two's complement codes with first bit equal to zero, while codes of the negative numbers begin with 1. Hence, given a four-bit two's complement number, it is easy to determine whether the number is positive or negative. Just examine the first (most significant) bit. This is true also for n-bit two's complement numbers.

3. A positive decimal number two's complement code is identical to its binary code.

4. While −8 has a four-bit two's complement representation, +8 does not. In the n-bit representation, $-2**(N-1)$ is represented but $+2**(N-1)$ is not.

5. The "two's complement" of 0001 is 1111, of 0101 is 1011, of 1010 is 0110. That is, to say that two's complement numbers "complement each other" means that they represent decimal negatives of each other, or that they *add to zero*. Do they sum to zero? Let us see.

```
  0 0 0 1          1 0 1 0          0 1 0 1
+1 1 1 1         +0 1 1 0         +1 0 1 1
─────────        ─────────        ─────────
1 0 0 0 0        1 0 0 0 0        1 0 0 0 0
```

Performing the preceding binary addition yields something that does not look like zero. But remember, we are using only 4-bit representations! Hence, by the time we carry the last one in our addition, we have run out of bits! Hence, the answer is zero. This is why we must always specify *number of bits* when we speak of a two's complement representation for decimal or other integers.

The last observation is especially important because it shows what is the essence of two's complement encoding. It facilitates addition of integers. It also facilitates subtraction because subtracting a number is equivalent to adding its two's complement. Given an n-bit binary number, how does one find its two's complement? We show you by means of a 4-bit example. Consider the number 0001. To determine its two's complement, first change every bit which is logic zero to logic one and every bit which is logic one to logic zero (result so far for this example is 1110); next add 0001 to yield 1111. Check the table to see if this is correct. Here are several examples.

Example 1

Find the two's complement of 1010.

$$\begin{array}{ll} \text{Step 1:} & 0101 \\ \text{Step 2:} & +0001 \\ \hline \text{Answer:} & 0110 \end{array}$$

Example 2

Find the two's complement of 0000.

$$\begin{array}{ll} \text{Step 1:} & 1111 \\ \text{Step 2:} & +0001 \\ \hline \text{Answer:} & 0000 \end{array}$$

Since $-0=0$ this is not surprising!

Example 3

Find the two's complement of 1000.

$$\begin{array}{ll} \text{Step 1:} & 0111 \\ \text{Step 2:} & +0001 \\ \hline \text{Answer:} & 1000 \end{array}$$

Note that the first bit is a logic one!
TROUBLE! The two's complement of a negative number should be positive. We have pointed out why we say that -8 (whose two's complement representation is 1000) has no two's complement. The reason for this is that its two's complement is $+8$ which has no 4-bit two's complement representation. All other 4-bit two's complement numbers (between -7 and $+7$) have 4-bit complements.

Let us examine some 8-bit two's complement representations.

Example 4

What is the largest positive integer that can be represented with 8-bit two's complement code?

Answer: A positive number must begin with 0, hence, the largest such integer is 0 1 1 1 1 1 1 1 = 127 (base 10)
What is the largest negative integer (largest in absolute value) that can be represented with 8-bit two's complement code? Is it

−127? What is the two's complement representation of −127? To figure this out, all we need to do is to form the two's complement of 0 1 1 1 1 1 1 1—

Step 1.   1 0 0 0 0 0 0 0
Step 2. +0 0 0 0 0 0 0 1
_____
          1 0 0 0 0 0 0 1

There is still one more number larger in absolute value than this—namely 1 0 0 0 0 0 0 0 which is the two's complement representation of −128. Hence, the 8-bit two's complement codes encompass the integers between −128 and +127.

Given an 8-bit two's complement code, how does one determine its decimal equivalent? Here are some more examples.

Example 5

What decimal number is represented by the following 8-bit two's complement numbers?

> a. 00001100
> b. 01100001
> c. 10001111
> d. 11100001

A. Since the code begins with a zero, it represents a positive integer and we interpret the two's complement code as if it were binary code. So, the answer is 12 (base 10).
B. Again we have a positive integer so we interpret the binary code in the usual manner and obtain 97 (base 10).
C. Here we have a negative integer. To determine which negative integer, form its two's complement and decode it:
> Two's complement of 10001111 is 01110001
> 01110001 is the two's complement representation of −113 (base 10)
> Thus, 10001111 is the two's complement representation of −113 (base 10).
D. We have another negative number so we follow the same procedure we followed in part C.
Step 1: Find the two's complement of 11100001 which is 00011111.
Step 2: Decode 00011111 as the two's complement representation of 31 (base 10).
Step 3: Thus 11100001 is the two's complement representation of −31 (base 10).

How about going the other way? That is, given a decimal integer between −128 and +127, how do we find its two's complement representation? The same basic techniques prevail as you will see in the following example.

Example 6

Give the two's complement representation of the following decimal numbers.

a. 100
b. −13

A. Since 100 is positive, all we need to do is find its binary code. This is easily seen to be 01100100.
B. We have a negative number this time so the old "complement and code-the-positive" trick applies here: in particular we find the two's complement representation for +13 and then take its two's complement!
   The two's complement representation for +13=the binary representation for +13=00001101
   The two's complement representation of 00001101= 11110011
   Hence, the two's complement representation of −13= 11110011.

Example 7 and the accompanying discussion are for those of our readers who wish to know a bit of the theory behind two's complement representation. We would like to point out that an understanding of Example 7 is *not* necessary to be able to utilize all of the considerable power of the Z-80 for indexed addressing and relative addressing. However, in our discussion of two's complement addition and subtraction in the following paragraphs, we will make reference to the expression $(2**n)-x$, just to indicate that some of the (seemingly) arbitrary rules we set forth do have some mathematical justification.

Thus far, we have not provided you with any reason why it makes sense to represent positive numbers with the standard binary code and negative numbers with a "crazy" code which is the result of a two-step operation on the code for the positive opposite of the number. The two-step operation, changing zeros to ones and ones to zeros and then adding one, did not just appear out of the blue sky. What you are doing with this procedure is finding the binary representation of $(2**n)-x$, where x is the positive integer whose binary representation you started with (n is the number of bits in the binary representation). Let us check this statement with an example:

Example 7

We know that 100 (base 10) has a two's complement representation of 01100100 from Example 6. Let us now find the two's complement of 100 (base 10) using the expression $(2**n)-x$.

$$(2**n)-x=(2**8)-100=156 \text{ (base 10)}$$

The binary representation of 156 is 10011100.

Finding -100 using the two-step method yields this same binary number. You should check this for yourself.

> NOTE: If you think back to the results when we added a number to its two's complement, you will recall that we always got a 1 followed by n zeros, where n was the number of bits in the representation. Of course, 1 followed by n zeros is the binary representation of $2**n$. So all we were doing was adding x and $(2**n)-x$ to get $2**n$!

TWO'S COMPLEMENT ADDITION AND SUBTRACTION

Let us take up the subject of addition first. Once you can add any two two's complement numbers, you are done. Why? Because any subtraction problem $(x-y)$ can be reduced to an addition problem $(x+(-y))$. Find the two's complement of y, add it to x, and you will have performed the subtraction.

Addition of two's complement numbers is performed exactly as if the numbers were binary representations. This is a major advantage of two's complement notation.

Example 8

a.
   0 0 0 0 0 1 1 1 (+7)
+0 0 0 0 0 0 1 0 (+2)
   0 0 0 0 1 0 0 1 (+9)

b.
   1 1 1 1 1 1 0 0 (−4)
+0 0 0 0 0 0 1 1 (+3)
   1 1 1 1 1 1 1 1 (−1)

c.
   1 1 1 1 1 0 0 1 (−7)
+1 1 1 1 0 0 1 1 (−13)
   1 1 1 0 1 1 0 0 (−20)

d.
   0 1 1 0 0 0 0 0 (+96)
+0 1 0 1 0 0 0 0 (+82)
   1 0 1 1 0 0 0 0 TROUBLE! Two positive numbers sum to a negative number?

e.
   1 0 1 1 1 0 0 1 (−71)
   1 0 1 1 1 0 0 0 (−72)
   0 1 1 1 0 0 0 1 TROUBLE! Two negative numbers sum to positive number.

In the last two addition problems (d and e), we ran into trouble. What happened is called *overflow*. As you remember, 8-bit two's complement numbers range between −128 and +127. When we add 96 and 82 in d, and −71 and −72 in e, our sums are 178 and −143, respectively. These are numbers outside of the −128 through +127 limit. This phenomenon, called *overflow* in computer science, exists whenever numbers are represented in codes of fixed bit length. The usual way to handle overflow is to detect its occurrence and branch to a set of instructions that print out an error message. So the question is: How to detect overflow? For some codes this is a nontrivial problem. Fortunately, one of the strengths of two's complement representation is ease of overflow detection. If two positive numbers sum to a negative, or if two negatives sum to a positive, then and only then does overflow exist. Checking for these conditions is easily accomplished by checking the first bit (most significant bit) of each addend and the sum. Also the Z-80 sets a bit (the P/V bit) in its FLAG REGISTER, if two's complement addition results in overflow. The FLAG REGISTER will be discussed in detail in a later chapter.

As we indicated earlier, subtraction is performed by complementing and adding the quantity to be subtracted.

This concludes our discussion of two's complement representation.

THE Z-80 ADDRESSING MODES

The next section covers the extensive addressing capabilities of the Z-80. It is the ten addressing modes which contribute greatly to the superiority of the Z-80 over the Intel 8080A microprocessor chip in terms of the richness of its instruction set. For each addressing mode, we give a fairly exhaustive discussion which includes definitions and examples. To reiterate what we stated earlier in Chapter 6, read what follows placing an emphasis on what the addressing mode does, how it compares to other addressing modes, and pay close attention to the notation used in mnemonics for each addressing mode.

The effort you put forth on this section will prepare you for reading and understanding the instruction tables which are essential for all further work in this book. At the end of this chapter we provide you with several exercises to help solidify your understanding of these important concepts.

REGISTER ADDRESSING

Register addressing occurs when the op code of an instruction contains information which specifies which CPU register(s) is/are involved in the instruction execution. The op codes that contain the 3-bit register codes listed in Chapter 6 are examples of this kind of addressing. Consider the instruction:

LD A,B

whose op code is: 0 1 <u>1 1 1</u> <u>0 0 0</u> or 78 hex.
                       A   B

Register addressing is implemented twice in this instruction, first for register A and second for register B.

IMMEDIATE ADDRESSING

The *immediate addressing* mode is used with multibyte instructions that actually contain the 8-bit data byte to be operated on. The following load instruction uses immediate addressing:

LD C,03H

whose associated hex code is: 0E 03. Execution of this instruction concludes with a hex 03 residing in the C register of the CPU. (Does this instruction utilize any other addressing modes? The op code indicates that register C is to be loaded, thus the register addressing mode is used.)

IMMEDIATE EXTENDED ADDRESSING

This addressing mode requires that the instruction provide two immediate data bytes following the op code instead of the one byte required by immediate addressing. Hence, this mode "extends" the immediate addressing mode. Clearly the machine code for any instruction utilizing this mode of addressing is at least three bytes long with one byte for the op code and two bytes for the data. The instruction:

LD BC,0421H

whose associated hex code is 01 21 04 uses immediate extended addressing. Be sure to note the order in which the data bytes appear in the machine code for this instruction. The byte for the C register (21) is the LO byte and, therefore, comes first. This is true for all of the register pair loads.

REGISTER INDIRECT ADDRESSING

We have seen modes for addressing registers and modes in which the data is part of the instruction. The *register indirect addressing* mode uses a register pair to indicate where in memory the data resides. That is, the register pair contains the address of the data that the instruction requires. An instruction that uses register indirect addressing is

LD A, (HL)

whose associated hex code is: 7E. To show that the contents of register pair HL are to be used as a pointer to memory, HL is enclosed in parentheses. This notation is standard for register indirect addressing.

For some instructions, indirect addressing is used to specify two bytes to be operated upon by an instruction. In such cases, the contents of the register pair specify the LO byte and the contents plus one point to the HI byte. For example the instruction

POP BC

whose associated hex code is: C1 loads (SP) into C and (SP+1) into B.

EXTENDED ADDRESSING

An instruction that uses *extended addressing* contains, as its last two bytes, a 16-bit address. This address can be used as a pointer to a memory location for required data or it can be the address to which the program should jump. An example of the former use is,

LD (1203H),A

whose associated hex code is: 32 03 12. This instruction causes memory location 1203 to be loaded with the contents of the accumulator. Notice that, consistent with register indirect addressing, the address is enclosed in parentheses. The generalized notation for this is (nn), where n is an 8-bit byte.

An instruction in which the nn represents an address to which the program should jump is the instruction JP nn, for example:

JP 1203H

whose associated hex code is: C3 03 12. Note that in this instruction we are not transferring data but, rather, program control to the instruction at address 1203. Hence, this time nn is not enclosed in parentheses.

MODIFIED PAGE ZERO ADDRESSING

There are eight Z-80 instructions that utilize modified page zero addressing. These instructions, called the *restart* instructions, cause program control to be transferred to a section of the program called a *subroutine*. We shall discuss this type of program control transfer later. All of the restart instructions are just one byte long. The op code specifies any one of eight possible addresses—0000, 0008, 0010, 0018, 0020, 0028, 0030, or 0038—one for each restart instruction. As the high address byte is always 00, the addressing mode is called *modified page zero*. The major purpose of restart instructions is to access subroutines which are used often. The advantages of the restart instructions are that they save time and space and they can be jammed into the microprocessor chip during an interrupt. Comparable subroutine "call" instructions use three bytes instead of the one required by a restart. Here is a sample restart instruction:

RST 10H

whose associated hex code is: D7. This instruction transfers program control to the subroutine located at 0010 (decimal 16).

IMPLIED ADDRESSING

Certain Z-80 instructions automatically apply to one particular register. This kind of instruction utilizes *implied addressing*. The 8-bit arithmetic and logic group of instructions are examples of implied addressing instructions because they all involve operations on the contents of the accumulator. The instruction

ADD A,B

whose associated hex code is: 80, adds the contents of the B register to the accumulator and loads the accumulator with the sum.

BIT ADDRESSING

The Z-80 instruction set contains many instructions that address individual bits within bytes stored in memory or registers. These bit manipulation instructions use a combination of addressing modes. Register, register indirect, or indexed addressing specifies the memory location or CPU register of the byte involved; a 3-bit code within the op code of the instruction specifies the bit—bit 0,1,2,3,4,5,6, or 7—where bits are numbered from right to left (low order to high order) within a byte:

Byte	MSB							LSB
BIT NUMBER	7	6	5	4	3	2	1	0

An example of a bit addressing instruction is

SET 3,B

whose associated hex code is **CB DB**. This instruction "sets" to logic 1 bit number decimal 3 of the B register. Many of the new Z-80 instructions not implemented on the Intel 8080A microprocessor are the BIT, SET, and RESET instructions, which all utilize the bit addressing mode.

INDEXED ADDRESSING

The Z-80 has two special purpose 16-bit registers called *index registers.* They are referred to as the IX and IY registers. Their major use is for the indexed addressing mode. Indexed addressing is very similar to register indirect addressing in that the contents of a 16-bit register point to the location in memory of the desired data. The one important difference is that for indexed addressing, one must specify a one-byte displacement in the first byte of the instruction after the op code. This byte is an 8-bit two's complement number which tells how many bytes lower or higher in memory from the address in the index register is the location of the data byte to be operated on. For example,

LD A,(IX+02H)

whose associated hex code is: DD 7E 02, loads the accumulator with the contents of the memory location two bytes higher than the location pointed to by IX. The instruction

LD (IY+FFH),A

whose associated hex code is: FD 77 FF loads the contents of the accumulator into the location one lower than the address in register IY, since FF is the two's complement representation of decimal −1. Table 7-1 lists the preceding LD instructions.

Table 7-1. LD Instructions

(IX+d)	Significance of Displacement With Respect to Memory Location (in decimal)
(IX+7FH)	127 bytes higher than IX
(IX+0FH)	15 bytes higher than IX
(IX+09H)	9 bytes higher than IX
(IX+01H)	1 byte higher than IX
(IX+00H)	(IX)
(IX+FFH)	1 byte lower than IX
(IX+FEH)	2 bytes lower than IX
(IX+FDH)	3 bytes lower than IX
(IX+FCH)	4 bytes lower than IX
(IX+F0H)	16 bytes lower than IX
(IX+E0H)	32 bytes lower than IX
(IX+D0H)	48 bytes lower than IX
(IX+80H)	128 bytes lower than IX

The notation for indicating indexed addressing is (IX+d) or (IY+d) where d represents the two's complement displacement byte. The parentheses indicate that IX+d and IY+d are pointers to a memory location. Fig. 7-1 summarizes the meaning of d in the instructions which use indexed addressing such as LD A,(IX+d).

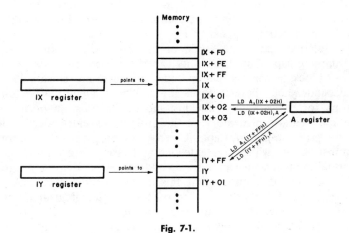

Fig. 7-1.

Indexed addressing is a powerful tool for accessing tables of data in memory. Typically, register IX or IY is loaded with the address of the first entry of the table and then all other table entries are referred to by their location relative to the first entry. That is, the displacement byte is appropriately changed according to the table entry accessed. This illustrates the important fact that execution of an instruction that uses indexed addressing does *not* change the contents of the index register.

Several programs which use indexed addressing to access a table appear at the end of this chapter.

RELATIVE ADDRESSING

Relative addressing is a very specialized addressing mode that applies only to jump instructions called the *relative jumps* (JR). As it is with indexed addressing, the first byte after the op code is an 8-bit two's complement number representing a displacement from some address. Consider the instruction

JR 09H

whose associated hex code is: 18 09. The 09 is the displacement from the address of the next instruction to the *instruction to be executed next*. That is, this is an unconditional relative jump to an instruction nine bytes further down in the program from the instruction that normally would have been executed next. The instruction

JR FCH

whose associated hex code is 18 FC causes program control to be transferred back four bytes from the next instruction since FC is the 8-bit two's complement representation for −4. Illustrations of these two instructions appear in Fig. 7-2.

The relative addressing mode of the Z-80 allows for a major programming capability, the ability to write *relocatable* code. A program or block of hex instruction codes is said to be relocatable if it is independent of where it physically resides in memory. To test a program for relocatability, one just moves the program *unchanged* to a new location in memory. If the program executes successfully, then the program is relocatable. Clearly, any program with a normal jump instruction, which uses extended addressing, is not relocatable. A normal jump specifies an absolute address, so moving the program to a new location requires that this absolute address be changed prior to successful execution. The process of changing all absolute addresses in conjunction with changing the location of a program is called *relocating* the program. Another advantage of relative jumps is that they require only two bytes of memory as opposed to the three bytes required by the absolute jumps, but their range is limited to +127 and −128 bytes.

This concludes the list of Z-80 addressing modes. As you undoubtedly noticed, there were a number of new instructions introduced. We felt that each addressing mode should be illustrated by at least one example, even if it meant introducing you to a new instruction. Rest assured that we shall come back to each of these new instructions with exhaustive discussions in subsequent chapters.

THE INSTRUCTION GROUP TABLES

Now that you are aware of all of the Z-80 addressing modes, we would like to introduce you to an extremely useful method for displaying the Z-80 instructions with their associated hex machine codes. The instruction group tables first appeared in Zilog's Z-80 CPU Technical Manual. Let us first examine the 8-bit load group table, Table 7-2.

Note that the rows down the left-hand side as well as the columns across the top are labeled with addressing modes. There are two addressing modes used by each 8-bit load instruction—one for the destination (rows) and one for the source (columns). Suppose you wish to move the contents of register C to register D. Then D is the destination register so you locate the (horizontal) row labeled D in

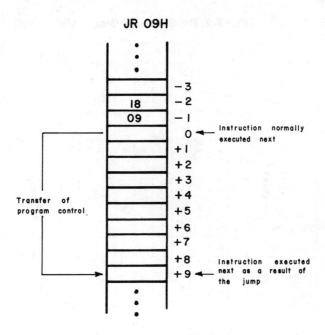

JR O9H

−3
18   −2
09   −1
0 ← Instruction normally executed next
+1
+2
+3
+4
+5
+6
+7
+8   Instruction executed
+9 ← next as a result of the jump

Transfer of program control

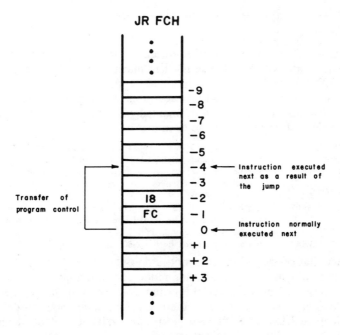

JR FCH

−9
−8
−7
−6
−5
−4 ← Instruction executed next as a result of the jump
−3
18   −2
FC   −1
0 ← Instruction normally executed next
+1
+2
+3

Transfer of program control

Fig. 7-2.

153

Table 7-2. The 8-Bit Load Group "LD"

		IMPLIED		REGISTER							REG INDIRECT			INDEXED		EXT. ADDR.	IMME.
		I	R	A	B	C	D	E	H	L	(HL)	(BC)	(DE)	(IX+d)	(IY+d)	(nn)	n
DESTINATION																	
REGISTER	A	ED 57	ED 5F	7F	78	79	7A	7B	7C	7D	7E	0A	1A	DD 7E d	FD 7E d	3A n n	3E n
	B			47	40	41	42	43	44	45	46			DD 46 d	FD 46 d		06 n
	C			4F	48	49	4A	4B	4C	4D	4E			DD 4E d	FD 4E d		0E n
	D			57	50	51	52	53	54	55	56			DD 56 d	FD 56 d		16 n
	E			5F	58	59	5A	5B	5C	5D	5E			DD 5E d	FD 5E d		1E n
	H			67	60	61	62	63	64	65	66			DD 66 d	FD 66 d		26 n
	L			6F	68	69	6A	6B	6C	6D	6E			DD 6E d	FD 6E d		2E n
REG INDIRECT	(HL)			77	70	71	72	73	74	75							36 n
	(BC)			02													
	(DE)			12													
INDEXED	(IX+d)			DD 77 d	DD 70 d	DD 71 d	DD 72 d	DD 73 d	DD 74 d	DD 75 d							DD 36 d n
	(IY+d)			FD 77 d	FD 70 d	FD 71 d	FD 72 d	FD 73 d	FD 74 d	FD 75 d							FD 36 d n
EXT. ADDR	(nn)			32 n n													
IMPLIED	I			ED 47													
	R			ED 5F													

Courtesy Zilog, Inc.

the table. Proceed across columns until you reach source register column C and you will locate the hex machine code for the instruction LD D,C which is 51. A hex code appears in each cell of this table for which a Z-80 load instruction exists. Hence, this table tells you *what* instructions are implemented, as well as their associated hex code. Let us look at some examples.

LD A, (IX+d)   has hex code DD 7E d, where the third byte d is the displacement byte in this application of indexed addressing.

LD (nn),A   has hex code 32 nn, where the first n is the LO byte and the second n is the HI byte in the address to be loaded with the contents of A.

LD (IY+d),n   has hex code FD 36 d n, where d is the displacement and n is the byte that will be loaded into the memory location d bytes displaced from location IY.

LD (HL),(BC)   is not implemented on the Z-80

Notice that certain addressing modes do not appear as labels for any rows or columns. If an addressing mode does not appear in the table for a group of instructions, the group does not use that addressing mode. Thus, we can see that there are four addressing modes not implemented by the 8-bit load group: bit, relative, extended immediate, and modified page zero.

The 16-bit load group table appears in Table 7-3.

This is certainly more sparsely populated with instructions than is the 8-bit load group in Table 7-2. Most of the 16-bit loads involve

Table 7-3. The 16-Bit Load Group "LD," "PUSH," and "POP"

		SOURCE							IMM. EXT.	EXT. ADDR.	REG. INDIR.
		REGISTER							nn	(nn)	(SP)
		AF	BC	DE	HL	SP	IX	IY			
DESTINATION — REGISTER	AF										F1
	BC								01 n n	ED 4B n n	C1
	DE								11 n n	ED 5B n n	D1
	HL								21 n n	2A n n	E1
	SP				F9		DD F9	FD F9	31 n n	ED 7B n n	
	IX								DD 21 n n	DD 2A n n	DD E1
	IY								FD 21 n n	FD 2A n n	FD E1
PUSH INSTRUCTIONS — EXT. ADDR.	(nn)		ED 43 n n	ED 53 n n	22 n n	ED 73 n n	DD 22 n n	FD 22 n n			
REG. IND.	(SP)	F5	C5	D5	E5		DD E5	FD E5			

NOTE: The Push & Pop Instructions adjust the SP after every execution

POP INSTRUCTIONS ↑

Courtesy Zilog, Inc.

either immediate extended or extended addressing with very few 16-bit transfers between register pairs. There is only one register pair for which register indirect addressing is possible. This register, the *stack pointer* SP, has a very special function that we will now discuss in detail.

Push and Pop the Stack

The Stack—In computer science, the word *stack* refers to a data structure, or way of storing data, that has the following "every-day life" analogue:

The scene is a cafeteria. Clean trays for use by the customers are kept in a stack on the counter. The most convenient tray to handle is the tray on the top of the stack. Thus as new customers are served, trays are "popped" or removed from the top of the stack. When used trays have been washed and dried, they are "pushed" or piled onto the top of the stack. The critical relationship to observe between using and replenishing the stack items is:

LAST IN, FIRST OUT

This rule (LIFO) is what characterizes stacks as a data structure of computer science. Let us illustrate this new concept with an example using bytes of computer memory instead of trays. Fig. 7-3

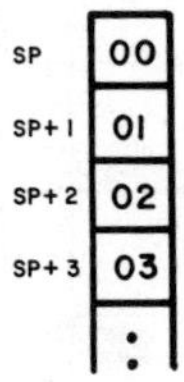

Fig. 7-3.

shows a memory section where each location is labeled with its address. Note that in this discussion of stack operations, memory addresses *increase* as you look *down* the page. This is a departure from our normal treatment of memory diagrams. We do this because the stack pointer, SP register, always points to the byte in the stack with the lowest address. This set of memory locations can be thought of as a stack with location SP (for *stack pointer*) representing the address of the top byte. The contents of the top of the stack, (SP), is shown to be 00.

One may perform two operations on this stack of bytes:

1. POP bytes off the top.
2. PUSH new bytes onto the stack.

Both of these operations produce a new top btye on the stack. The Z-80 microprocessor has two instructions, POP and PUSH, which accomplish 1 and 2 above for two bytes at a time. Both instructions require that a register pair be specified as the source (for PUSH) or the destination (for POP) of the data bytes being transferred. The examples in Fig. 7-4 should make all of this clear. The most important fact to keep in mind is that the *top byte in the stack has the lowest address*.

Fig. 7-4.

Example 1

The instruction POP BC is illustrated in Fig. 7-4.
Execution of the instruction POP BC has the following effects:

1. The top byte of the stack (SP) is loaded into register C

$$C \longleftarrow (SP)$$

2. The second byte of the stack (SP+1) is loaded into register B

$$B \longleftarrow (SP+1)$$

3. The stack pointer (register SP) is updated to point to the new top of the stack, thus eliminating the two bytes 00 and 01 from the stack. This change of SP just amounts to adding 2 to the original stack pointer to arrive at the new one.

$$SP \longleftarrow (SP+2)$$

Thus, POP operations cause the stack pointer to *increase!* Notice that even though the bytes 00 and 01 remain where they were before execution of POP BC, the *location* of the stack in memory has changed in such a way as to exclude them. This does represent a subtle difference between POPping bytes and POPping trays in a cafeteria since the trays are physically removed from the stack.

Example 2

The instruction PUSH HL is demonstrated in Fig. 7-5:

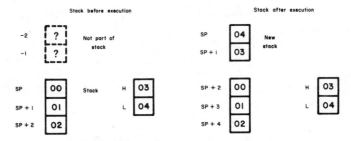

Fig. 7-5.

As you can see, PUSH HL has just the opposite effect as the POP instruction:

1. The byte in register H is loaded into the memory location one up from the top of the stack, SP-1.

$$(SP-1) \longleftarrow H$$

2. The byte in register L is loaded into the memory location two up from the top of the stack, SP-2.

$$(SP-2) \longleftarrow L$$

3. The stack pointer is updated to point to the new top of the stack.

$$SP \longleftarrow SP-2$$

(Two is subtracted from the stack pointer to give the new stack pointer)

Thus, PUSH operations cause the stack pointer to *decrease!*

Both of the examples illustrate some facts that are very important to remember:

A. The stack grows from high to low addresses in memory. That is, "the stack grows *downward* in memory." POP *increases* the SP and PUSH *decreases* the SP.
B. Two bytes are always pushed and popped. All pushing and popping takes place between the stack and register pairs or index registers: AF, BC, DE, HL, IX, or IY. The bytes come off of the top LO byte first, then HI byte last. The bytes are pushed on HI byte first, then LO byte last.
C. The PUSH and POP instructions differ from a normal 16-bit load because the data transfer is accompanied by an update of the stack pointer register.
D. The PUSH and POP instructions use register indirect addressing because the memory location of the data is pointed to by the contents of the 16-bit SP register.

The stack and its associated operations, PUSH and POP, are used most commonly in conjunction with a program control transfer called *subroutine calling.* The chapter on jumps, calls, and returns covers this subject. We will defer further stack discussions to that chapter. Our purpose in introducing the stack operations here is so that you may have a full understanding of the 16-bit load group of Z-80 instructions.

BLOCK TRANSFER AND EXCHANGES

Before concluding this chapter, we will present two more small tables: the block transfers and the exchanges in Tables 7-4 and 7-5, respectively.

Table 7-4. Block Transfer Group

SOURCE

		REG. INDIR. (HL)	
DESTINATION	REG. INDIR. (DE)	ED A0	'LDI' — Load (DE)◄—(HL) Inc HL & DE, Dec BC
		ED B0	'LDIR,' — Load (DE)◄—(HL) Inc HL & DE, Dec BC, Repeat until BC = 0
		ED A8	'LDD' — Load (DE)◄—(HL) Dec HL & DE, Dec BC
		ED B8	'LDDR' — Load (DE)◄—(HL) Dec HL & DE, Dec BC, Repeat until BC = 0

Reg HL   points to source
Reg DE   points to destination
Reg BC   is byte counter

Courtesy Zilog, Inc.

Table 7-5. Exchanges "EX" and "EXX"

		IMPLIED ADDRESSING				
		AF'	BC', DE' & HL'	HL	IX	IY
IMPLIED	AF	08				
	BC, DE & HL		D9			
	DE			EB		
REG. INDIR.	(SP)			E3	DD E3	FD E3

Courtesy Zilog, Inc.

We refer you to Chapter 6 for a discussion of block transfers.

The exchange instructions effect "swaps" of data bytes between 16-bit registers or register pairs. For example,

```
EX  DE,HL
```

whose associated hex code is EB, *swaps* the contents of DE with the contents of HL:

Before Execution of EX DE,HL		After Execution of EX DE,HL	
D	00	D	02
E	01	E	03
H	02	H	00
L	03	L	01

The instruction, EX (SP),HL swaps the contents of HL with the top two bytes of the stack, similar instructions exist for the index registers. The exchanges EXX and EX AF,AF' are the only Z-80 instructions that involve the second set of general-purpose registers B', C', D', E', H', L', A', and F'. Thus, you can see that these alternate registers can only be used as temporary storage for the main registers and cannot be accessed with any flexibility.

INTRODUCTION TO THE EXPERIMENTS AND EXERCISES

We have included both experiments and exercises at the end of this unit to help you solidify your understanding of two's complement binary representation, Z-80 addressing modes, stack operations, and the use of the Zilog instruction tables. We recommend that you work some of the exercises before performing the experiments. Therefore, we have positioned the review exercises ahead of the experiments to encourage you.

The experiments you will perform may be summarized as follows:

Experiment No.	Comments
1	Demonstrates table manipulation via indexed addressing.
2	Demonstrates alternative methods for performing table manipulation. A self-modifying program is one of the examples.
3	Demonstrates the stack operations PUSH and POP and the exchange instructions.

REVIEW

1. Find the 8-bit two's complement of the following 8-bit binary numbers:
   a. 0 0 0 0 0 0 0 1
   b. 1 1 0 1 1 0 1 0
   c. 0 1 0 1 0 1 0 1
   d. 1 1 1 0 1 1 1 0
   e. 0 0 0 0 1 1 1 0
   f. 1 0 0 0 0 0 0 0
   g. 1 1 1 1 1 1 1 1

2. a. What is the largest decimal integer which has a representation as an 8-bit two's complement number?
   b. What is the largest (in absolute value) negative decimal integer which has a representation as an 8-bit two's complement number?
   c. Answer a and b for 16-bit two's complement numbers.

3. Find the decimal number represented by the following 8-bit two's complement numbers.

    a. 0 1 1 1 1 0 0 0   e. 1 1 1 1 0 0 1 1
    b. 1 0 1 0 0 0 1 1   f. 0 1 0 1 0 1 0 0
    c. 0 0 0 0 0 0 1 1   g. 1 1 0 1 1 0 0 1
    d. 1 1 1 1 1 1 1 1

4. Find the 8-bit two's complement representation of the following decimal numbers.

    a. 1   e. 128
    b. 16   f. 121
    c. −16   g. −90
    d. −128

5. The following is a list of relative jump instructions with their associated hex machine code. Use this information to convert all "absolute" jump (JP) instructions to relative jump (JR) instructions in the following programs.

Relative Jump Instruction	Hex Operation Code
JR	18
JR NZ	20
JR Z	28
JR PE	not implemented

    a. Program No. 9 in Experiment No. 3 of Chapter 6.
    b. Program No. 10 in Experiment No. 3 of Chapter 6.
    c. Program No. 12 in Experiment No. 5 of Chapter 6.

6. For each of the following instructions, give the Z-80 addressing modes used and give the associated hex code from the Zilog tables.

    a. LD A,B   g. LD SP,HL
    b. JR FBH (Exercise 5 gives the hex code)   h. LD BC,0109H
    c. LD A,(IX+06H)   i. LD (1030H),BC
    d. LD (IX+06H),A   j. LD IX,(1000H)
    e. LD (1234H),A   k. PUSH BC
    f. LD (IX+09H),33   l. POP IX

7. Indicate whether the following instructions are implemented on the Z-80 microprocessor. If so, give the associated hex code.

    a. LD AF,BC   f. LD (1234H),56H
    b. LD B,(BC)   g. LD (1234H),B
    c. LD (BC),B   h. LD (DE), 45H
    d. LD IX,IY   i. PUSH 1234H
    e. LD HL,BC   j. POP SP

Answers

1. a. 1 1 1 1 1 1 1 1   e. 1 1 1 1 0 0 1 0
    b. 0 0 1 0 0 1 1 0   f. none exists
    c. 1 0 1 0 1 0 1 1   g. 0 0 0 0 0 0 0 1
    d. 0 0 0 1 0 0 1 0

2. a. 0 1 1 1 1 1 1 1 = +127(base 10)
    b. 1 0 0 0 0 0 0 0 = −128(base 10)
    c. 0 1 1 1 1 1 1 1 1 1 1 1 1 1 1 = (2**15−1) (base 10) = highest
    d. 1 0 0 0 0 0 0 0 0 0 0 0 0 0 0 = (−2**15) (base 10) = lowest

3. a. 120   e. −13
    b. −93   f. 84
    c. 3   g. −39
    d. −1

4. a. 0 0 0 0 0 0 0 1
   b. 0 0 0 1 0 0 0 0
   c. 1 1 1 1 0 0 0 0
   d. 1 0 0 0 0 0 0 0
5. a.

e. none exists
f. 0 1 1 1 1 0 0 1
g. 1 0 1 0 0 1 1 0

Memory Location	Object Code	Source Code
0120	0E 00	LD C,00H
0122	0D	LOOP: DEC C
0123	20 FD	JR NZ,LOOP
0125	FF	RST 38H

To determine what relative address should be used as $<B2>$ of the JR NZ instruction, use the following equation:

relative address = 8-bit two's complement of (absolute address of instruction after the relative jump instruction less the absolute address of the destination of the jump)

= 8-bit two's complement of (0125-0122)*

= 8-bit two's complement of the 8-bit byte 03

= 1 1 1 1 1 1 0 1

= FD

* Note that the difference between these two 16-bit hex addresses must have an 8-bit two's complement representation for a relative jump to be defined between the two addresses.

This program was shortened by one byte by replacing an absolute with a relative jump.

5. b.

Memory Address	Object Code	Source Code
0130	06 00	LD B,00H
0132	0E 00	LOOP1:LD C,00H
0134	0D	LOOP2:DEC C
0135	20 FD	JR NZ,LOOP2
0137	05	DEC B
0138	20 F8	JR NZ,LOOP1
013A	FF	RST 38H

For the instruction JR NZ,LOOP2:

relative address = two's complement (0137-0134)

= two's complement 03

= FD

For the instruction JR NZ,LOOP1:

relative address = two's complement (013A-0132)

= two's complement (08)

= F8

This program was shortened by two bytes by replacing two absolute jumps with relative jumps.

5. c.

Memory Location	Object Code	Source Code
0180	21 A0 01	LD HL,01A0H
0183	11 C0 01	LD DE,01C0H
0186	01 10 00	LD BC,0010H

0189	7E	LOOP: LD A,(HL)
018A	B7	OR A
018B	28 05	JR Z,QUIT
018D	ED A0	LDI
018F	EA 89 01	JP PE,LOOP
0192	FF	QUIT: RST 38H

Of the two jumps in this program, only one, JP Z,QUIT, can be converted to a relative jump. A JP PE has no relative jump counter-part in the Z-80 instruction set. Thus, for the instruction JP Z,QUIT:

relative address = two's complement (address after jump instruction less the destination address)

= two's complement (018D-0192)

= (0192-018D)

= 05

Note that for jumps to higher addresses, the computation is easier because the two's complement operation is avoided by changing the order of subtraction of addresses (the two's complement of A-B is equal to B-A). Also the two's complement of the two's complement of A is A.

6. a. Register addressing for both source and destination—Hex code:78
   b. Relative addressing—Hex code: 18 FB
   c. Destination: register addressing—Hex code: DD 7E 06
      Source: Indexed addressing—(IX+d)
   d. Destination: Indexed addressing—(IX+d)—Hex code:DD 77 06
      Source: register addressing
   e. Destination: extended addressing—(nn)—Hex code 32 34 12
      Source: register addressing
   f. Destination: Indexed addressing—(IX+d)—Hex code: DD 36 09 33
      Source: Immediate addressing—n
   g. Destination: register addressing—Hex code: F9
      Source: register addressing
   h. Destination: register addressing—Hex code: 01 09 01
      Source: Immediate extended—nn
   i. Destination: extended addressing—(nn)—Hex code: ED 43 30 10
      Source: register addressing
   j. Destination: register addressing—Hex code: DD 2A 00 10
      Source: extended addressing—(nn)
   k. Destination is (SP) and (SP-1): register indirect addressing—hex code C5
      Source is BC register pair: register addressing
   l. Destination is IX: Register addressing—Hex code: DD E1
      Source is (SP) and (SP+1): register indirect addressing
7. None of these instructions are implemented.

EXPERIMENT NO. 1

Purpose

The purpose of this experiment is to demonstrate table manipulation via indexed addressing.

Program No. 15

Memory Location	Object Code	Source Code	Comments
0100	01 03 00	LD BC,0003H	;3 bytes per line
0103	FD 21 20 01	LD IY,0120H	; Table start address=0120
0107	FD 7E 00	LOOP: LD A,(IY)	;Load column 1 to A
010A	B7	OR A	;Is it zero?
010B	28 0A	JR Z,END	;If so, quit
010D	FD 86 01	ADD (IY+01H)	;if not, add column 2
0110	FD 77 02	LD (IY+02H),A	;Store sum in column 3
0113	FD 09	ADD IY,BC	;IY points to next line
0115	18 F0	JR LOOP	;Repeat above procedure
0117	FF	END: RST 38H	;Return control to operating ;system.

Step 1

Load the preceding program starting at location 0100. Verify that you have loaded it correctly.

Step 2

This program manipulates a table made up of entries each three bytes long. For each successive row or line of the table, the first two columns or line entries are added together and the sum stored in column three. This process continues until a line is encountered whose first byte is 00. At that time, control is returned to the Nano-computer operating system. For the sake of simplicity, we shall assume for now that the addends in columns 1 and 2 are small enough so that there is no possibility of additive overflow. Consider the following diagram of a table in memory:

	Address	Col 1	Col 2	Col 3
Line 1	0120	01	02	?
Line 2	0123	10	04	?
Line 3	0126	23	13	?
Line 4	0129	06	24	?
Line 5	012C	00		

IY is initially set to 0120 and incremented by 0003 for each sequential row entry.

Step 3

Initialize memory locations 0120 through 012C to the values appearing in the above table.

Step 4

Execute the program in single-step mode watching what happens to the IY and A registers as well as memory locations 0122, 0125, 0128, and 012B.

By now you have certainly noticed how suitable indexed addressing is for manipulation of two dimensional tables of information. The line in the table is established via the contents of the IY register while the entry within each line is specified via the displacement from IY.

EXPERIMENT NO. 2

Purpose

The purpose of this experiment is to show you that there can be many alternative ways to write a program to perform a given task. One technique is self-modification, in which a program modifies its own instructions as it executes. WARNING: WE ARE NOT ADVOCATING THAT YOU EVER ADOPT THIS TECHNIQUE BUT YOU SHOULD BE AWARE OF ITS EXISTENCE.

Program No. 16

Memory Location	Object Code		Source Code	Comments
02FD	01 07 00		LD BC,0007H	;BC = the number of columns per row
0300	1E 06		LD E,06H	;The E-register will be used as a ;counter for the number of lines ;processed
0302	FD 21 80 03		LD IY,0380H	;IY points to the line currently ;being processed
0306	21 11 03		LD HL,0311H	;HL points to the location of the ;displacement byte in the ADD(IY+d) ;instruction
0309	36 00	ROW:	LD (HL),00H	;Initialize the displacement
030B	3E 00		LD A,00H	;Initialize the A register
030D	16 06		LD D,06H	;The D-register counts the number ;of column bytes added.
030F	FD 86 d	COL:	ADD A,(IY+d)	;We use d here because the dis- ;placement changes as the program ;executes
0312	00		NOP	;No operation
0313	34		INC (HL)	;Change the displacement
0314	15		DEC D	;Update the column counter
0315	20 F8		JR NZ,COL	;If not zero, add more
0317	FD 77 06		LD (IY+06H),A	;Store the sum in column 7
031A	FD 09		ADD IY,BC	;Set IY to next row
031D	1D		DEC E	;Update the row counter
031D	20 EA		JR NZ,ROW	;If not zero, process next row
031F	FF		RST 38H	;If zero, pass control back to ;operating system

Program No. 17

Memory Location	Object Code	Source Code
0320	01 07 00	LD BC,0007H
0323	1E 06	LD E,06H

```
0325    FD 21 80 03         LD IY,0380H
0329    3E 00         ROW: LD A,00H
032B    FD 86 00           ADD A,(IY)
032E    FD 86 01           ADD A,(IY+01H)
0331    FD 86 02           ADD A,(IY+02H)
0334    FD 86 03           ADD A,(IY+03H)
0337    FD 86 04           ADD A,(IY+04H)
033A    FD 86 05           ADD A,(IY+05H)
033D    FD 77 06           LD (IY+06H),A
0340    FD 09              ADD IY,BC
0342    1D                 DEC E
0343    20 E4              JR NZ,ROW
0345    FF                 RST 38H
```

Program No. 18

```
0360    1E 06              LD E,06H
0362    FD 21 80 03        LD IY,0380H
0366    3E 00         ROW: LD A,00H
0368    16 06              LD D,06H
036A    FD 86 00      COL: ADD (IY)
036D    FD 23              INC IY
036F    15                 DEC D
0370    20 F8              JR NZ,COL
0372    1D                 DEC E
0373    FD 77 00           LD (IY+00H),A
0376    FD 23              INC IY
0378    20 EC              JR NZ,ROW
037A    FF                 RST 38H
```

Step 1

First look at all of the above programs and notice that they all perform exactly the same task. There is a table stored at memory location 0380 with 6 rows and 6 columns. Each of these programs computes a line total by adding successive column bytes of a given row to the accumulator. These programs vary in their memory and time requirements because they use different techniques. Let us discuss each program in detail.

For all three programs, the overall program structure may be represented by the flow chart in Fig. 7-6. The programs differ in the methods chosen to implement the flow chart process boxes that have been marked with an asterisk.

Program No. 16

The algorithm used by this program modifies the displacement byte in the instruction ADD A,(IY+d). More specifically, the HL register pair is loaded with the memory location of the third byte of this instruction, namely the displacement. First the displacement is initialized to zero and the accumulator is set to zero. As a column counter tracks the number of entries processed, (IY+d) is added

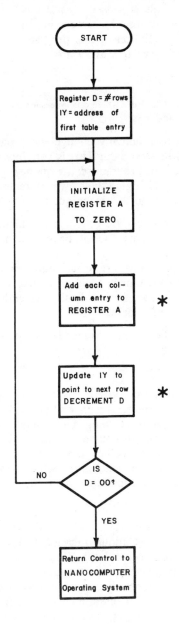

Fig. 7-6.

to the accumulator, and the displacement incremented, INC (HL). Once all columns have been added, the column counter has been decremented to zero. This is sensed by a JR NZ instruction which causes a branch to instructions for processing the next row.

As we have already mentioned, this program modifies itself. The four instructions which give this away are

```
LD  HL,0311H
LD  (HL),00H
ADD A,(IY+d)    where d is in location 0311
INC (HL)
```

Two of these instructions actually change the program. Hence the program is treated as its own data! This is certainly a technique that stimulates the imagination. Programs can write new programs or alter themselves, dynamically changing their own characteristics. However, three major disadvantages to this technique must be mentioned:

a. Self-modifying programs are often quite difficult to debug.
b. Self-modifying programs cannot be executed from read-only memory.
c. Self-modifying programs are often quite difficult to change. It is not easy to document such programs. Even the original programmer may have great difficulty remembering the details of how the program works.

Self-modification techniques are tremendously powerful and must be used with extreme care.

Program No. 17

The algorithm used by this program is quite straightforward. The six ADD A,(IY+d) instructions with d=00, . . . ,05 quite clearly document what the program is doing. Unfortunately this is not efficient with respect to space. Of course, as the number of bytes to be ADDed increases, the more inefficient this method becomes. Thus, this method is limited to applications in which few bytes must be referenced, e.g., the program in Experiment No. 1.

Program No. 18

This program uses an algorithm which makes no use of nonzero displacement bytes. The technique increments the IY register for each byte ADDed to the accumulator. This works quite well in this application and results in the smallest (number of bytes) program. The technique used here somewhat obscures the tabular form of the data because it is treated as a one dimensional array with IY as its index. One reason this technique works out so nicely here is because the locations to be referenced are in sequence, i.e., one right after the other in memory. If the locations to be added were IY+01H, IY+09H, IY+43H, IY+44H, and IY+56H, this technique would clearly have to be changed. In contrast, the technique of Program No. 17 would work as is, i.e., just list the columns to be summed.

In the preceding paragraphs we alluded to several qualities attributed to alternative programming techniques. Here is a summary:

   a. *Space*—the number of memory bytes required to store the program
   b. *Time*—the number of CPU states required to execute the program
   c. *Flexibility*—the ease with which a program can be changed
   d. *Self-Modifying*—whether or not the program modifies itself during execution
   e. *Logical Simplicity*—the ease with which the program can be read and understood.

This is certainly not an exhaustive list, but each of these attributes must be considered as you try to determine the best way to build a program. Typically, tradeoffs exist because you cannot optimize one attribute without sacrificing on another. For example, to write programs which economize on memory space, one often has to settle for slower execution times. This is a *time-space* tradeoff. Similarly, we have seen that logical simplicity often requires more space, a *simplicity-space* tradeoff.

Step 2

Load Program No. 16 and execute it in single-step mode, paying special attention to memory location 0311, the displacement byte of the ADD A,(IY+d) instruction. Use the following table for data:

Memory	Col 1	Col 2	Col 3	Col 4	Col 5	Col 6	Col 7	
0380	01	02	03	04	05	06	X	ROW 1
0387	02	02	02	02	02	02	X	ROW 2
038E	01	03	01	03	01	03	X	ROW 3
0395	03	03	03	03	03	03	X	ROW 4
039C	08	08	01	01	08	08	X	ROW 5
03A3	04	04	04	04	08	08	X	ROW 6

NOTE: X means this byte computed by the program.

Step 3

Carefully scrutinize Program No. 17 to see if there is a change which will result in making the program shorter. One improvement that we saw is to replace all references to IY with HL. In general, the analogous HL instruction is one byte shorter.

We hope that you have seen in this experiment how programming is as much an art as a science. A given task can be performed by many different sets of instructions with some sets more efficient than others with respect to time, or space, or logical simplicity, or many other attributes. The art lies in taking the trouble to analyze the pros and cons of each alternative and working the tradeoffs to meet the unique situation. It is not unusual for a programmer to rewrite a program three or four times, if his constraints merit such perfection. For example, a typical constraint is memory space. A 2708 EPROM will hold exactly 1024 bytes. A program may have to be reworked many times to utilize those 1024 bytes most effectively.

EXPERIMENT NO. 3

Purpose

The purpose of this experiment is to demonstrate the use of the stack operations PUSH and POP and the exchange instructions.

Program No. 19

Memory Location	Object Code	Source Code	Comments
0130		PUSH AF	;AF to top of stack
		PUSH BC	;BC to top of stack
		PUSH DE	;DE to top of stack
		PUSH HL	;HL to top of stack
		EX, AF,AF'	;Exchange AF and AF'
		EXX	;Exchange register pairs
		POP HL	;Top of stack to HL
		POP DE	;Top of stack to DE
		POP BC	;Top of stack to BC
		POP AF	;Top of stack to AF
		RST 38H	;Return control to operating ;system

Step 1

For this program, we will ask you to perform your own hand assembly. Thus, you are given a start address and the source which uniquely determines the object code. Below is a hex memory dump for you to use to check your hand assembly:

0130	F5	C5	D5	E5	08	D9	E1	D1
0138	C1	F1	FF					

Step 2

Load the object code starting at 0130 and verify its correctness.

Step 3

The next step is to locate the stack in read/write memory. We have two choices: We can leave it where it is now or we can change it. The following are the only instructions provided by the Z-80 to affect the location of the stack:

```
LD  SP,HL
LD  SP,IX
LD  SP,IY
LD  SP,nn
LD  SP,(nn)
```

Any one of these can be used at the beginning of the above program to locate the stack because the stack pointer, SP, contains the memory location of the top of the stack. For most programs, once established, the SP register is updated only as a result of PUSH and POP instructions.

Let us utilize a nice capability of the Nanocomputer operating system and set the Stack Pointer to 0150 by positioning the selector lamp at SP and SToring 0150 (Fig. 7-7).

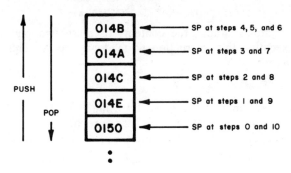

Fig. 7-7.

Step 4

Execute the program in single-step mode with the selector lamp at position SP. Watch the stack first grow in size from 0 to 8 bytes and then shrink back again:

Step 5

To help track which registers are stored in which order, initialize the registers as follows:

A = 01	D = 05
F = 02	E = 06
B = 03	H = 07
C = 04	L = 08

Execute the program in single-step mode until the last PUSH instruction has been executed, i.e., until the PC=0134. Verify that the register pairs have been pushed onto the stack as follows:

```
0148   L = 08    SP
       H = 07
```

014A	E = 06
	D = 05
014C	C = 04
	B = 03
014E	F = 02
	A = 01
0150	

The HI byte occupies the memory location with the higher address.

Step 6

The next instruction to be executed is

> 08   EX AF,AF'   (AF' = A' and F')

This instruction "swaps" the contents of these two register pairs. Before executing this instruction write down the contents of these register pairs:

> AF = 0102   AF' =   (we observed 0044)

Recall that AF' may be observed by using the ARS key. When the ARS lamp is lit, the alternate registers are being displayed. Press the single-step key once to execute the EX AF,AF' instruction. Then

> AF =   (we observed 0044)   ;AF' = 0102

The next instruction is EXX which exchanges BC and BC', DE and DE', HL and HL'. Write the contents of all these registers, first before and then after EXX is excuted:

			Our Observation
Before	BC = 0304	BC' =	FFFF
	DE = 0506	DE' =	FFFF
	HL = 0708	HL' =	FFFF

Press the ss key.

		Our Observation	
After	BC =	FFFF	BC' = 0304
	DE =	FFFF	DE' = 0506
	HL =	FFFF	HL' = 0708

Step 7

The next four instructions are all POP instructions which load the top two bytes on the stack into the specified register pairs. Watch the HL register pair as you press the ss key to execute POP HL. The byte 08 in memory location 0148 is loaded into register L and the 07 in memory location 0149 is loaded into register H.

172

Similarly, the next two POP instructions load register pairs DE and BC with 0304 and 0102, respectively. Thus, we see that execution of this program leaves each register pair loaded with the same contents as its alternate register pair.

Step 8

Two very important facts about the stack operations should be made clear:

1. PUSH and POP *always* move 16 bits or two bytes of information. Instructions such as POP C and PUSH F do not exist.
2. The order in which register pairs are PUSHed onto the stack is opposite to the order in which the register pairs should be POPped off if register contents are to be restored to their original values. Specifically

```
PUSH HL
PUSH DE
POP HL
POP DE
```

is a sequence of instructions equivalent to the instruction

```
EX DE,HL.
```

Whereas,

```
PUSH HL
PUSH DE
```

(Any sequence of instructions including instructions which alter DE and HL)

```
POP DE
POP HL
```

preserve the DE and HL registers as they were before the sequence of instructions was executed. This last sequence of instructions is quite useful as you will see later when you study subroutines.

CHAPTER 8

Jumps, Calls, and Returns

Jump, call, and return instructions comprise the class of Z-80 instructions called *branch* instructions. They all cause the instruction flow of the program to be transferred to places in memory other than what normally would have occurred had the branch instruction not appeared. In this chapter, you will extend your knowledge of these instructions beyond the simple ones that you have already seen, namely, JP and JR. In particular, you will learn about the technique of using subroutines. The jump, call, and return instructions appear in Table 8-1.

OBJECTIVES

After completing this chapter, you will be able to:

- Define *transfer of program control* in terms of what happens to the program counter (PC) register.
- Define the *zero, carry, parity/overflow,* and *sign* flags.
- Define *subroutine call* and *return* in terms of what happens to the program counter (PC), the stack pointer (SP), and the stack.
- Define and use the *restart instructions.*

PROGRAM CONTROL TRANSFERS

By now, you are well aware that a program is merely a set of memory bytes that represent instructions and data. Normally these instructions are executed sequentially, i.e., one right after the next,

Table 8-1. JUMP, CALL, and RETURN Group

CONDITION

			UN-COND.	CARRY	NON CARRY	ZERO	NON ZERO	PARITY EVEN	PARITY ODD	SIGN NEG	SIGN POS	REG B≠0
JUMP 'JP'	IMMED. EXT.	nn	C3 n n	DA n n	D2 n n	CA n n	C2 n n	EA n n	E2 n n	FA n n	F2 n n	
JUMP 'JR'	RELATIVE	PC+e	18 e-2	38 e-2	30 e-2	28 e-2	20 e-2					
JUMP 'JP'		(HL)	E9									
JUMP 'JP'	REG. INDIR.	(IX)	DD E9									
JUMP 'JP'		(IY)	FD E9									
'CALL'	IMMED. EXT.	nn	CD n n	DC n n	D4 n n	CC n n	C4 n n	EC n n	E4 n n	FC n n	F4 n n	
DECREMENT B, JUMP IF NON ZERO 'DJNZ'	RELATIVE	PC+e										10 e-2
RETURN 'RET'	REGISTER INDIR.	(SP) (SP+1)	C9	D8	D0	C8	C0	E8	E0	F8	F0	
RETURN FROM INT 'RETI'	REG. INDIR.	(SP) (SP+1)	ED 4D									
RETURN FROM NON MASKABLE INT 'RETN'	REG. INDIR.	(SP) (SP+1)	ED 45									

NOTE—CERTAIN FLAGS HAVE MORE THAN ONE PURPOSE. REFER TO SECTION 6.0 FOR DETAILS

Courtesy Zilog, Inc.

until something (like a JP instruction) changes that mode of execution. Let us examine in detail how the Z-80 actually executes a program stored somewhere in memory.

The Z-80 CPU stores the address of the *next* instruction to be executed in the PC (program counter) register. Hence, executing a program amounts to repeating the following steps until the HALT instruction is executed:

Step 1. Read (PC) into an instruction register internal to the Z-80 chip. Recall that the notation (PC) means the contents of the memory location addressed by the 16-bit program counter. (PC) is the first instruction byte, and, therefore, is an op code that will begin to define the instruction to be executed. In some cases, this byte will be the entire instruction. In other cases, the CPU will have to read another byte before it will actually know how long, in bytes, the instruction is.

Step 2. Decode the first instruction byte and determine if additional bytes need to be read. Increment the address in the PC so that it points to the next memory location, i.e., the next byte in the program.

If decoding indicates that the instruction is just one byte, then go to step 4.

Step 3. Continue to read (PC) and increment PC until the entire instruction has been read, a maximum of four bytes in all.

Step 4. Execute the instruction, then return to Step 1.

Notice that when it is time to begin execution of an instruction, the 16-bit PC register always holds the address in memory of the first byte of the next instruction. As you will see, all branch instructions, namely jumps, calls, and returns, act directly on the PC register to change the sequence in which memory locations are read and executed as instructions.

UNCONDITIONAL JUMP INSTRUCTIONS

Jump instructions cause program control to be transferred to an address specified within the instruction itself. After the first byte of the jump instruction has been read and decoded by the Z-80 CPU, the instruction type is fully determined. Hence, the execution of the instruction is carried out by reading the next byte or bytes to determine the jump address, after which the jump address is loaded into the PC register. When the CPU begins the next *instruction cycle*, the PC contains the address of the instruction addressed by the address byte(s) of the previous jump instruction. We illustrate the effect of a JP instruction on the PC below:

Address Sequence	Instruction	(PC = 1000 initially)
1000	LD A	
1001	00H	
1002	INC A	PC = 1002 after execution of LD A,00H
1003	JP	PC = 1003 after execution of INC A
1004	02H	
1005	10	
		PC = 1002 after execution of JP FDH (A nonbranching three-byte instruction would have left PC = 1006 after execution).

Notice that the JP instruction affects only the PC register. No other operations take place. In the case of the JP instruction, the full jump address is contained as the second and third (last) bytes of the instruction. Thus, execution of the jump amounts to loading the last two instruction bytes into the PC register. The effect of jump instructions on program control is illustrated in Fig. 8-1.

Jumps can go "forward" or "backward." The program flow just follows the changes in the PC register from location to location.

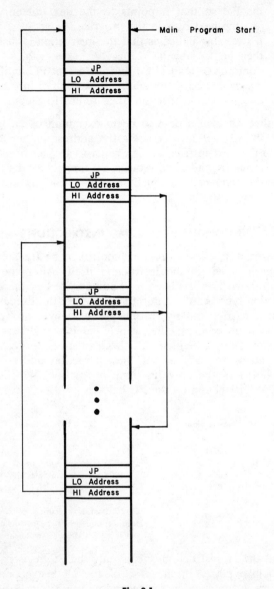

Fig. 8-1.

Generally, the more jumps in a program, the more difficult it will be to change and de-bug.

There are two major classes of jump instructions implemented on the Z-80 microprocessor. *Absolute jumps* and *relative jumps*. The

JP instruction used in the above example is an absolute jump because the actual two-byte jump address is specified as part of the instruction. Relative jumps (JR) specify a one-byte two's complement displacement in the instruction. Thus, execution of a relative jump involves the extra step of determining the jump address from the sum of the current PC value and the displacement byte. Here we list the same program as above, only in this case we use a relative jump.

Address	Instruction	(PC = 1000, initially)
1000	LD A,	
1001	00H	
1002	INC A	PC = 1002 after execution of LD A,00H
1003	JR	PC = 1003 after execution of INC A
1004	FDH	
		PC = 1002 after execution of JR FDH (A nonbranching two-byte instruction would have left PC = 1005 after execution)

Note that FD is the two's complement representation of −3. In the relative jump instruction, the displacement byte gives the number of bytes before (negative) or after (positive) the location pointed to by a *normally updated program counter*. In the above example, the PC would have normally become 1005 after execution of a nonbranching two-byte instruction. Three bytes BEFORE 1005 is location 1002, the jump address, thus the displacement is −3 or FD. A common mistake made by programmers is to determine the displacement byte relative to the PC just BEFORE execution of the JR instruction. This is incorrect and invariably leads to trouble. *Displacement for a relative jump instruction is always determined relative to the first location after the two-byte JR instruction.*

Let us list some differences between relative and absolute jumps:

1. The instruction JP uses three bytes per instruction, a one-byte op code plus a two-byte address. A JR uses two bytes per instruction, a one-byte op code plus a one-byte displacement.
2. The instruction JP can cause program control to transfer to any location in memory. The JR instruction can cause program control to transfer only to locations in memory within the range of −128 to +127 bytes of the memory location just after the displacement byte. This is the limitation of a one-byte displacement.
3. The JP instructions are generally *not relocatable* while JR instructions are. A very important attribute of the JR instruction is that it relates only to relative memory locations of instructions. This implies that JR instructions maintain their integrity independent of their *absolute* memory location. Every pro-

grammer who has had to move a large portion of a program down one byte in memory to insert a new instruction can appreciate the convenience of writing relocatable code (assuming hand-assembly).

Before we consider conditional jumps, we would like to note that there are three absolute jumps that use register indirect addressing. That is, these jumps, JP (HL), JP (IX), and JP (IY), indicate the jump address as the contents of one of the register pairs HL, IX, or IY. These, as well as all Z-80 branch instructions, are contained in Table 8-1.

FLAGS AND CONDITIONAL JUMPS

The JP and JR instructions are both unconditional jumps. This means that program control is *always* transferred to the specified absolute or relative address when the instruction is executed. Conditional jumps are instructions that transfer program control to a different location *contingent* on some condition that must be met. For example, the instruction JP NZ causes a branch to occur if the zero flag is at logic 0. (Though the NZ, not zero, and logic 0 seem contradictory, they really are not, as you will see.) When we introduced this instruction in Chapter 6, we did not discuss the flag registers. We will do so now.

The Z-80 CPU contains two flag registers F and F', one each for the two sets of general-purpose registers. Each flag register contains six *flags,* or bits of information, that are individually affected by various Z-80 instructions. We say that a flag is *set* if its value is logic 1, and *reset* if its value is logic 0. Four of the six flags are used as conditions for jump, call, and return instructions. They are:

1. *CARRY FLAG (C)*—This flag is affected primarily by the add, subtract, and rotate and shift instructions. During an add operation, it is set if there is a carry from the most significant bit of the accumulator. During a subtract operation, the carry flag is set if a borrow occurs to the most significant bit of the accumulator. Many rotates and shifts append the carry flag to the accumulator as a ninth bit to manipulate. We shall introduce and fully discuss arithmetic and logic instructions in subsequent chapters.

Two instructions directly manipulate the carry flag:

SCF—set carry flag forces the C bit to logic 1.
CCF—complement carry flag changes the current logic level of the C bit. IF C = 1, CCF resets C (to logic 0). IF C = 0, CCF sets C (to logic 1).

2. *ZERO FLAG (Z)*—The state of this flag is affected by many instructions. Operations that change the accumulator usually affect the zero flag by setting it if the accumulator is zero, and resetting it if the accumulator is not zero. The BIT instruction sets the zero flag if a specified bit is zero, and resets the zero flag if the bit is one. The compare instruction, CP, checks for equality of a specified byte with the accumulator. If there is equality, the zero flag is set; if not, it is reset. Other instructions that affect the zero flag will be discussed later. The Z flag is the only flag for which there is some seeming inconsistency and confusion with respect to the conditions on which the flag is zero or one. The reason for this is the way in which the flag is manipulated: the Z flag equals one means a result was zero and the Z flag equals zero means a result was not zero. Thus, when the instruction JP NZ appears in a program, it means jump if the *result is not zero;* or, in terms of the Z flag, jump if the *Z flag is zero*. The Z flag equal to zero means that the result of a previous operation was not zero. This is most confusing. Our best advice is to suggest that you memorize this fact and think carefully when you use the Z flag as a condition for jumping. The important fact is that the condition NZ refers to the *result* of the previous operation, and *not* to the flag.

3. *SIGN FLAG (S)*—This flag is just a copy of the most significant bit of the result of an operation. Results are usually, but not always, stored in the accumulator. The purpose of the S flag is to indicate that the two's complement result is positive or negative. Thus, the S flag is set (= 1) for negative and reset (= 0) for positive results.

4. *PARITY/OVERFLOW FLAG (P/V)*—The P/V flag serves two purposes:
   (a) To indicate parity of the result of a logical, rotate, shift, or input instruction.
   (b) To indicate overflow as a result of two's complement arithmetic.

The word *parity* refers to the number of bits in a byte that are at logic 1. If the number of set bits is odd, then one says that the byte has *odd parity*. If the number of set bits is even, then one says that the byte has *even parity*. For example, the parity of FF is even, and the parity of 01 is odd.

The parity flag is *set* if the parity of the result is *even* and is *reset* if the parity of the result is *odd*.

In Chapter 6, we discussed overflow detection for two's complement arithmetic. If the addition of two positive two's complement numbers results in a negative two's complement number, the overflow flag is *set*. Similarly, the flag is *set* if addition of two negatives yields a positive result. The V flag is *reset* if no overflow occurs.

It is important to understand the difference between the *carry flag* (*C*) and the *overflow flag* (*V*). If two binary numbers are added or subtracted, the C flag is used to detect any overflow. If two two's complement numbers are being added or subtracted, the V flag is used to detect any overflow. These two flags are *not* interchangeable. Here is an example that proves this.

$$1\ 1\ 1\ 1\ 1\ 0\ 1\ 1 \quad \text{is the two's complement representation for } -5$$
$$+\ 1\ 1\ 1\ 1\ 0\ 0\ 0\ 0 \quad \text{is the two's complement representation for } -16$$
SUM: $1\ 1\ 1\ 0\ 1\ 0\ 1\ 1$ is the two's complement representation for -21

C = 1 because there is a carry from the most significant bit
V = 0 because −21 is correct; there is no overflow.

5. *HALF-CARRY* (*H*) and *SUBTRACT* (*N*) *FLAGS*—The last two flags are highly specialized flags used only for arithmetic based on a binary encoding scheme called *binary coded decimal* (*BCD*). At this time we shall only say that the two flags are called the *Half-Carry* (*H*) and the *Subtract* (*N*) flags. Both are important for the *decimal adjust accumulator* (*DAA*) instruction. Neither the H nor N flags are used in connection with *branching,* as are the first four flags, i.e., they cannot be "tested" with any of the conditional branch instructions. The format of the flag registers is:

S	Z	X	H	X	P/V	N	C

where X means that the value of the bit is not of interest. The X is sometimes referred to as the "don't care" condition because no attention is ever paid to it. The SGS–ATES Z-80 CPU programming reference card, as well as the Table in Appendix I, summarizes all of the Z-80 instructions that affect the flags.

We have already discussed the JP NZ conditional jump, which transfers program control to a specified address contingent on the zero flag (Z) being reset. For each of the flags, S, Z, P/V, and C, there is a conditional JP instruction that is subject to the flag's being set or reset:

         JP NZ—Jump if Z-flag is reset (result not zero)
         JP Z—Jump if Z-flag is set (result zero)
         JP NC—Jump if C-flag is reset (no carry)
         JP C—Jump if C-flag is set (carry)

JP PO—Jump if P-flag is reset (parity odd or no overflow on previous operation

JP PE—Jump if P-flag is set (parity even or overflow on previous operation

JP P—Jump if S-flag is reset (result positive)

JP M—Jump if S-flag is set (result "minus")

There are four conditional relative jumps—JR NZ, JR Z, JR NC, and JR C—in addition to the unconditional relative jump, JR.

Let us look at the relative jumps whose actions are contingent on the state of the carry-flag (C). The effects of these instructions JR NC and JR C are diagrammed in Fig. 8-2A and 8-2B. In Fig. 8-2C, the decision symbol, which is commonly used in program flowcharting, indicates that what happens next depends on the state of a flag. Later in this chapter, and in subsequent chapters, you will see many examples of programs that use conditional jumps.

There is one specialized conditional relative jump instruction whose mnemonic is DJNZ. The instruction executes in three steps:

a. Register B is decremented (by 1).
b. A check is made to see if the contents of register B is 00.
c. If B is not 00, then the relative jump takes place. Otherwise, the next sequential instruction is executed.

The flow chart in Fig. 8-3 shows how the DJNZ instruction works.

Quite often in programming, one may need to execute the same group of instructions a specified number of times. The DJNZ instruction is designed for this purpose. Fig. 8-4 shows how the DJNZ instruction can be used. As you will see, this instruction is quite useful.

CALLS AND RETURNS

A *call* instruction is a jump instruction that "remembers" where it jumped from. The *return* instruction causes the CPU to resume program execution at the statement following the last executed call statement. See Fig. 8-5.

As you may imagine, the CALL and RET instructions are very useful for allowing the same block of code to be executed through the use of call instructions from many different places in a program. One of the common uses of subroutines is for program delay loops. A delay subroutine can be written for one time period, say one millisecond. Any time that the program requires a delay of n milliseconds, the subroutine is called n times. Manufacturers of hardware, software developers, and various computer user groups keep collections of useful subroutines for use by programmers on their computers. These collections are called *libraries*. Sample libraries

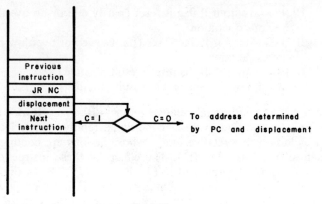

Fig. 8-2A.

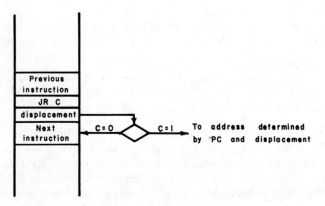

Fig. 8-2B.

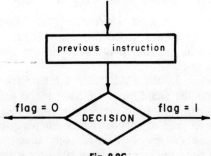

Fig. 8-2C.

might include multiply and divide subroutines, subroutines to compute trigonometric, logarithmic, and exponential function values, and other special-purpose tasks.

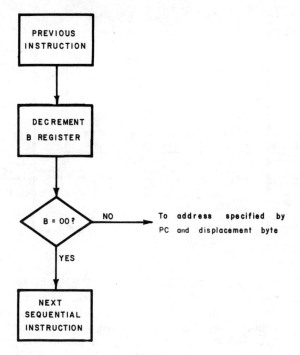

Fig. 8-3.

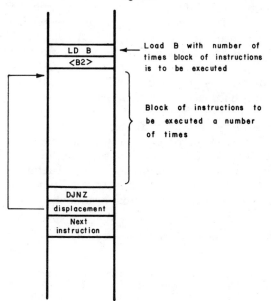

Fig. 8-4.

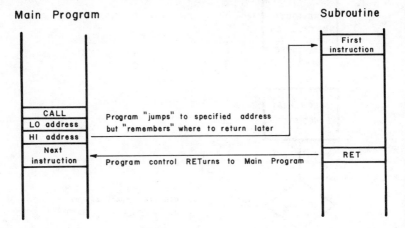

Fig. 8-5.

Now that you know *what* the CALL and RET instructions do, you must learn *how* they do it. First the CALL instruction. Just as it was with the JP addr instruction, the CALL instruction specifies a memory location in the second and third bytes of the instruction. These two bytes are loaded into the PC register to accomplish the transfer of program control. However, before the PC is changed, the CALL instruction performs a first step that distinguishes it from the JP instruction. To remember where in the main program to return to, the PC is pushed onto the stack—first HI byte, then LO byte— *while the PC still points to the next instruction after the three-byte call.*

The subroutine stays in control until a return instruction is encountered. The unconditional return, RET, causes the PC to be loaded with the top two bytes of the stack—the top byte becoming the LO address byte, and the next stack byte becoming the HI address byte. If the stack has been properly used, the RET should come when the top two stack bytes are the bytes pushed onto the stack by the previous CALL. Hence, program control returns to the first instruction after the CALL. To illustrate this process let us step through a CALL and then a RET from a subroutine.

Address				
0300	LD SP	Program start: Initialize the stack pointer at	SP=	0400 [1]
0301	00H	0400	PC=	0303
0302	04			
0303	CALL	Call the subroutine at 0310: Push 0306 onto	SP=	03FE [2]
0304	10H	stack; Decrement SP by 2; Load PC with 0310	PC=	0310
0305	03			
0306	HALT	Halt		

0310	INC A	Subroutine Start	SP=	03FE
0311	INC B		PC=	0311
0312	INC C			
0313	DEC D			
0314	DEC E		PC=	0314
0315	RET	Return to main program: Pop top two bytes off stack into PC; Increment SP by 2.	SP= PC=	0400 [3] 0306

STACK: The stack is changed only by the following instructions

[1]   0300 LD SP
[2]   0303 CALL
[3]   0315 RET

(Note that for the diagrams, addresses *increase* downwards.)

Stack
After [1]

```
03FE  [X]
03FF  [X]
0400  [X]        SP=0400
      [X]
      [·]
      [·]
      [·]        PC=0303
```

Stack
After [2]

```
      [06]       SP=03FE
      [03]
      [X]
      [X]
      [·]
      [·]
      [·]        PC=0310
```

Stack
After [3]

```
      [06]
      [03]
      [X]        SP=0400
      [X]
      [·]
      [·]
      [·]        PC=0306
```

(X is unknown and don't care)

Three critical pitfalls can trap even the most experienced programmers:

1. The stack grows so large that it expands down in RAM until it begins to "eat up" the program that is using it, or the data that the program is operating on; or, the stack grows so large that it tries to expand into ROM or PROM and can no longer accept new bytes.
2. The subroutine called begins to manipulate the stack in such a manner that the RET instruction is executed with the wrong pair of bytes sitting at the top of the stack. Who knows where the CPU will then send program control?
3. You forget to initialize the stack pointer and wind up with the stack sitting *anywhere* in memory. In particular, *"anywhere"* could be in the middle of your *program,* or in the "bit bucket" at location FFFF, where you do not have read-write memory.

All three of the above instances of stack mismanagement may well result in execution of stack data which is always adventuresome, if not guaranteed trouble!

Even with these risks, the technique of subroutine calling is very, very useful and is an excellent practice to develop. Rarely can it be overdone. Programs that are structured around subroutines are usually easier to understand, easier to change, and easier to debug than if they had not used subroutines. Experiment No. 2 investigates the issue of when to use subroutines.

Similar to the JP instruction, CALL and RET have conditional counterparts that perform a call or return contingent on the status of a flag. These all appear in Table 8-1. Table 8-2 lists the restart instructions, RST N. These are one-byte instructions that perform a

Table 8-2. Restart Group

	CALL ADDRESS	OP CODE	
	0000_H	C7	'RST 0'
	0008_H	CF	'RST 8'
	0010_H	D7	'RST 16'
	0018_H	DF	'RST 24'
	0020_H	E7	'RST 32'
	0028_H	EF	'RST 40'
	0030_H	F7	'RST 48'
	0038_H	FF	'RST 56'

Courtesy Zilog, Inc.

call to an address specified within the op code. In other words, the RST instructions are one-byte unconditional CALLS. The two-byte address necessary in a CALL instruction is circumvented by modified page zero addressing. Depending on three bits within the op code, one of eight hex subroutine addresses can be specified:
0000, 0008, 0010, 0018, 0020, 0028, 0030, and 0038.

INTRODUCTION TO THE EXPERIMENTS

This set of exercises concentrates on important programming techniques that utilize the various Z-80 branching instructions. The first experiments introduce you to the instructions by giving you simple programs to execute while closely watching the program counter (PC) register as well as other affected registers and memory locations. The latter experiments discuss such techniques as passing parameters to subroutines and using jump tables. The experiments you will perform may be summarized as follows:

Experiment No.	Comments
1	Demonstrates the DJNZ instruction for use in a delay loop routine. Also execution breakpoints are demonstrated.
2	Demonstrates how to convert the program of Experiment No. 1 to a subroutine and gives a sample calling program. The question of when to use subroutines is discussed.
3	Demonstrates the RST N instruction.
4	Demonstrates four techniques for passing parameters to subroutines.
5	Demonstrates the technique of using jump tables.

EXPERIMENT NO. 1

Purpose

The purpose of this experiment is to demonstrate the DJNZ instruction by using it to implement a delay loop. Also, the technique for inserting, using, and removing program execution breakpoints is demonstrated.

Program No. 20

Memory Location	Object Code	Source Code		Comments
0100	06 09		LD B,09H	;Initialize register B
0102	0E FF	LOOP1:	LD C,FFH	;Initialize register C
0104	16 FF	LOOP2:	LD D,FFH	;Initialize register D
0106	15	LOOP3:	DEC D	;Inner-most loop
0107	20 FD		JR NZ,LOOP3	;Decrements register D
0109	0D		DEC C	;Middle loop decrements
010A	20 F8		JR NZ,LOOP2	;register C
010C	10 F4		DJNZ LOOP1	;Outer loop decrements ;register B
010E	FF		RST 38H	:Return control to the Nanocomputer ;operating system

Step 1

Load the above program and execute it with several different initial values for register B. As you can see, we used 09 above. Notice how widely you can vary the time the display remains dark by changing the initial value of register B. Appendix D contains a complete discussion of how to calculate the execution time of a given program. We have calculated the following execution times for three different initial values of the B register.

B Register	Total Execution Time of Program in Experiment No. 1
01	0.4420844 second (approximately)
09	3.66123772 seconds (approximately)
FF	105.47 seconds (approximately)

The DJNZ instruction automatically decrements the B register. Thus one instruction, namely DEC B, is saved by using this specialized jump.

Step 2

Suppose that you wish to observe what happens to register B as the above program executes the DJNZ instruction. You could single step through decrementing C and D, with C decremented 255 times for every time D is decremented once. However, this could be time consuming. The best alternative is to insert a program breakpoint just before the DJNZ instruction is executed. For example, the breakpoint could be inserted at location 010C, since the instruction at the breakpoint address is not executed before the program stops. Then, placing the selector lamp at position BC and pressing the ss key will allow you to see register B being decremented. Press GO again and execution will stop at the next time the PC equals the breakpoint address, i.e., when the DJNZ instruction is about to be executed again.

To set the breakpoint, enter Breakpoint Mode by pressing the BRK key. The BRK lamp should light and you should see a lone zero in the data display. Press and hold down the INC key. You should see the 0 change to 1,2,3, up to 7 and back to zero again. If there are no other breakpoints set, no other digits should appear in either the data or address displays. Increment the breakpoint counter (the single displayed digit) to read 3. Enter 010C and press LA. You should then see:

$$0 \; 1 \; 0 \; C \qquad 3 \; 1 \; 0$$

0 1 0 C is the breakpoint address, 1 0 is the content of that address (the DJNZ op code), and 3 is the breakpoint counter. This breakpoint could have been entered as any breakpoint number 0 through 7. We chose 3 arbitrarily. Exit Breakpoint Mode by pressing the BRK key again. The BRK lamp will go dark. Execute the program at full speed starting at location 0100. The display should darken momentarily, then come up reading:

$$0 \; 1 \; 0 \; C \qquad 1 \; 0$$

That is, the PC=010C and the next instruction to be executed is DJNZ. Position the selector lamp at BC and press the ss key once. The B register should decrease by 1 and the PC register should read

0102. To see the DJNZ instruction execute a second time, press GO again. Execution will stop at PC=010C again. It is possible for you to single step through each occurrence of the DJNZ instruction in the execution of the program in this manner.

Step 3

Remove the breakpoint by entering Breakpoint Mode, displaying the breakpoint to be deleted by using the INC key, and finally pressing GO.

EXPERIMENT NO. 2

Purpose

The purpose of this experiment is to demonstrate how to convert the program of Experiment No. 1 into a subroutine and give an example program to call the subroutine. The question of when to use subroutines is also discussed.

Program No. 21

Memory Location	Object Code	Source Code	Comments
011B	31 FF 01	LD SP,01FFH	;Locate the system stack
011E	06 03	LD B,03H	;Specify B register value
0120	CD 02 01	CALL DELAY	;Call the subroutine
0123	3E 00	LD A,00H	;Load the accumulator with 00
0125	FF	RST 38H	;Return control to the operating system

Subroutine Delay

Memory Location	Object Code	Source Code
0102	0E FF	DELAY: LD C,FFH
0104	16 FF	LOOP2: LD D,FFH
0106	15	LOOP3: DEC D
0107	20 FD	JR NZ,LOOP3
0109	0D	DEC C
010A	20 F8	JR NZ,LOOP2
010C	10 F4	DJNZ DELAY
010E	C9	RET

Step 1

The program from Experiment No. 1 appears above under the heading Subroutine Delay. We have converted it to a subroutine by, among other things, replacing the final RST 38H statement with the RET statement. Thus, now the subroutine returns control to the calling routine, listed as Program 21, instead of jumping back to the Nanocomputer operating system. Two other modifications were made. First the label LOOP1 was changed to DELAY. This was purely for aesthetic reasons as it seemed more "self-documenting" for the calling program to call subroutine DELAY instead of subroutine LOOP1. So this change was not really a necessary one. The second change was to omit the LD B,<B2> statement from the subroutine. We moved this statement to the calling program so that the calling program could specify the length of the delay by loading register B just prior to turning control over to subroutine DELAY. This was not a required change to make the program of Experiment No. 1 into a subroutine. However, it does add a great deal of flexibility to the way the subroutine can be used. In particular, the subroutine can be used to cause delays of 256 different time intervals depending on the contents of register B just prior to its being called. This technique of having the calling program specify values crucial to the operation of a subroutine is termed *parameter passing*. In this case, the parameter is the content of the B register that determines the duration of delay. There are other ways of passing parameters to subroutines which are discussed in Experiment No. 4.

In conclusion, let us summarize the changes necessary to make a program into a subroutine. Moreover, let us also identify the necessary elements of a calling routine.

To change a program to a subroutine:
The only necessary change is to insert conditional or absolute RET statements where control should be passed back to the calling program. Since the RET statement uses one byte of memory, this may result in a savings of memory space, for example, if the RET statements replace two- or three-byte JR or JP statements. At worst, the program is lengthened by one byte for each new RET instruction.

For a calling program:
It is critical to explicitly specify where the system stack should reside in memory. This is accomplished via the three-byte instruction

LD SP,<B3><B2>

If the program has no other use for the stack, i.e., there are no PUSH and POP instructions in the program, then subroutine calls have cost three bytes of memory to set up the stack. If the program uses the stack for other purposes already, then the stack has to be set up anyway.

For each call to a subroutine, three bytes are normally required. (The RST instructions can be used only for special cases.) If the call statement replaces an absolute jump (JP) statement, the program is not lengthened. At worst, the program is increased by three bytes for each call.

Load the PROGRAM and SUBROUTINE at the indicated addresses. (Much of the SUBROUTINE should already be loaded from Experiment No. 1.)

Step 2

Insert an execution breakpoint at location 010E, i.e., just before the RET instruction. Execute the calling program in single-step mode starting at location 011B. Look at the SP register just before and just after execution of the CALL DELAY statement:

Before: SP=_____
After: SP=_____

We observed that before the subroutine call SP=01FF, and after the subroutine call SP=01FD.

Step 3

Observe the top two bytes on the stack, i.e., locations 01FE and 01FD. You should see that the address of the next instruction after the CALL DELAY statement has been PUSHed onto the stack (i.e., (SP)=(01FD)=23 and (SP+1)=(01FE)=01). Note also, that the PC = 0102, the address of the first instruction of the DELAY subroutine.

Step 4

Press the GO key to continue program execution until the RET instruction at location 010E is encountered. Check the SP and PC registers before and after the RET instruction is executed:

Before: SP=_____   PC=_____
After: SP=_____   PC=_____

We observed that before, SP=01FD and PC=010E, while after, SP=01FF and PC=0123. The top two bytes of the stack have been POPped into the PC register so that execution may resume at the next instruction, LD A,00H, after the CALL DELAY instruction.

Step 5

Let us now analyze when to use subroutines. Two criteria must be applied in making a decision concerning whether or not a group of instructions should be a subroutine:

1. *Functional Criterion*—Does the set of instructions form a logical unit with well-defined inputs and well-defined outputs? That is, does it make sense to separate the function of the instruction group from the rest of the program.
2. *Efficiency Criterion*—Does converting a set of instructions to a subroutine cost more in time and memory space than is

merited by the functional considerations of the first criterion? Consider the following "worst case analysis":

Suppose we are analyzing whether or not a set of instructions equivalent to M bytes of memory should be converted to a subroutine and then called from the program of which it is currently a part. Suppose further that this group of instructions appears R times in the program. Then,

# of bytes used as part of program	= (# occurrences in program) × (# bytes per occurrence)
	= R×M
Maximum # bytes used as subroutine	= (# bytes in subroutine including RET)
	+(# calls in program)×(# bytes per call)
	+(3 bytes for setting up stack)
	+(2 bytes of stack for return address)
	= M + (# RETs) + 3 R + 3 + 2
	= M + (# RETs) + 3 R + 5

The criterion of space efficiency is satisfied as long as:

$$R \times M > M + (\#RETs) + 3R + 5$$

With respect to the criterion of time efficiency, the use of subroutines is always slower than repeating sets of instructions over and over again in a program. The CALL instruction is one of the more time consuming instructions in the Z-80 instruction set. The reason for this is that the CPU not only has to read three bytes of memory to interpret the instruction and change the PC register, but also the old PC value has to be PUSHed on the stack.

The RET instruction is time consuming because it POPs the stack to change the PC register. For every set of instructions which are extracted from a sequential flow of program logic to form a subroutine, the addition of the CALL and RET statements is pure overhead in terms of time. In most cases, the space savings outweigh the timing considerations. In cases where timing is critical, the slightly faster RST instructions can be used, or, in the extreme, space efficiency will be sacrificed in the interest of speed.

Step 6

Analyze the sample program and subroutine given in this experiment to determine if using a subroutine was efficient in terms of time and space. Defend your answer.

Our answer is that, based *strictly* on the space criterion, it was not a good idea to use a subroutine. Since subroutine DELAY was called only once, the memory space utilized is smaller for the "non-subroutine" implementation:

```
          LD  B,03H
DELAY:    LD  C,FFH
LOOP2:    LD  D,FFH
LOOP3:    DEC D
          JR  NZ,LOOP3
          DEC C
          JR  NZ,LOOP2
          DJNZ DELAY
          LD  A,00H
          RST 38H
```

Total bytes = 19

Savings = (# bytes used in sample program and subroutine)
          + 2 bytes of stack for return address −19
        = 9 bytes

Note: 9 = (2 bytes for stack) + (3 bytes for LD SP,<B3>)
          + (3 bytes for CALL DELAY) + (1 byte for RET).

It is NEVER FASTER to use a subroutine than to insert the desired instructions in-line with no branching. However, a sacrifice in speed or a sacrifice in memory utilization (as would be necessary in the example above) is often overshadowed by the advantages inherent in writing well-structured, modular programs which are easier to debug and easier to maintain and modify.

Step 7

Execute the calling program varying the value of the timing parameter passed to the subroutine via the B register.

EXPERIMENT NO. 3

Purpose

The purpose of this experiment is to demonstrate the RST N instruction.

Program No. 22

Memory Location	Object Code	Source Code	Comments
0130	31 FF 01	LD SP,01FFH	;Locate the system stack
0133	01 00 01	LD BC,0100H	;BC = # bytes of memory to zero out
0136	21 00 04	LD HL,0400H	;HL = start address
0139	D7	RST 16	;Call the zero-out routine
013A	FF	RST 38H	;Return control to the operating system

195

Subroutine

Memory Location	Object Code	Source Code	Comments
0010	F5	PUSH AF	;Save the registers as they were be-
0011	C5	PUSH BC	;fore the subroutine call
0012	D5	PUSH DE	
0013	E5	PUSH HL	
0014	36 00	LD (HL),00H	;Load 1st location with zeros
0016	54	LD D,H	;Move address in register pair HL to ;register pair DE
0017	5D	LD E,L	
0018	13	INC DE	;Increment DE
0019	ED B0	LDIR	;Zero out all locations from DE
001B	06 03	LD B,03H	;Set timing byte for Delay
001D	CD 02 01	CALL DELAY	;Call the DELAY routine
0020	F1	POP HL	;Restore registers to original
0021	C1	POP DE	;Status prior to subroutine
0022	D1	POP BC	;call
0023	E1	POP AF	
0024	C9	RET	

Step 1

Load the above program and subroutine at the indicated addresses. Be sure that subroutine DELAY from Experiment No. 2 is also loaded into memory.

Step 2

The main program (listed under PROGRAM No. 22) uses BC and HL register pairs to pass two parameters to the subroutine located at 0010. BC contains the number of memory bytes to load 00 into, HL contains the address of the first byte, and the subroutine uses the LDIR instruction to zero out "BC" consecutive memory locations starting at location "HL." Notice that due to the special start address of the subroutine, 0010, there are two call instructions used to call the subroutine, namely CALL 0010H and RST 16H. The CALL 0010H instruction occupies three bytes of memory since its associated hex code is CD 10 00. The RST 16H instruction hex code is D7, just one byte. Both perform the identical function.

The subroutine at 0010 uses a standard technique for preserving the registers A, F, B, C, D, E, H, and L exactly as they were when the subroutine was called. The first four instructions of the subroutine PUSH the registers onto the stack. The last four instructions prior to RETurning restore the registers using four POP instructions. Pay special attention to the relationship between the order in which the register pairs were PUSHed and POPped. The "PUSHing-order" is the exact reverse of the "POPping-order." The reason for this is the last-in-first-out processing discipline of the stack. When the net effect of a subroutine on all the registers is zero, the subroutine is said to *preserve the state of the CPU*. Thus, the subroutine at 0010 preserves the state of the CPU, while subroutine DELAY (at location 0102) does not.

Note that the subroutine at 0010 itself calls a subroutine, see the CALL DELAY statement at location 001D. This is called a *nested subroutine call*. Thus, there is no rule against subroutines calling subroutines which, in turn, may call subroutines. Subroutines can even call themselves! The technique of *recursive programming,* in which subroutines call themselves, is very powerful, but also very difficult to conceptualize. We shall not discuss it here.

What happens with nested subroutine calls? Basically return addresses keep getting pushed onto the stack until finally a subroutine executes a RET, RET NZ, RET Z, RET C, RET NC, RET P, RET M, RET PE, or RET PO statement, at which time an address pops off the stack.

Execute the program at location 0130. Insert program breakpoints judiciously so that you can watch the stack grow and shrink as execution proceeds.

Step 3

Currently, a program, two subroutines, a stack, and a memory block of program data occupy read/write memory. It is often an

00 00		
00 10 00 20 00 25	SUBROUTINE	Loads BC bytes of memory starting at location HL (preserves CPU state)
00 30 01 00		
01 02 01 0D	SUBROUTINE DELAY	Delay dependent on contents of B register
01 10 01 20		
01 30 01 3D	MAIN PROGRAM	All routines called from this program
01 40		
01 E0 01 E8 01 F0 01 F8 01 FF 02 00	STACK	
04 00 05 00	DATA	The memory block to be loaded with zeros

Fig. 8-6. Memory map.

excellent idea to keep a map of memory utilization. Fig. 8-6 gives a memory map for this experiment.

EXPERIMENT NO. 4

Purpose

The purpose of this experiment is to demonstrate four techniques for passing parameters to subroutines.

Technique No. 1

Passing parameters via registers.

Program No. 23

Memory Location	Object Code	Source Code	Comments
0200	31 FF 08	LD SP,08FFH	;Locate the system stack
0203	01 00 01	LD BC,0100H	;BC=bytes of memory to zero out
0206	21 00 04	LD HL,0400H	;HL=start address
0209	CD 10 02	CALL ZERO1	;Call the zero out routine
020C	FF	RST 38H	;Return control to the operating system

Subroutine

Memory Location	Object Code	Source Code	Comments
0210	36 00	ZERO1: LD (HL),00H	;Set first location to zeros
0212	54	LD D,H	;Move the address in register
0213	5D	LD E,L	;pair HL to register pair DE
0214	13	INC DE	;Increment DE
0215	ED B0	LDIR	;Zero out locations starting at DE
0217	C9	RET	;Return control to main program

Technique No. 2

Passing parameters via the stack.

Program No. 24

0220	31 FF 08	LD SP,08FFH	
0223	01 00 01	LD BC,0100H	
0226	21 00 04	LD HL,0400H	
0229	C5	PUSH BC	;Push parameters onto stack
022A	E5	PUSH HL	
022B	CD 31 02	CALL ZERO2	
022E	FF	RST 38H	

Subroutine

0231	D1	ZERO2: POP DE	;Pop return address off stack
0232	E1	POP HL	;Pop parameters off stack
0233	C1	POP BC	
0234	D5	PUSH DE	;Push return address back onto
0235	36 00	LD (HL),00H	;stack

```
0237    54                    LD D,H
0238    5D                    LD E,L
0239    13                    INC DE
023A    ED B0                 LDIR
023C    C9                    RET
```

Technique No. 3

Passing parameters via a control block in memory.

Program No. 25

```
0240    31 FF 08              LD SP,08FFH
0243    01 00 01              LD BC,0100H
0246    21 00 04              LD HL,0400H
0249    ED 43 00 08           LD (0800H),BC     ;Store parameters in control
                                                ;block in memory
024D    22 02 08              LD (0802H),HL
0250    CD 56 02              CALL ZERO3
0253    FF                    RST 38H
```

Subroutine

```
0256    ED 4B 00 08   ZERO3:  LD BC,(0800H)     ;Load parameters stored
025A    2A 02 08              LD HL,(0802H)     ;in memory to proper
025D    36 00                 LD (HL),00H       ;registers
025F    54                    LD D,H
0260    5D                    LD E,L
0261    13                    INC DE
0262    ED B0                 LDIR
0264    C9                    RET
```

Technique No. 4

Passing parameters via memory locations immediately following the CALL statement.

Program No. 26

```
0265    31 FF 08              LD SP,08FFH
0268    CD 72 02              CALL ZERO4
026B    00 01                 DEFW 0100H        ;DEFW is a "pseudo operator"
026D    00 04                 DEFW 0400H        ;implemented by many
                                                ;assemblers
026F    FF                    RST 38H           ;to allow data to be interspersed
                                                ;with instructions.
```

Subroutine

```
0272    DD E1         ZERO4:  POP IX            ;IX= address of first parameter
0274    DD 4E 00              LD C,(IX)
0277    DD 46 01              LD B,(IX+01H)     ;Load data into registers
027A    DD 6E 02              LD L,(IX+02H)
027D    DD 66 03              LD H,(IX+03H)
0280    11 04 00              LD DE,0004H       ;Add 0004 to IX to obtain the re-
0283    DD 19                 ADD IX,DE         ;turn address of the subroutine
0285    DD E5                 PUSH IX           ;Push return address onto stack
```

199

```
0287    36  00        LD  (HL),00H
0289    54            LD  D,H
028A    5D            LD  E,L
028B    13            INC DE
028C    ED  B0        LDIR
028E    C9            RET
```

Step 1

Load all four sets of programs and subroutines. Verify that you have loaded them correctly.

Step 2

Study all four parameter passing techniques carefully to make sure you understand how each works. Note that each program-subroutine pair performs exactly the same function. Also, one cannot use any program to call any subroutine. These are *matched* pairs in the sense that coordination as to how parameters will be passed must take place between calling program and called subroutine. How do these techniques compare? Let us first look at memory requirements.

Technique	Program	Subroutine	Total No. Bytes
1	15	8	23
2	17	12	29
3	22	15	37
4	13	27	40

Although Technique No. 1 has the lowest overall memory requirements in this set of examples, other examples could easily be devised in which Technique No. 4 is lowest. Each time subroutine ZERO1 is called, it takes nine bytes of space in the calling program to set up the parameters and call the subroutine. To set up and call ZERO4 only takes seven bytes. The large number of bytes added to ZERO4 to implement the more complicated technique is a *ONE-TIME-COST*. The more ZERO4 is called, the less significant the additional subroutine bytes become, and the more significant the savings in the calling sequence become.

To use Technique No. 1, all parameters must fit into the available registers. Sometimes this can be a serious constraint. Techniques No. 2 and No. 3 both use memory for passing parameters. Technique No. 2 is excellent for passing lots of parameters which get used and discarded by the subroutine in a particular sequence. Technique No. 3 is the only practical way to pass matrices or long character strings between routines.

Step 3

Execute all the program-subroutine pairs. Pay special attention to Technique No. 4 which is less straightforward than the rest.

EXPERIMENT NO. 5

Purpose

The purpose of this experiment is to demonstrate the use of jump tables.

Program

Memory Location	Object Code	Source Code	Comments
0900	61	DEFB 61H	;Value #1
0901	41 09	DEFW 0941H	;Address for Process #1
0903	62	DEFB 62H	;Value #2
0904	45 09	DEFW 0945H	;Address for Process #2
0906	63	DEFB 63H	;Value #3
0907	50 09	DEFW 0950H	;Address for Process #3
0909	64	DEFB 64H	;Value #4
090A	55 09	DEFW 0955H	;Address for process #4
090C	00	DEFB 00H	;END OF JUMP TABLE INDICATOR
0915	21 FD 08	START:LD HL,08FDH	;Initialize HL
0918	23	NEXT: INC HL	;Increment HL to point to
0919	23	INC HL	;value entry in jump table
091A	23	INC HL	
091B	7E	LD A,(HL)	;Load value to accumulator
091C	B7	OR A	;Set zero flag if A is zero
091D	CC 38 00	CALL Z,0038H	;If A=0, then end of jump table ;has been reached—pass control ;back to operating system
0920	B8	CP B	;Does B=A?
0921	20 F5	JR NZ,NEXT	;If not, try next value in ;jump table
0923	23	INC HL	;If so, next two positions hold ;address of routine to perform
0924	5E	LD E,(HL)	;Load the address into DE—
0925	23	INC HL	;First LO, then HI
0926	56	LD D,(HL)	
0927	62	LD H,D	;Move contents of DE to HL
0928	6B	LD L,E	
0929	E9	JP (HL)	;Jump to address in HL

Step 1

Let us first discuss the new instructions appearing in the above program. To understand DEFB and DEFW, examine closely the object code associated with these instructions. For example DEFB 41H has 41 as its associated hex code. In general,

$$\text{DEFB } <B1>$$

has <B1> as its associated hex code. Instruction DEFB appropriately stands for DEFine Byte because all the instruction does is give a byte which is placed directly into memory. A DEFW has a similar effect for two-byte addresses:

DEFW <B2><B1>

has <B1><B2> as its associated hex code. Instruction DEFW
stands for DEFine Word, where *word* in this context is a two-byte
absolute address. It is important to notice a very subtle difference
between the DEFB or DEFW instructions and all the other instructions discussed so far. All instructions we have discussed so far correspond to operations which the Z-80 CPU performs. DEFB and
DEFW do *not* correspond to operations performed by the Z-80, but
rather cause direct insertion of data into memory. In this manner,
the assembler (either human or software) initializes memory to
desired values.

The DEFB and DEFW statements described previously are called
assembly language pseudo-op codes. The reason these statements are
called *pseudo*-ops is because they are not Z-80 executable instructions. Instead, they are instructions which the ASSEMBLER executes in generating the object code. Another pseudo-op implemented
by most assemblers is the DEFINE STORAGE statement whose
format is

DEFS n

The DEFS pseudo-op is used to tell the assembler to reserve a specified number, n, of bytes in the object code for storage. The assembler
does not insert any particular values in the storage space, it just
skips the next n bytes before continuing to load memory with generated object code. The number n can be a hexadecimal number
(followed with an H) or a decimal number (followed with a
period .).

The CP B instruction at location 0920 will be discussed in detail
in a subsequent chapter. The associated hex code for this instruction
is B8. The instruction compares the contents of register B with those
of register A. If they are equal, the zero flag is set to logic 1, otherwise it is reset to logic 0. Thus, the program of this experiment uses
the CP B and JR NZ instructions to determine if A and B are equal
and branch in either of two directions according to the result.

Load the program at the indicated location.

Step 2

A jump table is a very efficient method for implementing program
branching logic which looks like the example in Fig. 8-7.
That is, a process ends with a certain result, and then based on the
result, one of many other processes (N above, 4 in the sample jump
table) is performed. The software term for this is *case analysis*. Each
possible result constitutes a *case;* or, in CASE the result is X, perform
process J. The sample jump table given previously has the general
format:

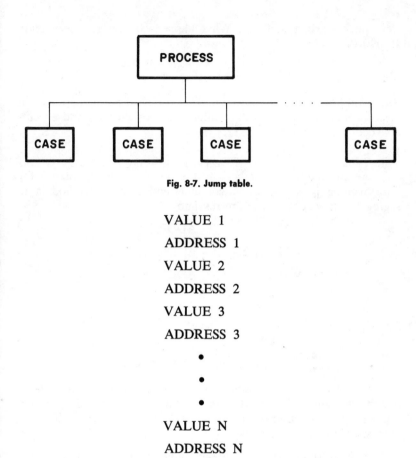

Fig. 8-7. Jump table.

VALUE 1

ADDRESS 1

VALUE 2

ADDRESS 2

VALUE 3

ADDRESS 3

•

•

•

VALUE N

ADDRESS N

00

Each possible result is listed with the address of its associated routine immediately following. 00 denotes the end of the jump table. To perform the case analysis, the result (in register B) is compared (CP B) with each *value* in the jump table until a match is found or until the end of the table is reached. On finding a match, control is passed to the address immediately following the VALUE byte by jumping to the address contained in the HL register pair.

Store a jump back to the operating system (FF) at each address in the jump table. Normally, a special–purpose set of instructions would be stored at these addresses, of course.

Load the B register (via the operating system) with values such as 45, 55, and 41 which are in the jump table, and 01, or 09 which are not in the jump table, and then execute the program in single step mode starting at 0915. What happens if you start execution at 0900?

Then you are executing your data. This is almost never a good idea. Keep in mind the fundamental difference between data and executable code (the computer won't).

Step 3

There are alternative methods to the one presented in Step 2 for implementing jump tables. A common and efficient method is to segregate the values and addresses into two separate tables:

VALUE 1	ADDRESS 1
VALUE 2	ADDRESS 2
VALUE 3	ADDRESS 3
•	•
•	•
•	•
VALUE N	ADDRESS N

The value table is first searched for a match. If the Ith value was a match then control is passed to the routine at the Ith address in the address table. As an exercise, try to implement this method for case analysis. Here are some hints:

1. Use 00 to mark the end of each table. Note that if 00 is a possible value or address byte, a new end marker must be chosen; or a new method of detecting the end of the table must be devised.
2. Note that the value table has one-byte entries, but the address table has two-byte entries.
3. As in the sample program assume the value to be matched is already in one of the CPU registers (pick the most convenient one).
4. Use the DEFB and DEFW instructions to set up the tables.

Once you have the program written, load and execute it. You will know then how you did.

CHAPTER 9

Logical Instructions

Table 9-1 contains the Z-80 Arithmetic and Logic Instructions. Table 9-2 contains the Z-80 instructions which manipulate just the accumulator and flags, the general-purpose AF instructions. We will cover the instructions contained in these tables in this chapter and in Chapter 11. This chapter will introduce you to logical instructions which perform logical operations on 8-bit binary words. The mnemonics for these instructions are AND, XOR, OR, and CPL. Since a full understanding of multibit logic operations is required in order to effectively use these instructions, we have included introductory material on this subject.

At the completion of this chapter, you will be able to do the following:

- Summarize the truth tables for the one-bit AND, OR, XOR, and NOT logic operations.
- List the correct Boolean symbols for AND, OR, XOR, and NOT.
- Explain how multibit logic operations are performed.
- Perform the logic operations AND, OR, and XOR on pairs of 8-bit data bytes. The NOT operation is performed on single data bytes.
- Write De Morgan's theorem in Boolean algebra.
- State De Morgan's theorem using logic symbols.
- List the logic instructions in the Z-80 instruction set.
- Explain how logic instructions can be used in a microcomputer program.
- Define *masking*.

Table 9-1. The 8-Bit Arithmetic and Logic Groups

SOURCE

	REGISTER ADDRESSING							REG. INDIR.	INDEXED		IMMED.
	A	B	C	D	E	H	L	(HL)	(IX+d)	(IY+d)	n
'ADD'	87	80	81	82	83	84	85	86	DD 86 d	FD 86 d	C6 n
ADD w CARRY 'ADC'	8F	88	89	8A	8B	8C	8D	8E	DD 8E d	FD 8E d	CE n
SUBTRACT 'SUB'	97	90	91	92	93	94	95	96	DD 96 d	FD 96 d	D6 n
SUB w CARRY 'SBC'	9F	98	99	9A	9B	9C	9D	9E	DD 9E d	FD 9E d	DE n
'AND'	A7	A0	A1	A2	A3	A4	A5	A6	DD A6 d	FD A6 d	E6 n
'XOR'	AF	A8	A9	AA	AB	AC	AD	AE	DD AE d	FD AE d	EE n
'OR'	B7	B0	B1	B2	B3	B4	B5	B6	DD B6 d	FD B6 d	F6 n
COMPARE 'CP'	BF	B8	B9	BA	BB	BC	BD	BE	DD BE d	FD BE d	FE n
INCREMENT 'INC'	3C	04	0C	14	1C	24	2C	34	DD 34 d	FD 34 d	
DECREMENT 'DEC'	3D	05	0D	15	1D	25	2D	35	DD 35 d	FD 35 d	

Courtesy Zilog, Inc.

Table 9-2. General-Purpose AF Operations

Decimal Adjust Acc, 'DAA'	27
Complement Acc, 'CPL'	2F
Negate Acc, 'NEG' (2's complement)	ED 44
Complement Carry Flag, 'CCF'	3F
Set Carry Flag, 'SCF'	37

Courtesy Zilog, Inc.

WHAT IS A LOGICAL INSTRUCTION?

In this section we shall be concerned with the logical operations AND, OR, XOR (Exclusive OR), and CPL (complement). A two-byte logic operation or logic instruction is performed with two 8-bit data bytes, the corresponding bits of each byte being subject to a 2-bit logic operation such as AND, OR, or XOR. In the Z-80 microprocessor, one of the data bytes is originally present in the accumulator, and the final result is stored in the accumulator. This is one indication of why we call the *accumulator* an "ACCUMULATOR"; it *accumulates* the final results of logic and arithmetic operations. The one-byte logical instruction, CPL, operates directly on the accumulator and no other register or memory cell is involved.

Truth Table for One-Bit Logic Operations

AND			OR			XOR			NOT	
B	A	Q	B	A	Q	B	A	Q	A	Q
0	0	0	0	0	0	0	0	0	0	1
0	1	0	0	1	1	0	1	1	1	0
1	0	0	1	0	1	1	0	1		
1	1	1	1	1	1	1	1	0		

We call these truth tables "1-bit tables" because the data words, A and B, each contain only a single bit. The XOR is an abbreviation for Exclusive-OR.

BOOLEAN ALGEBRA

When we discuss logic instructions, it is helpful to use *Boolean symbols*. Such symbols originate from the subject of *Boolean algebra,* which is the mathematics of logic systems. Alphabetic symbols such as A, B, C, . . ., Q are used to represent logical variables and the symbols 1 and 0 are used to represent logic states. This particular form of mathematics was originated in England by George Boole in 1847. It did not become widely used until 1938, when Claude Shannon adapted it to analyze multicontact networks for telephone systems.

What you should learn about Boolean algebra are the basic Boolean symbols that are employed in Boolean algebra computations and thus, are employed in all digital logic. These symbols include the following:

- $+$ which means logical addition and given the name OR
- $\bullet$ which means logical multiplication and is given the name AND
- $\oplus$ which is given the name Exclusive-OR or XOR

— which means logical complementation and is given the name
NOT

The complementation symbol is a solid bar over a logical variable such as A, B, C, . . . , Q. Thus, the Boolean statement for a 2-input AND state is Q=A • B, or simply Q=AB. The Boolean statements for different types of gates are shown in Fig. 9-1. Note the use of the bar, ‾‾ , for the NAND and NOR gates.

It is useful to summarize the symbol operations for the four logic operations that we are considering:

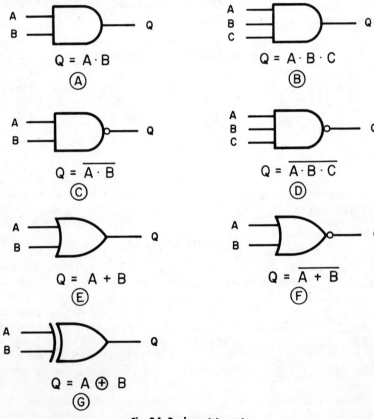

Fig. 9-1. Boolean statements.

AND	OR	XOR	NOT
$0 \cdot 0 = 0$	$0 + 0 = 0$	$0 \oplus 0 = 0$	$\overline{0} = 1$
$0 \cdot 1 = 0$	$0 + 1 = 1$	$0 \oplus 1 = 1$	$\overline{1} = 0$
$1 \cdot 0 = 0$	$1 + 0 = 1$	$1 \oplus 0 = 1$	
$1 \cdot 1 = 1$	$1 + 1 = 1$	$1 \oplus 1 = 0$	

These are 1-bit logic operations.

MULTIBIT OPERATIONS

Multibit logic operations are treated as many one-bit logic operations. No new principles of logic are involved. The corresponding bits of one binary word logically operate with the corresponding bits of the second binary word to produce an overall multibit logic result. Consider the 8-bit logic variable, A. The individual bits in the 8-bit word can be labeled as A7, A6, A5, A4, A3, A2, A1, and A0, with A0 being the least significant bit (the $2**0$ bit) and A7 being the most significant bit (the $2**7$ bit). Also consider the 8-bit logic variable, B, which has individual bits B7, B6, B5, B4, B3, B2, B1, and B0, with B0 being the least significant bit and B7 being the most significant bit. The logic operation, $A \cdot B = Q$, means the following:

$$A0 \cdot B0 = Q0$$
$$A1 \cdot B1 = Q1$$
$$A2 \cdot B2 = Q2$$
$$A3 \cdot B3 = Q3$$
$$A4 \cdot B4 = Q4$$
$$A5 \cdot B5 = Q5$$
$$A6 \cdot B6 = Q6$$
$$A7 \cdot B7 = Q7$$

The result of the logic operation is the logic variable, Q, which has a least significant bit of Q0 and a most significant bit of Q7. In other words, *multibit logic operations are performed bit by bit in a series of one-bit logic operations.*

It is easier to perform multibit logic operations if the multibit binary words are placed one under the other. Thus, if A=11110000 and B=00111100, then AB is

$$\begin{array}{c} 11110000 \\ \underline{00111100} \\ 00110000 \end{array}$$

or Q=00110000. We have performed a logical AND, and have used the relationships $0 \cdot 1 = 0$ and $1 \cdot 1 = 1$ in deriving the final result.

In a similar manner, the multibit logic operation, $A + B = Q$, means the following:

$$A0 + B0 = Q0$$
$$A1 + B1 = Q1$$
$$A2 + B2 = Q2$$
$$A3 + B3 = Q3$$
$$A4 + B4 = Q4$$
$$A5 + B5 = Q5$$
$$A6 + B6 = Q6$$
$$A7 + B7 = Q7$$

Again, the result of the logic operation is the logic variable, Q, which contains eight bits. If A = 11110000 and B = 00111100, then Q=A + B becomes

```
11110000
00111100
11111100
```

or Q=11111100. We have performed a logical OR, and have used the relationships 0+1=1, 1+1=1, and 0+0=0 in deriving the final result. *Note that the + sign represents the* OR *logical operation and the "plus" arithmetic operation.* There is a bit of confusion here, and you will have to watch out for it.

The final logic operation of interest, $A \oplus B = Q$, means the following:

$$A0 \oplus B0 = Q0$$
$$A1 \oplus B1 = Q1$$
$$A2 \oplus B2 = Q2$$
$$A3 \oplus B3 = Q3$$
$$A4 \oplus B4 = Q4$$
$$A5 \oplus B5 = Q5$$
$$A6 \oplus B6 = Q6$$
$$A7 \oplus B7 = Q7$$

The result of this Exclusive-OR operation is an 8-bit logic variable, Q. If A=11110000 and B=00111100, then $Q=A \oplus B$ becomes

```
11110000
00111100
11001100
```

or Q=11001100. We have performed a logical Exclusive-OR and have used the relationships $0 \oplus 0 = 0$, $0 \oplus 1 = 1$, $1 \oplus 0 = 1$, and $1 \oplus 1 = 0$ in deriving the final result.

NOT

The NOT logic operation complements any binary digit or group of binary digits. If A = 11110000, then Q = 00001111.

DE MORGAN'S THEOREM

An important theorem in Boolean algebra is *De Morgan's Theorem,* which can be written in either of two different ways:

$$\overline{A \cdot B} = \overline{A} + \overline{B}$$
$$\overline{A + B} = \overline{A} \cdot \overline{B}$$

A more interesting statement of De Morgan's theorem occurs through the use of logic symbols (Fig. 9-2). This is an important result, and

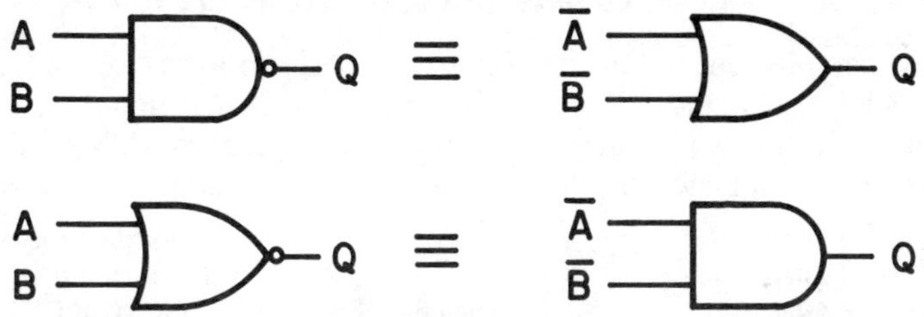

Fig. 9-2. Logic symbols.

one that you will find to be quite useful in digital electronics and microcomputer interfacing. It states that you can accomplish a NOR function by negating all of the inputs and applying them to an AND gate; alternatively, you can accomplish a NAND function by negating all of the inputs and applying them to an OR gate.

De Morgan's theorem can also be represented by the logic symbols in Fig. 9-3. They state that you can accomplish an AND func-

Fig. 9-3. Logic symbols.

tion by negating all of the inputs and applying them to a NOR gate; alternatively, you can accomplish an OR function by negating all of the inputs and applying them to a NAND gate. NAND gate integrated-circuit chips are very common and quite inexpensive. De Morgan's theorem demonstrates how you can readily create OR and NOR gates from NAND gates. We will discuss NAND, NOR, AND, OR, and other gates in detail in Book 2.

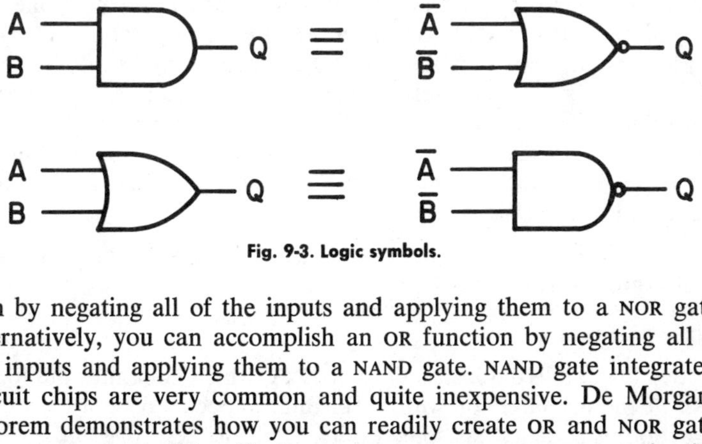

Z-80 LOGICAL INSTRUCTION GROUP

All of the logical operations which we have discussed are implemented by the Z-80 CPU as instructions in the 8-bit logical instruction group. Let us investigate these instructions in detail. Pay particular attention to the manner in which these instructions affect the flag register F as this aspect of their operation is often essential to their effective use.

COMPLEMENT ACCUMULATOR: CPL

To complement the accumulator is to perform a NOT operation on the 8-bit accumulator byte. This single-byte instruction has a hex code of 2F and a mnemonic of CPL. The carry, zero, P/V, and sign flags are not affected by this instruction, for example:

		Accumulator Contents
Before	Execution of CPL	10111010
After	Execution of CPL	01000101

A good application of the CPL instruction is as follows:

```
CPL A
INC A
```

These two instructions find the 8-bit *two's complement* of the contents of the accumulator.

AND WITH ACCUMULATOR: AND

The 11 different AND instructions in the Z-80 instruction set have the general mnemonic AND S where S depends on the addressing mode. The carry flag is reset by this instruction and both the sign and the zero flags are affected as a result of the operation. The P/V flag senses the parity of the result and is set if the parity (number of set bits) is even and reset otherwise. For example, consider the execution of the instruction AND B. This instruction causes the Z-80 to perform a logical AND between the contents of the B register and the contents of the accumulator. The result is stored in the accumulator. For example:

	Accumulator	B-Register	S Flag	Z Flag	P/V Flag
Before Execution of AND B	11001100	10001011	X	X	X
After Execution of AND B	10001000	10001011	1	0	1
(X = Don't Care)					

Notice that while the instruction AND A, which computes the logical AND of the accumulator with itself, might appear to be a useless instruction, it actually has some utility. Both the zero flag and the sign flag are affected as a result of this instruction. The AND A sets the zero flag if and only if the contents of the accumulator is 00. Similarly, AND A sets the sign flag if, and only if, the contents of the accumulator is a negative two's complement number. For example:

	Accumulator	S Flag	Z Flag	P/V Flag
Before execution of AND A	10000001	X	X	X
After execution of AND A	10000001	1	0	1
(X = Don't Care)				

Another useful application of the AND instruction is to implement a technique called masking. The term *masking* is defined as follows:

masking—A logical technique in which certain bits of a multibit word are blanked out or inhibited.

A face mask covers part of the face. In the same sense, a mask, used in a computer operation, covers some or most of the bits of a multibit word, leaving only those bits that are important for the continued execution of the program. Consider the following sequence of instructions:

```
LD  A,(0F32H)
AND 01H
```

The zero flag is set or reset depending on the value of the least significant bit of the byte at memory location ∅F32. This instruction sequence uses a mask to test bit D∅ of a byte in memory, the mask being the byte 01 of the AND instruction. Similarly, the technique can be used to test other bits. Masking can also be used to look at subsets of bits in a byte. For example, the instruction sequence

```
LD  A,(0F32H)
AND 0FH
```

zeros out the most significant four bits and leaves unchanged the least significant four bits of the accumulator, allowing a program to look at just the least significant half of the byte located at 0F32.

EXCLUSIVE-OR WITH ACCUMULATOR: XOR

The general mnemonic for the exclusive-OR instruction is XOR S, where S depends on the addressing mode. As with the AND instruction, the carry flag is reset and the sign, zero, and parity/overflow flags are affected as a result of the operation.

For example, consider the instruction XOR (HL) where register pair HL contains the address 1AB6. This instruction causes the Z-80 to perform a logical exclusive-OR between the contents of the accumulator and the contents of the memory location 1AB6 pointed to by the HL register pair, and leave the result in the accumulator.

	Accumulator	HL	(HL)	S Flag	Z Flag	P/V Flag
Before Execution	10010001	1AB6	00110000	X	X	X
After Execution	10100001	1AB6	00110000	1	0	0

Thus, XORing the byte 00 with the contents of the accumulator leaves the accumulator unchanged, but affects the sign and zero flags in informative ways. The instruction XOR A zeros out the accumulator via a one-byte instruction and, thus, is preferable to LD A,00H. The process of XORing FF with the accumulator has the same effect as the CPL instruction except that the carry, zero, and sign flags are affected.

OR WITH ACCUMULATOR: OR

The eleven OR instructions have the general mnemonic OR S, where S depends on the addressing code. The flags are affected by the OR instruction in the same manner as are the flags for the XOR and the AND instructions. That is, the carry flag is reset and the sign, zero, and parity/overflow flags are affected according to the result of the operation. For example, consider instruction OR (IX+02H). This instruction causes the Z-80 to perform a logical OR between the contents of the accumulator and the contents of the memory location two bytes above the location addressed by index register IX.

	Accumulator (binary)	IX (hex)	(IX+02) (binary)	S Flag	Z Flag	P/V Flag
Before Execution	00000011	1AB4	00110010	X	X	X
After Execution	00110011	1AB4	00110010	0	0	1

Thus, the OR instruction cannot be used to zero out the accumulator. As you have already seen in several experiments, OR A can be used to determine if the accumulator is zero. An excellent use of the OR instruction is for determining if a register pair is zero. For example, the following sequence of instructions determines if DE=0000:

LD A,D
OR E

The only way the OR E operation can leave the zero flag set is if both D and E are equal to 00. You saw this technique applied to the BC register pair in the last experiment of Chapter 6. The reason this technique is so useful is that the 16-bit increment and decrement instructions *do not* affect any of the flags. Thus, if a register pair is used as a loop counter, the zero flag has to be explicitly set if the register pair equals 0000 is a loop termination condition.

LOGICAL INSTRUCTIONS AND
EXTERNAL DEVICE MONITORING

Logical instructions permit you to determine whether external devices are on or off or whether specific events have occurred or not. As an example, assume that you use logic 0 and logic 1 to represent one of the following situations:

A. On/off state of a device
   Logic 0=device is off
   Logic 1=device is on

B. Occurrence of an event
   Logic 0=the event has not occurred
   Logic 1=the event has occurred

In a subsequent chapter, you will learn how to use the IN micro-computer instruction to input eight bits of data into the accumulator. You will learn that you can use each bit to represent the on/off state of a specific device, or the occurrence or nonoccurrence of a specific event. With eight bits, you can represent the state of eight different devices or events. Consider the following eight devices, each of which can be either on or off:

Bit 0: Pressure measuring device
Bit 1: Temperature measuring device
Bit 2: Velocity measuring device
Bit 3: Flow measuring device
Bit 4: Voltage measuring device
Bit 5: Current measuring device
Bit 6: ASCII terminal input device (keyboard)
Bit 7: ASCII terminal output device (printer or crt screen)

These eight devices have eight associated bits, which can be collectively input at the same instant of time into the accumulator of the Z-80 microprocessor chip. Once inside the microprocessor, you can employ logical instructions to determine whether specific devices are on or off.

INTRODUCTION TO THE EXPERIMENTS

The following experiments are designed to demonstrate what you have learned in Chapter 9 about logic instructions. The experiments you will perform may be summarized as follows:

Experiment No.	Comments
1	Demonstrates a 16-bit AND routine
2	Demonstrates the use of the AND, CPL, and XOR instructions in device monitoring applications. These instructions are used to determine whether a device has changed status, and if so, in which direction, on to off or off to on.

EXPERIMENT NO. 1

Purpose

The purpose of this experiment is to demonstrate a program which performs a logical AND between the contents of register pairs BC and DE and leaves the result in HL.

Program No. 28

Memory Location	Object Code	Source Code	Comments
0200	78	AND16: LD A,B	
0201	A2	AND D	;AND the most significant 8 bits
0202	67	LD H,A	;Load result into register H
0203	79	LD A,C	
0204	A3	AND E	;AND the least significant 8 bits
0205	6F	LD L,A	;Load result into register L
0206	B4	OR H	;Set the zero flag if the contents of HL ;is 00, otherwise reset the zero flag.
0207	FF	RST 38H	

Step 1

Load the above program at the indicated address. Initialize the BC and DE register pairs to each of the following values and then execute the program. Enter your observations for the contents of register pair HL and the zero, sign, P/V, and carry flags.

Note that the zero flag is bit D6 of the F register, the sign flag is bit D7, the P/V flag is bit D2, and the carry flag is bit D0, as illustrated next:

```
        7  6  5  4  3   2   1  0
       ┌──┬──┬──┬──┬──┬─────┬──┬──┐
       │S │Z │X │H │X │P/V  │N │C │
       └──┴──┴──┴──┴──┴─────┴──┴──┘
```

BC = 0 0 1 1 0 0 1 1   1 1 0 0 1 0 0 1   or   33 C9
DE = 1 1 1 1 0 0 0 0   0 1 1 1 0 0 1 1   or   F0 73
HL =
Zero flag =   Sign flag =   P/V flag =   Carry flag =

We observed that HL= 30 41 and that the flags were set as follows:

Zero Flag = 0   Sign Flag = 0   P/V Flag = 1   Carry Flag = 0
BC = 1 0 1 0 0 1 0 1   1 0 1 0 0 1 0 1   or   A5 A5
DE = 1 1 0 0 1 1 0 0   0 1 0 1 1 1 1 1   or   CC 5F
HL =
Zero Flag =   Sign Flag =   P/V Flag =   Carry Flag =

We observed that HL= 84 05 and that the flags were set as follows:

Zero Flag = 0   Sign Flag = 1   P/V Flag = 0   Carry Flag = 0
BC = 1 1 1 1 1 1 1 1   0 0 0 0 0 0 0 0   or   FF 00
DE = 0 0 0 0 0 0 0 0   1 1 1 1 1 1 1 1   or   00 FF
HL =
Zero Flag =   Sign Flag =   P/V Flag =   Carry Flag =

We observed that HL= 00 00 and that the flags were set as follows:

Zero Flag = 1   Sign Flag = 0   P/V Flag = 1   Carry Flag = 0

Step 2

Write, load, and debug a program to perform a 16-bit OR between register pairs BC and DE, leave the result in HL, and set or reset the

Z-flag accordingly. Test the program to verify its correctness by loading sample data values into BC and DE and checking predicted versus program generated values for HL and the zero flag.

<h2 style="text-align:center">EXPERIMENT NO. 2</h2>

Purpose

The purpose of this experiment is to determine which of eight devices has changed status between two status readings and in which direction the status change occurred, on to off or off to on. The eight devices are listed next with their associated bit number:

Bit 0: Pressure measuring device
Bit 1: Temperature measuring device
Bit 2: Velocity measuring device
Bit 3: Flow measuring device
Bit 4: Voltage measuring device
Bit 5: Current measuring device
Bit 6: Liquid-level measuring device
Bit 7: Frequency measuring device

A logic 1 will indicate that a device is on, and a logic 0 will indicate that a device is off. The input of two distinct status bytes is simulated by two LD r,<B2> instructions.

Program No. 29

Memory Location	Object Code	Source Code	Comments
0100	06 88	LD B,88H	;Simulate the input of a previous status byte to ;the B register
0102	3E 09	LD A,09H	;Simulate the input of a current status byte to ;the accumulator
0104	4F	LD C,A	;Copy current status to C register
0105	A8	XOR B	;Exclulsive-OR between the contents of A and ;B. In the result logic 1 marks devices whose ;status changed
0106	57	LD D,A	;Save this information in register D
0107	A0	AND B	;AND between the contents of A and B. In the ;result, logic 1 marks the devices which changed ;status from on to off
0108	67	LD H,A	;Save this information in H
0109	2F	CPL	;Complement the accumulator. In the result, ;logic 1 marks a device which did NOT change ;status from on to off, i.e., a device which main-;tained constant status or changed from off to ;on.
010A	A2	AND D	;AND between the contents of A and D. In the ;result, logic 1 marks a device whose status ;changed from off to on.
010B	6F	LD L,A	;Save this information in register L
010C	FF	RST 38H	;Return control to the operating system

Step 1

Load the preceding program at the indicated memory location. Verify that you have loaded the program correctly.

Step 2

Examine the program carefully to verify the following summary:

a. If bit n in register D is a logic 1, then the associated device changed status.
b. If bit n in register L is at logic 1, then the associated device went from off to on.
c. If bit n in register H is at logic 1, then the associated device went from on to off.
d. If bit n in register L is a logic 0, then the associated device either did not change status or went from on to off.
e. If bit n in register H is at logic 0, then the associated device either did not change status or went from off to on.

To summarize, with the aid of logical instructions, you can answer the following types of questions via microcomputer programs:

- Is the logic state of the status bit 0 or 1?
- When compared to the previous logic state, has the status bit state changed or does it remain unchanged?
- If the staus bit logic state has changed, has the change been from 0 to 1 or 1 to 0?

Step 3

Before you execute the program, perform the following logical operations.

Let 10001000= Previous status byte
Let 00001001= Current status byte

a. 10001000 XOR 00001001

$$\underline{\begin{array}{l} 10001000 = \text{Previous status byte} \\ 00001001 = \text{Current status byte} \end{array}}$$

The result of this logical operation tells you which of the devices have changed state. Device n has changed state if and only if bit n is set in the result of the XOR operation.

b. 10000001 AND 10001000

$$\begin{array}{l} 10001000 = \text{Previous status byte} \\ \underline{10000001} = \text{Result form part (a) telling which devices have} \\ \qquad\qquad\qquad \text{changed state} \end{array}$$

The result of this logical operation tells you which of the devices have changed state from on to off. Device n has changed state from on to off if and only if bit n is set.

c. CPL 10000000, the complement of 10000000

10000000 is the result from part (b) and tells you which devices have changed state from on to off. Thus the result of this logical operation will tell you which devices did NOT change their state from on to off.

d. 01111111 AND 10000001
01111111 = result from (c)
10000001 = result from (a)

The result of this logical operation tells you which of the devices have changed state from off to on.

Step 4

Execute the preceding program on your microcomputer. What information appears in register L after execution?

Those devices that have changed state from off to on have their associated bits set in register L.

Step 5

What information appears in register H?

Those devices that have changed state from on to off have their associated bits set in register H.

Step 6

What information appears in register C?

The current status byte, i.e., which devices are on and which devices are off.

REVIEW

The following questions will help you review the use of logical instructions, Boolean algebra, and multibit operations.

1. Perform the indicated multibit Boolean logic operations.

    a. 11001011 · 01011010
    b. 00100000 + 11011111
    c. 00100000 · 11011111
    d. 10101010 ⊕ 10100100
    e. CC · 0B
    f. A6 ⊕ 80
    g. 37 ⊕ 04
    h. 49 · 1B

2. An 8-bit status byte is associated with eight different devices:

> Bit 0: Pressure measuring device
> Bit 1: Temperature measuring device
> Bit 2: Velocity measuring device
> Bit 3: Flow measuring device
> Bit 4: Voltage measuring device
> Bit 5: Current measuring device
> Bit 6: Liquid-level measuring device
> Bit 7: Frequency measuring device

For the hex status bytes given next, indicate which of the devices given in Question No. 2 are on. A logic 1 for the indicated bit means that the device is on.

    a. 53
    b. 40
    c. 64
    d. 20
    e. 02
    f. 30
    g. 30
    h. C0
    i. 01
    j. 28

3. For the hex status bytes given next, including both the prior status byte and the current status byte, use Boolean algebra techniques to determine which of the eight different devices listed in Question No. 2 changed state from on to off or off to on. Show your Boolean algebra calculations.

	Prior Status Byte	Current Status Byte
a.	84	46
b.	27	63
c.	02	07
d.	A7	DB

Answers

1. a. 01001010
    b. 11111111
    c. 00000000

d. 00001110
e. 00001000 = 08
f. 00100110 = 26
g. 00110011 = 33
h. 00001001 = 09

2. a. liquid-level, voltage, temperature, and pressure measuring devices
   b. liquid-level measuring device
   c. liquid-level, current, and velocity measuring devices
   d. current measuring device
   e. temperature measuring device
   f. current and voltage measuring devices
   g. velocity and temperature measuring devices
   h. frequency and liquid-level measuring devices
   i. pressure measuring device
   j. current and flow measuring devices

3. a. You first convert the two bytes into binary code.

   $$84 = 10000100 \text{ (prior status byte)}$$
   $$46 = 01000110 \text{ (current status byte)}$$

   Next, you perform an Exclusive-OR operation on these two data bytes.

   $$10000100 \oplus 01000110 = 11000010$$

   Using the result, 11000010, you perform an AND operation between it and the prior status byte,

   $$10000100 \cdot 11000010 = 10000000$$

   You perform a NOT operation on this result,

   $$\overline{10000000} = 01111111$$

   Finally, you employ the result of the NOT operation and perform an AND operation between it and the result of the initial Exclusive-OR operation,

   $$01111111 \cdot 11000010 = 01000010$$

   Now we can make the proper conclusions.
   1. The frequency, liquid-level, and temperature measuring devices changed state.
   2. The frequency measuring device went from on to off.
   3. The liquid-level and temperature measuring devices went from off to on.

   By inspection of the two status bytes, you should conclude that the Boolean algebra has provided the correct answers.

   b. Convert hex status bytes into binary code,

   $$27 = 00101111 \text{ (prior status byte)}$$
   $$63 = 01100011 \text{ (current status byte)}$$

   Perform an Exclusive-OR operation.

   $$00101111 \oplus 01100011 = 01001100$$

   Use the result and perform an AND operation with prior status byte,

$$00101111 \cdot 01001100 = 00001100$$

So far, we can conclude that the liquid-level, flow, and velocity measuring devices have changed state. The flow and velocity measuring devices have gone from on to off.

Complement the result of the AND operation.

$$\overline{00001100} = 11110011$$

AND this result with the result of the initial XOR operation,

$$11110011 \cdot 01001100 = 01000000$$

Therefore, the liquid-level measuring device went from off to on.

c. Convert hex status bytes into binary code,

$$02 = 00000010 \text{ (prior status byte)}$$
$$07 = 00000111 \text{ (current status byte)}$$

Perform an XOR operation,

$$00000010 \oplus 00000111 = 00000101$$

Use this result and perform an AND operation with prior status byte,

$$00000010 \cdot 00000101 = 00000000$$

The velocity and pressure measuring devices changed state. Neither went from on to off.

Complement the result of the AND operation.

$$\overline{00000000} = 11111111$$

AND this result with the result of the initial XOR operation,

$$11111111 \cdot 0000101 = 00000101$$

Both the velocity and pressure measuring devices went from off to on.

d. Convert hex status bytes into binary code,

$$A7 = 10100111 \text{ (prior status byte)}$$
$$DB = 11011011 \text{ (current status byte)}$$

Perform an XOR operation,

$$10100111 \oplus 11011011 = 01111100$$

Use this result and perform an AND operation with prior status byte,

$$01111100 \cdot 10100111 = 00100100$$

The liquid-level, current, voltage, flow, and velocity measuring devices changed state. The current and velocity measuring devices went from on to off.

Complement the result of the AND operation,

$$\overline{00100100} = 11011011$$

AND this result with the result of the initial XOR operation,

$$11011011 \cdot 01111100 = 01011000$$

The liquid-level, voltage, and flow measuring devices went from off to on.

CHAPTER **10**

Bit Manipulation, Rotate and Shift Instructions

In this chapter, we shall examine two groups of instructions that significantly enrich the instruction set of the Z-80, the *BIT MANIPU-LATION* group and the *ROTATE AND SHIFT* group. The instructions in the bit manipulation group will allow you to test and/or change register and memory cell values at the individual bit level. Actually, the bit manipulation instructions comprise over 50% of the new Z-80 instructions that are not available on 8080-based systems.

OBJECTIVES

At the completion of this chapter, you will be able to do the following:

- Use the bit manipulation instructions, BIT, SET, and RESET.
- Use the rotate and shift instructions.
- Understand why each of the bit manipulation, rotate and shift instructions are useful.
- Understand the applicability of the RRD and RLD instructions to processing bcd numbers.

BIT SET, TEST, AND RESET PROCESS

One simple and universal example of the use of the *set, reset,* and *test bit process* is the procedure followed by rural mail carriers and residents to facilitate the delivery of mail. Every mailbox, like those in Fig. 10-1, on a rural mail route in the United States has a red flag attached to it which can be in either the up position, flag set (logic one state), or in the down position, flag reset (logic zero state). If the resident wants the postman to stop at his mailbox to pick up

Fig. 10-1. Flag positions.

some letters, the resident SETS the flag (raises the flag to the up position). The postman drives by and looks (TESTS the flag) to see if the flag is set. If the flag is set, the postman stops, picks up the letters, and then RESETS the flag so that the process can be repeated with the same convention the next day.

If the flag is not set, the postman does not "service" the mailbox unless he has some letters to deliver to the resident. Thus, without the flag setting and resetting convention, the only time that the resident could send a letter would be on those days that the resident was receiving letters and the postman had to stop anyway. This would be an awkward situation for those of us who never get any mail.

A lot of information is being conveyed from the resident to the postman with this one flag convention. The reason this procedure works is, of course, because there is an agreement between the resident and the postman as to the conditions under which each shall SET and RESET the flag. This is an example of a very simple *protocol*. According to Webster, a *protocol* can be defined as a code prescribing strict adherence to correct etiquette and precedence. The notion of a protocol will be very important when you begin interfacing microcomputers to other devices and other microcomputers.

The Z-80 instruction set in Table 10-1 includes 240 different bit manipulation instructions:

> 80 set bit instructions ("SET"),
> 80 reset bit instructions ("RES"), and
> 80 test bit instructions ("BIT").

For example the set bit instruction, SET 0,A (op code: CB C7), puts a logic 1 into bit number zero of the accumulator. Note that the

Table 10-1. Bit Manipulation Group Instructions

		REGISTER ADDRESSING							REG. INDIR.	INDEXED	
	BIT	A	B	C	D	E	H	L	(HL)	(IX+d)	(IY+d)
TEST 'BIT'	0	CB 47	CB 40	CB 41	CB 42	CB 43	CB 44	CB 45	CB 46	DD CB d 46	FD CB d 46
	1	CB 4F	CB 48	CB 49	CB 4A	CB 4B	CB 4C	CB 4D	CB 4E	DD CB d 4E	FD CB d 4E
	2	CB 57	CB 50	CB 51	CB 52	CB 53	CB 54	CB 55	CB 56	DD CB d 56	FD CB d 56
	3	CB 5F	CB 58	CB 59	CB 5A	CB 5B	CB 5C	CB 5D	CB 5E	DD CB d 5E	FD CB d 5E
	4	CB 67	CB 60	CB 61	CB 62	CB 63	CB 64	CB 65	CB 66	DD CB d 66	FD CB d 66
	5	CB 6F	CB 68	CB 69	CB 6A	CB 6B	CB 6C	CB 6D	CB 6E	DD CB d 6E	FD CB d 6E
	6	CB 77	CB 70	CB 71	CB 72	CB 73	CB 74	GB 75	CB 76	DD CB d 76	FD CB d 76
	7	CB 7F	CB 78	CB 79	CB 7A	CB 7B	CB 7C	CB 7D	CB 7E	DD CB d 7E	FD CB d 7E
RESET BIT 'RES'	0	CB 87	CB 80	CB 81	CB 82	CB 83	CB 84	CB 85	CB 86	DD CB d 86	FD CB d 86
	1	CB 8F	CB 88	CB 89	CB 8A	CB 8B	CB 8C	CB 8D	CB 8E	DD CB d 8E	FD CB d 8E
	2	CB 97	CB 90	CB 91	CB 92	CB 93	CB 94	CB 95	CB 96	DD CB d 96	FD CB d 96
	3	CB 9F	CB 98	CB 99	CB 9A	CB 9B	CB 9C	CB 9D	CB 9E	DD CB d 9E	FD CB d 9E
	4	CB A7	CB A0	CB A1	CB A2	CB A3	CB A4	CB A5	CB A6	DD CB d A6	FD CB d A6
	5	CB AF	CB A8	CB A9	CB AA	CB AB	CB AC	CB AD	CB AE	DD CB d AE	FD CB d AE
	6	CB B7	CB B0	CB B1	CB B2	CB B3	CB B4	CB B5	CB B6	DD CB d B6	FD CB d B6
	7	CB BF	CB B8	CB B9	CB BA	CB BB	CB BC	CB BD	CB BE	DD CB d BE	FD CB d BE
SET BIT 'SET'	0	CB C7	CB C0	CB C1	CB C2	CB C3	CB C4	CB C5	CB C6	DD CB d C6	FD CB d C6
	1	CB CF	CB C8	CB C9	CB CA	CB CB	CB CC	CB CD	CB CE	DD CB d CE	FD CB d CE
	2	CB D7	CB D0	CB D1	CB D2	CB D3	CB D4	CB D5	CB D6	DD CB d D6	FD CB d D6
	3	CB DF	CB D8	CB D9	CB DA	CB DB	CB DC	CB DD	CB DE	DD CB d DE	FD CB d DE
	4	CB E7	CB E0	CB E1	CB E2	CB E3	CB E4	CB E5	CB E6	DD CB d E6	FD CB d E6
	5	CB EF	CB E8	CB E9	CB EA	CB EB	CB EC	CB ED	CB EE	DD CB d EE	FD CB d EE
	6	CB F7	CB F0	CB F1	CB F2	CB F3	CB F4	CB F5	CB F6	DD CB d F6	FD CB d F6
	7	CB FF	CB F8	CB F9	CB FA	CB FB	CB FC	CB FD	CB FE	DD CB d FE	FD CB d FE

Courtesy Zilog, Inc.

number specifying the bit (0 in this example) is not a data or address byte and is not followed by an H meaning hexadecimal or meaning decimal. Consider the following two examples:

Example 1
Accumulator

Before Execution of SET 0,A	1 1 0 0 1 0 0 0
After Execution of SET 0,A	1 1 0 0 1 0 0 1

Example 2

Before Execution of SET 0,A	1 1 1 1 0 0 1 1
After Execution of SET 0,A	1 1 1 1 0 0 1 1

Remember that the eight bits in any register or memory location are always numbered from right to left, starting with bit zero and ending with bit seven.

A common way of describing the SET 0,A instruction is to say that it "SETS" the zeroth bit of the accumulator to 1. A shorter and, hence, more popular way of saying this is to say that the instruction "SETS" the zeroth bit of the accumulator. Common usage has determined that the phrase "SETTING" a bit implies that the value of the bit is 1 after the instruction has been executed. Similarly, the phrase "RESETTING" a bit means that the value of the bit is 0 after the "RESETTING" instruction has been executed.

One should note that both the set bit instruction and the reset bit instruction are independent of the original value of the bit. Thus, a previously "SET" bit can be "SET" again for no net change on the bit. The instruction, RES 0,D (op code: CB 82), will reset bit zero of the D register.

Example 3
D Register

Before Execution of RES 0,D	1 1 0 0 1 1 1 1
After Execution of RES 0,D	1 1 0 0 1 1 1 0

Example 4

Before Execution of RES 0,D	0 0 0 0 0 0 0 0
After Execution of RES 0,D	0 0 0 0 0 0 0 0

Neither the "SET" nor the "RESET" instructions affect any flags.

A somewhat more complicated instruction is the test bit instruction. For example, the instruction, BIT 0,A (op code: CB 47), tests bit zero of the accumulator. If bit zero of the accumulator is a zero then this instruction will set the zero flag. That is, the value of the zero flag will be 1 if the zeroth bit of the accumulator is zero.

Example 5

	Accumulator	Zero Flag
Before Execution of BIT 0,A	1 0 0 1 1 1 0 0	X
After Execution of BIT 0,A	1 0 0 1 1 1 0 0	1

Example 6

Before Execution of BIT 0,A	1 1 1 0 0 1 1 1	X
After Execution of BIT 0,A	1 1 1 0 0 1 1 1	0

Example 7

Before Execution of BIT 0,A	1 1 1 1 1 1 1 1	X
After Execution of BIT 0,A	1 1 1 1 1 1 1 1	0

(X = Don't care)

Note that in no case does this instruction, BIT 0,A, change the value of the accumulator.

You will find the test bit instruction to be quite useful. For example, this instruction allows you to determine the value of a particular bit in any register or any memory location without having to create a mask byte and alter the contents of the accumulator. Consider the following two instruction sequences which perform the same function, namely that of determining whether bit D4 of location 01FF is logic 1 or logic 0:

Sequence 1:   LD A,(01FFH)
                      AND 08H

Sequence 2:   LD A,(01FFH)
                      BIT 4,A

Sequence 1 uses the mask byte 08 to change the contents of the accumulator with the zero flag set according to the result. Sequence 2 affects the zero flag in precisely the same manner as does Sequence 1 without changing the contents of register A. Both sequences require five bytes of memory.

ROTATE AND SHIFT INSTRUCTION GROUP

There are 74 rotate and shift instructions for the Z-80, as presented in Table 10-2. The four Intel 8080A compatible rotate accumulator instructions RLCA, RRCA, RLA, and RRA are *almost* redundant. They were included in the Z-80 instruction set only to maintain compatibility with the Intel 8080A instruction set. One should note that these four instructions affect no flag other than the carry flag. The execution of any of these four instructions does not affect the zero, parity/overflow, or sign flags. However, all of the remaining 70 rotate instructions affect all of the carry, zero, parity/ overflow, and sign flags. In addition to these 74 instructions, there are two very special decimal-digit instructions that we will discuss separately.

Table 10-2. Rotates and Shifts

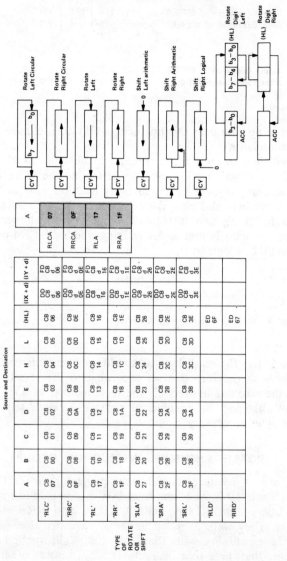

Courtesy Zilog, Inc.

ROTATE INSTRUCTIONS

First, let us consider the four classes of rotate instructions. For each instruction we give several diagrams to illustrate the particular rotate operation associated with it.

Rotate Left Circular (RLC) (Fig. 10-2)

We can interpret this diagram by examining the contents of the carry bit and the accumulator both before and after the execution of the instruction RLC A. Thus:

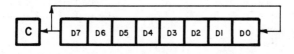

Fig. 10-2.

	Carry Bit	Accumulator
Before Execution of RLC A	C	D7 D6 D5 D4 D3 D2 D1 D0
After Execution of RLC A	D7	D6 D5 D4 D3 D2 D1 D0 D7

For example:

Before Execution of RLC A	X	1 1 0 1 1 1 0 0
After Execution of RLC A	1	1 0 1 1 1 0 0 1
(X = Don't care)		

Rotate Right Circular (RRC) (Fig. 10-3)

This diagram implies that the following changes are made to the carry bit and to the C register during the execution of the instruction RRC C:

Fig. 10-3.

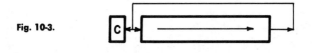

	Carry Bit	C Register
Before Execution of RRC C	C	D7 D6 D5 D4 D3 D2 D1 D0
After Execution of RRC C	D0	D0 D7 D6 D5 D4 D3 D2 D1

For example:

Before Execution of RRC C	X	1 1 0 1 1 1 0 0
After Execution of RRC C	0	0 1 1 0 1 1 1 0

Note that, for both the RRL and RRC instructions, the original content of the carry flag is destroyed by the execution of the instruction.

Fig. 10-4.

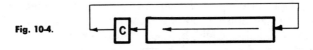

Rotate Left (RL) (Fig. 10-4)

This diagram implies that the following changes are made to the carry bit and to the accumulator for the RL A instruction.

	Carry Bit	Accumulator
Before Execution of RL A	C	D7 D6 D5 D4 D3 D2 D1 D0
After Execution of RL A	D7	D6 D5 D4 D3 D2 D1 D0 C

For example:

	Carry Bit	Accumulator
Before Execution of RL A	0	1 1 0 1 1 1 0 0
After Execution of RL A	1	1 0 1 1 1 0 0 0

Rotate Right (RR) (Fig. 10-5)

This diagram implies that the following changes are made to the carry bit and to the D register for the RR D instruction:

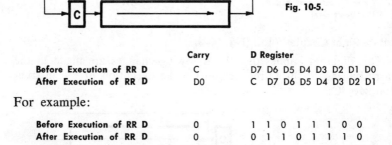

Fig. 10-5.

	Carry	D Register
Before Execution of RR D	C	D7 D6 D5 D4 D3 D2 D1 D0
After Execution of RR D	D0	C D7 D6 D5 D4 D3 D2 D1

For example:

	Carry	D Register
Before Execution of RR D	0	1 1 0 1 1 1 0 0
After Execution of RR D	0	0 1 1 0 1 1 1 0

The four rotate instructions are often used to examine successive bits in a particular register or memory location. For example, if you want to find the highest order nonzero bit in the accumulator, you can perform successive "rotate left" instructions until the carry flag is set equal to 1:

```
        LD A,X          ;Load Accumulator with byte X to be tested
        LD C,08H        ;Bit counter
CHECK:  DEC C           ;Update bit counter
        JP M,END        ;All bytes checked?
        RL A            ;Rotate next most significant bit to C
        JP NC,CHECK     ;Is it 0 or 1? If 0, then try next bit
END:    RST 38H         ;Otherwise, return control to the operating system
```

In the preceding instruction sequence, register C returns the number (7 for most significant bit, . . . ,0 for least significant bit) of the highest order nonzero bit in the accumulator. Note that the one-byte RLA instruction could be used instead of the two-byte RL A instruction previously given because only the carry flag is important to the program logic.

Another interesting application of the rotate instructions can be seen in the following example. Suppose there are eight processes that must be performed in sequence, i.e., Process 1 first, Process 2 second, etc. However, not all processes are always performed. For example, in some situations, the appropriate sequence of processes is:

Process 1		Process 5		Process 3	
Process 3	OR	Process 7	OR	Process 6	
Process 5				Process 8	
Process 8					

or any other of the 256 possible sequences. To implement the program logic required to handle this situation, one can use a rotate right instruction.

First, subroutines for each process, SUB1 for Process 1, . . . ,SUB8 for Process 8, are developed. Then each time a sequence of processes must be performed, a one-byte description of the sequence is generated by setting bit 0 if Process 1 is to be performed, setting bit 1 if Process 2 is to be performed, setting bit 7 if Process 8 is to be performed. If a bit is at logic 0, its associated process is not performed. The branching logic for performing any so specified process sequence can be implemented as follows: (Note that the instruction RRA is almost identical to the instruction RR.)

```
            RRA
            CALL C,SUB1
            RRA
            CALL C,SUB2
            RRA
            CALL C,SUB3
            RRA
            CALL C,SUB4
            RRA
            CALL C,SUB5
            RRA
            CALL C,SUB6
            RRA
            CALL C,SUB7
```

We assume that the sequence byte has been loaded into the accumulator. Note that the above instruction sequence uses the one-byte RRA instruction instead of the two-byte RRA instruction because only the carry flag is important to the program logic.

The next group of instructions that we will discuss is called the *SHIFT GROUP*. The rotate and shift instructions are often used in conjunction with each other to perform many important programming functions. We will discuss several of these examples in this and the next chapters.

SHIFT INSTRUCTIONS

Shift Left Arithmetic (SLA) (Fig. 10-6)

This diagram implies that the following changes are made to the carry bit and to the accumulator.

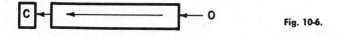

Fig. 10-6.

	Carry Bit	Accumulator
Before Execution of SLA A	C	D7 D6 D5 D4 D3 D2 D1 D0
After Execution of SLA A	D7	D6 D5 D4 D3 D2 D1 D0 0

This instruction has the effect of multiplying the contents of the accumulator by 2 with an overflow signal provided when the carry bit is set equal to 1. Consider the following examples:

Example 1

	Carry Bit	Accumulator
Before Execution of SLA A	X	0 0 1 1 0 0 1 1 = 51 (decimal)
After Execution of SLA A	0 (no overflow)	0 1 1 0 0 1 1 0 = 102 (decimal)

Example 2

	Carry Bit	Accumulator
Before Execution of SLA A	X	0 1 1 0 0 1 1 0 = 102 (decimal)
After Execution of SLA A	0 (no overflow)	1 1 0 0 1 1 0 0 = 204 (decimal)

Example 3

	Carry Bit	Accumulator
Before Execution of SLA A	X	1 0 0 1 1 0 0 0 = 152 (decimal)
After Execution of SLA A	1 (overflow)	0 0 1 1 0 0 0 0 = 48 (decimal)

In the first two examples, the contents of the accumulator were doubled by the SLA A instruction. But in Example 3, the contents of the accumulator went from 152 to 48, hardly doubling the initial value. The reason for this is that 2 times 152 equals 304 which is greater than 256, the maximum positive integer that can be represented in eight bits (using binary, not two's complement, representation). When the original number being shifted is larger than 128, the result of the shift will not be 2 times the number (but rather 2 times the number minus 256) and the carry bit will be set to indicate this.

The SLA instruction can also be used in conjunction with the RL instruction to perform multibyte left shifts. The following instruction sequence shifts the DE register pair left one bit, zero-filling the vacated bit:

```
SLA E
RL  D
```

Note that we can also shift left pairs of memory bytes. To shift left and zero fill memory locations 0100 and 0101, we can use the following instruction sequence.

```
            LD  IX,0100H
            SLA (IX)
            RL  (IX+01H)
```

Multibyte shifts are extremely important in programming multibyte arithmetic operations such as multiplication and division.

Shift Right Arithmetic (SRA) (Fig. 10-7)

This diagram implies that the following changes are made to the carry bit and to the accumulator.

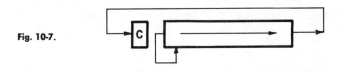

Fig. 10-7.

	Carry Bit	Accumulator
Before Execution of SRA A	C	D7 D6 D5 D4 D3 D2 D1 D0
After Execution of SRA A	D0	D7 D7 D6 D5 D4 D3 D2 D1

Note that the value of the carry bit is destroyed.

This instruction has the effect of dividing the contents of the given register by 2, putting the "remainder" of this division into the carry bit. Division is carried out in two's complement form, i.e., the instruction assumes that the number in the register is in two's complement form and produces a quotient in the same register in two's complement form. Consider the following examples:

Example 4

	Carry Bit	Accumulator
Before Execution of SRA A	X	0 0 0 0 1 1 1 1 = 15 (decimal)
After Execution of SRA A	1 (remainder)	0 0 0 0 0 1 1 1 = 7 (decimal)

Example 5

Before Execution of SRA A	X	1 0 0 0 1 1 1 0 = −114 (decimal)
After Execution of SRA A	0 (remainder)	1 1 0 0 0 1 1 1 = −57 (decimal)

The SRA instruction can be used in conjunction with the RR instruction to perform multibyte right shifts in much the same manner as the SLA and RL instructions perform left shifts. For example, the HL register pair can be right shifted, with bit D7 of the H register filling in the vacated bit, as follows:

```
            SRA H
            RR  L
```

Shift Right Logical (SRL) (Fig. 10-8)

	Carry Bit	Accumulator
Before Execution of SRL A	C	D7 D6 D5 D4 D3 D2 D1 D0
After Execution of SRL A	D0	0 D7 D6 D5 D4 D3 D2 D1

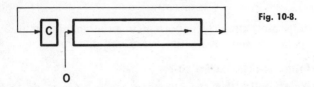

Fig. 10-8.

0

This instruction has the effect of dividing the number in the register by 2, when the number in the register is viewed as a positive 8-bit binary number. The quotient appears in the register after the execution of the instruction and the remainder appears in the carry bit.

Example 6

	Carry Bit	Accumulator
Before Execution of SRL A	X	1 0 0 0 0 0 1 1 = 131 (decimal)
After Execution of SRL A	1 (remainder)	0 1 0 0 0 0 0 1 = 65 (decimal)

To shift right, zero-fill multibyte sequences, you can use the SRL and RR instructions. For example, to shift right zero-fill an eight-byte sequence residing at memory locations 0100 through 0107 you can use the following instruction sequence:

```
        LD B,08H
        LD HL,0107H
        SRL (HL)
SHIFT:  DEC HL
        DEC B
        JP Z, END
        RR (HL)
        JP SHIFT
END:    RST 38H
```

Let us now discuss the two special rotate decimal-digit instructions. First we describe the RLD and RRD instructions and then we give examples of how they can be used.

Rotate Digit Left (RLD) (Fig. 10-9)

	Accumulator	Memory Cell Pointed to by HL
Before Execution of RLD	D7 D6 D5 D4 D3 D2 D1 D0	B7 B6 B5 B4 B3 B2 B1 B0
After Execution of RLD	D7 D6 D5 D4 B7 B6 B5 B4	B3 B2 B1 B0 D3 D2 D1 D0

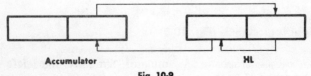

Accumulator   HL

Fig. 10-9.

For example:

Before Execution of RLD	1 1 0 1 1 0 0 0	0 0 1 0 1 1 0 0
After Execution of RLD	1 1 0 1 0 0 1 0	1 1 0 0 1 0 0 0

Note that this instruction rotates half bytes (*NIBBLES*) at a time. It does not simply rotate bits at a time. In other words, the four bits 1000 in the low order nibble of the accumulator appear at their final destination as 1000, not as 0001.

Rotate Digit Right (RRD) (Fig. 10-10)

	Accumulator	Memory Cell Pointed to by HL
Before Execution of RRD	D7 D6 D5 D4 D3 D2 D1 D0	B7 B6 B5 B4 B3 B2 B1 B0
After Execution of RRD	D7 D6 D5 D4 B3 B2 B1 B0	D3 D2 D1 D0 B7 B6 B5 B4

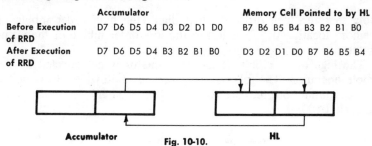

Accumulator   **Fig. 10-10.**   **HL**

For example:

Before Execution of RRD	1 1 0 1 0 0 0 1	1 0 1 1 1 1 1 0
After Execution of RRD	1 1 0 1 1 1 1 0	0 0 0 1 1 0 1 1

The RLD and RRD instructions are especially useful for processing which involves manipulating nibbles instead of bits and bytes. Programs which use the binary coded decimal (bcd) representation for numbers are excellent examples of this kind of nibble-oriented processing. Recall that bcd number representation equates four bits to a decimal number, thus, allowing for two decimal numbers per byte. For example, the bcd representation for the decimal number 83 is

$$\underbrace{1\ 0\ 0\ 0}_{\text{nibble 1}=8}\ \underbrace{0\ 0\ 1\ 1}_{\text{nibble 2}=3}$$

Conversely, the bcd interpretation of the byte:

$$\underline{0\ 1\ 1\ 1}\ \ \underline{0\ 0\ 0\ 0}$$

is the decimal number 70. Thus, in terms of bcd representation, the RLD instruction rotates decimal digits left between the memory cell pointed to by HL and the accumulator. Similarly, the RRD instruction rotates bcd digits to the right.

For example, the following sequence of instructions will shift left zero-fill a sequence of eight bcd digits residing in the four sequential memory locations from 0100 through 0103:

```
          LD  B,04H
          LD  HL,0100H
          LD  A,00H
AGAIN:    RLD
          INC HL
          DEC B
          JP  NZ,AGAIN
          RST 38H
```

Note that the high order decimal digit (the high order nibble of memory location 0103) is left in the low order nibble of the accumulator.

The high order nibble of the accumulator is not affected by the whole operation. The following diagram illustrates the effects of the above routine on the accumulator and memory locations 0100 through 0103.

	Accumulator		0103		0102		0101		0100	
Before:	X	X	8	7	6	5	4	3	2	1
After:	0	8	7	6	5	4	3	2	1	0

An additional application for these rotate instructions, translation of bcd to ASCII representation, is explored in Experiment No. 2.

INTRODUCTION TO THE EXPERIMENTS

The following experiments are designed to help you understand how the bit manipulation, rotate and shift instructions work and to illustrate their uses to you. In Experiment No. 1, we introduce you to the ASCII representation of numbers. In each of the three experiments, we give you programs that convert numbers between three forms of representation: binary, bcd, and ASCII.

Experiment No.	Comments
1	Demonstrates the use of the BIT and RR instructions in program to convert binary to ASCII representation.
2	Demonstrates the use of the RL instruction in a program to convert ASCII to binary representation.
3	Demonstrates the use of the RRD instruction in a program to convert bcd to ASCII representation.

EXPERIMENT NO. 1

Purpose

The purpose of this experiment is to demonstrate the use of the BIT instruction in a program to convert binary to ASCII representation. The ASCII representation of the numbers 0 through 9 is given by the following table:

DECIMAL NO.	ASCII REPRESENTATION IN HEX
0	30
1	31
2	32
3	33
4	34
5	35
6	36
7	37
8	38
9	39

ASCII is just another method for representing numbers using 8-bit bytes. For many crt and printer terminals, ASCII is the standard code for representing numbers, letters, and special characters such as ;, !, <, >, ?, etc. Binary to ASCII conversion means inputting a string of 0s and 1s and outputting a corresponding sequence of 30s and 31s. For example, the byte 0 1 0 0 1 1 0 1 would be converted to the following eight-byte string (represented in hex):

$$30 \ 31 \ 30 \ 30 \ 31 \ 31 \ 30 \ 31$$

The following program converts the byte currently in the B register to an eight-byte string stored in memory beginning at location 0200.

Program No. 29

Memory Location	Object Code	Source Code		Comments
0100	0E 08		LD C,08H	;Bit counter
0102	21 00 02		LD HL,0200H	;Start of ASCII string
0105	36 30	NXTBIT:	LD (HL),30H	;ASCII zero
0107	CB 40		BIT 0,B	;Test the bit
0109	28 01		JR Z,ZERO	;If not zero, increment
010B	34		INC (HL)	;the 30 to 31
010C	23	ZERO:	INC HL	;Increment ASCII string pointer
010D	CB 18		RR B	;Rotate B to look at next bit
010F	0D		DEC C	;Update the bit counter
0110	20 F3		JR NZ,NXTBIT	;All bits translated?
0112	FF		RST 38H	

Step 1

Load the above program at the indicated address. Execute it using several different sample bytes in the B register. For example, if the contents of the B register are

$$0\ 1\ 1\ 1\ 1\ 0\ 0\ 0$$

then memory locations 0200 through 0207 should read (in hex)

$$(0200)=30$$
$$(0201)=30$$
$$(0202)=30$$
$$(0203)=31$$
$$(0204)=31$$
$$(0205)=31$$
$$(0206)=31$$
$$(0207)=30$$

Step 2

Replace the preceding program to utilize a rotate instruction and the carry flag to translate each bit from binary to ASCII. Test and debug your program to make sure it works properly.

EXPERIMENT NO. 2

Purpose

The purpose of this experiment is to demonstrate the use of the RL instruction in a program to convert ASCII to binary representation. In this program, a string of eight ASCII 0s and 1s (hex 30s and 31s) is input and a single byte with the proper bits set to logic 0 and logic 1 is output. The following program converts the string of eight bytes starting at location 0200 to a single byte which is contained in the B register.

Program No. 30

Memory Location	Object Code	Source Code	Comments
0120	0E 08	LD C,08H	;Bit counter
0122	21 00 02	LD HL,0200H	;Start address of ASCII string
0125	7E	NXT: LD A, (HL)	;Get byte
0126	1F	RRA	;Move bit 0 to C flag
0127	CB 18	RR B	;Rotate C flag into register B
0129	23	INC HL	;Point to next byte
012A	0D	DEC C	;Update bit counter
012B	20 F8	JR NZ,NXT	;Have we looked at all bytes?
012D	FF	RST 38H	

Step 1

Load and execute the above program using several sample ASCII strings as input.

Step 2

Rewrite the program to process the ASCII byte string from location 0207 down to 0200. How will this influence the rotate instructions? Test and debug your program to make sure that it works properly.

EXPERIMENT NO. 3

Purpose

The purpose of this experiment is to demonstrate the use of the RRD instruction in a program to convert bcd to ASCII representation. In this program, bcd to ASCII conversion means inputting a string of "packed bcd" bytes, i.e., bytes which contain two four-bit bcd numbers, and outputting a string of ASCII numbers, one per byte. For example,

Byte 1	0 0 1 1 1 0 0 1	= 39 (bcd)
Byte 2	0 1 0 1 1 0 0 0	= 58 (bcd)
Byte 3	0 0 0 0 0 0 0 1	= 01 (bcd)
Byte 4	0 1 1 1 0 0 0 0	= 70 (bcd)

converts to the eight-byte ASCII string (written in hex)

$$33 \quad 39 \quad 35 \quad 38 \quad 30 \quad 31 \quad 37 \quad 30$$

The following program converts a string of packed bcd bytes, whose start address is contained in register pair HL, to a string of ASCII bytes whose start address is contained in register pair DE. Register pair HL is set to 0210 and DE is set to 0301 initially. Register C contains the number of packed bcd bytes to be converted. We have set the contents of C to 04.

Program No. 31

Memory Location	Object Code	Source Code	Comments
0130	3E 30	LD A,30H	;Initialize high order nibble of ;accumulator to 3
0132	21 10 02	LD HL,0210H	;Source address (packed bcd)
0135	11 01 03	LD DE,0301H	;Destination address (ASCII ;string)
0138	0E 04	LD C,04H	;Number of source bytes
013A	ED 67	BCD: RRD	;Rotate low order nibble to ac- ;cumulator. Since high order

				;nibble is 3 we have the ASCII ;equivalent.
013C	12	LD	(DE),A	;Store ASCII byte
013D	1B	DEC	DE	;Decrement destination pointer ;for high order bcd number
013E	ED 67	RRD		;Rotate high order nibble to ;accumulator
0140	12	LD	(DE),A	;Store ASCII byte
0141	ED 67	RRD		;Rotate high order nibble back ;to source byte restoring it to ;initial form
0143	13	INC	DE	;Update destination pointer
0144	13	INC	DE	
0145	13	INC	DE	
0146	23'	INC	HL	;Update source pointer
0147	0D	DEC	C	;Update source byte counter
0148	20 F0	JR	NZ,BCD	;Are we done?
014A	FF	RST	38H	

Step 1

Load the above program at the indicated address. Execute the program in single step mode for several sample packed bcd strings to try to understand how it works.

Step 2

Let us discuss how the above program operates. Consider the diagram in Fig. 10-1.

Memory Location	High Order BCD No.	Low Order BCD No.
	D7 D6 D5 D4	D3 D2 D1 D0
0210	BCD1	BCD2
0211	BCD3	BCD4
0212	BCD5	BCD6
0213	BCD7	BCD8

0300	ASCII1	loaded after 2nd RRD
0301	ASCII2	loaded after 1st RRD
0302	ASCII3	loaded after 5th RRD
0303	ASCII4	loaded after 4th RRD
0304	ASCII5	loaded after 8th RRD
0305	ASCII6	loaded after 7th RRD
0306	ASCII7	loaded after 11th RRD
0307	ASCII8	loaded after 10th RRD

	Accumulator	Memory Location 0210
Initial configuration	3 0	BCD1 BCD2
After first RRD instruction	3 BCD2	0 BCD1

Note: 3 BCD2 = ASCII2 is stored in (0301)

After second RRD instruction

3	BCD1	BCD2	0

Note: 3 BCD1 = ASCII1 is stored in (0300)

After third RRD instruction

3	0	BCD1	BCD2

Note: Everything is restored, translation of source byte is complete.

(Everything restored, translation of source byte complete.)

There are three crucial facts to understand about this program:

1. The RRD instruction operates to move nibbles between memory and the accumulator. This is shown in Fig. 10-1.
2. The operation of the RRD instruction requires that BCD2 is converted to ASCII2 *before* BCD1 is converted to ASCII1. This explains why register DE is initialized to 0301, decremented, and then incremented three times.
3. The operation of the RRD instruction allows us to initialize the accumulator to 30 and perform the bcd to ASCII translation by merely rotating bcd digits into the low order nibble, keeping the high order nibble constant.

Note that this program departs from our normal practice of associating high order halves of pairs with higher memory locations: BCD1, the high order nibble, is translated to ASCII1 at location 0300 and BCD2, the low order nibble, is translated to ASCII2 at location 0301. This departure is due to the fact that it is normally desirable to print the high order digit first. Thus, the ASCII string starting at location 0300 can be output in sequence to a printer and, thus, appear in the normal "printed" order with high order digits preceding low order digits.

CHAPTER 11

Arithmetic and Block Search Instructions

In this chapter we shall continue our discussion of the 8-bit Arithmetic and Logic Instruction Group and the General-Purpose AF Instruction Group. We shall also investigate the 16-bit Arithmetic Instruction Group and the powerful Block Search Instruction Group. These four instruction groups appear in Tables 11-1, 11-2, 11-3, and 11-4, respectively. At the end of this chapter, you will have had experience in using every instruction that the Z-80 microprocessor can perform except the input, output, and interrupt related instructions, which will be covered in detail in a subsequent volume.

OBJECTIVES

At the completion of this chapter you will be able to:

- Write programs to add, subtract, multiply, and divide 8-bit binary integers.
- Write programs to add, subtract, multiply, and divide 16-bit binary integers.
- Understand and use the decimal adjust accumulator (DAA) instruction in conjunction with bcd arithmetic.
- Describe the functions of the H and N flags in conjunction with bcd arithmetic and the DAA instruction.
- Understand and use the add-with-carry and subtract-with-carry instructions.

Table 11-1. The 8-Bit Arithmetic and Logic Groups

SOURCE

	REGISTER ADDRESSING							REG. INDIR.	INDEXED		IMMED.
	A	B	C	D	E	H	L	(HL)	(IX+d)	(IY+d)	n
'ADD'	87	80	81	82	83	84	85	86	DD 86 d	FD 86 d	C6 n
ADD w CARRY 'ADC'	8F	88	89	8A	8B	8C	8D	8E	DD 8E d	FD 8E d	CE n
SUBTRACT 'SUB'	97	90	91	92	93	94	95	96	DD 96 d	FD 96 d	D6 n
SUB w CARRY 'SBC'	9F	98	99	9A	9B	9C	9D	9E	DD 9E d	FD 9E d	DE n
'AND'	A7	A0	A1	A2	A3	A4	A5	A6	DD A6 d	FD A6 d	E6 n
'XOR'	AF	A8	A9	AA	AB	AC	AD	AE	DD AE d	FD AE d	EE n
'OR'	B7	B0	B1	B2	B3	B4	B5	B6	DD B6 d	FD B6 d	F6 n
COMPARE 'CP'	BF	B8	B9	BA	BB	BC	BD	BE	DD BE d	FD BE d	FE n
INCREMENT 'INC'	3C	04	0C	14	1C	24	2C	34	DD 34 d	FD 34 d	
DECREMENT 'DEC'	3D	05	0D	15	1D	25	2D	35	DD 35 d	FD 35 d	

Courtesy Zilog, Inc.

Table 11-2. General-Purpose AF Operations

Decimal Adjust Acc, 'DAA'	27
Complement Acc, 'CPL'	2F
Negate Acc, 'NEG' (2's complement)	ED 44
Complement Carry Flag, 'CCF'	3F
Set Carry Flag, 'SCF'	37

Courtesy Zilog, Inc.

- Understand and use the compare instruction, CP, and the powerful block search instructions which are an extention of it.

Table 11-3. The 16-Bit Arithmetic Group

SOURCE

			BC	DE	HL	SP	IX	IY
		HL	09	19	29	39		
	'ADD'	IX	DD 09	DD 19		DD 39	DD 29	
DESTINATION		IY	FD 09	FD 19		FD 39		FD 29
	ADD WITH CARRY AND SET FLAGS 'ADC'	HL	ED 4A	ED 5A	ED 6A	ED 7A		
	SUB WITH CARRY AND SET FLAGS 'SBC'	HL	ED 42	ED 52	ED 62	ED 72		
	INCREMENT 'INC'		03	13	23	33	DD 23	FD 23
	DECREMENT 'DEC'		0B	1B	2B	3B	DD 2B	FD 2B

Courtesy Zilog, Inc.

Table 11-4. Block Search Group

SEARCH LOCATION

REG. INDIR.	
(HL)	
ED A1	'CPI' Inc HL, Dec BC
ED B1	'CPIR', Inc HL, Dec BC repeat until BC = 0 or find match
ED A9	'CPD' Dec HL & BC
ED B9	'CPDR' Dec HL & BC Repeat until BC = 0 or find match

HL points to location in memory
   to be compared with accumulator
   contents
BC is byte counter

Courtesy Zilog, Inc.

8-BIT ARITHMETIC GROUP

The instructions in the 8-bit arithmetic group all involve addition or subtraction of 8-bit bytes. The INC and DEC instructions add or subtract hexadecimal 01 from a specified register or memory byte. The ADD and SUB instructions specify a byte in a register or memory location to be ADDed or SUBtracted to/from the byte in the accumulator with the resultant sum/difference residing in the accumulator. The INC, DEC, ADD, and SUB instructions for 8-bit operations all affect the flags as follows:

Zero Flag: If the result in the accumulator is zero then the Z-flag is set, otherwise it is reset.

Sign Flag: If the result in the accumulator is negative (i.e., most significant bit is logic 1), the S-flag is set, otherwise it is reset.

Carry Flag: If the operation, INC, DEC, ADD, or SUB, resulted in a carry or borrow to/from a "phantom" 9th bit, the C-flag is set, otherwise it is reset.

P/V (parity/overflow) Flag: The P/V flag performs strictly as a two's complement arithmetic overflow indicator. See the discussion of this in Chapter 8.

H Flag: The Half Carry (H) flag is set if there is a carry or borrow as a result of adding or subtracting the low order digits of two packed bcd numbers, otherwise it is reset. We will discuss this flag at length in the section on the DAA instruction.

N Flag: The Subtract Flag (N) is set for all operations related to subtraction, and reset for all operations related to addition. This flag will also be discussed at length in the section on the DAA instruction.

Here are several examples which illustrate the operations INC, DEC, ADD, and SUB. The entry , • , under a column labeled with a flag indicates that the flag is not affected by the operation, i.e., the instruction leaves it unchanged.

Instruction	Accumulator Before Execution	Accumulator After Execution	Flags After Execution (X=don't care)					
			S	Z	H	P/V	N	C
INC A	04	05	0	0	0	0	0	•
INC A	FF	00	0	1	1	0	0	•
DEC A	00	FF	1	0	1	0	1	•
ADD A,80H	00	80	0	0	0	0	0	0
ADD A,80H	80	F0	1	0	0	1	0	0
ADD A,F0H	F0	E0	1	0	0	0	0	1
ADD A,11H	22	33	0	0	0	0	0	0
ADD A,18H	29	41	0	0	1	0	0	0
ADD A,94H	93	27	0	0	0	1	0	1

ADD A,99H	99	32	0	0	1	1	0	1
SUB 33H	33	00	0	1	0	0	1	0
SUB 02H	10	0E	0	0	1	0	1	0
SUB 22H	10	EE	1	0	1	0	1	1

To understand each of the above examples, perform the indicated binary arithmetic and follow the rules described previously for setting and resetting the affected flags. For example, consider the instruction.

ADD 18H

where the accumulator already contains 29. Then the binary addition can be written:

```
     0  0  1  0  1  0  0  1    Accumulator
  +  0  0  0  1  1  0  0  0
     ─────────────────────
     0  1  0  0  0  0  0  1
```

S Flag: 0 because bit D7 is zero
Z Flag: 0 because result not zero
H Flag: 1 because there was a carry from bit D3 to bit D4 during the bit by bit addition
P/V Flag: 0 because two positive two's complement numbers summed to a positive two's complement number
N Flag: 0 because the operation is addition
C Flag: 0 because there was no carry beyond bit D7

The 8-bit ADC, *add-with-carry,* and the SBC, *subtract-with-carry,* instructions perform a three-step operation:

Step 1: Add or subtract the indicated byte to/from the accumulator as if performing an ADD or SUB instruction. Do not change any flag bits.

Step 2: Add or subtract the C-flag to/from the accumulator. That is, if the C flag was set just prior to execution of the ADC or SBC instruction, add or subtract 01 from the byte in the accumulator. If the C-flag was reset, the accumulator is not changed.

Step 3: Adjust the flags based on the results of both previous steps.

Here are some examples to illustrate the ADC and SBC instructions.

Instruction	Accumulator Before Execution	C-Flag	Accumulator After Exec.	Flags After Execution							
				S	Z	X	H	X	P/V	N	C
ADC A,00H	01	1	02	0	0		0		0	0	0
ADC A,00H	01	0	01	0	0		0		0	0	0
ADC A,90H	97	1	28	0	0		0		1	0	1
ADC A,19H	39	1	53	0	0		1		0	0	0
SBC A,00H	00	1	FF	1	0		1		0	1	1
SBC A,01H	00	1	00	0	1		0		0	1	0
SBC A,80H	00	1	7F	1	0		1		1	1	1

The ADC and SBC instructions are especially useful for multibyte binary arithmetic operations. Consider the following program which performs a multibyte or *multiple precision* addition of two binary numbers stored in memory. The maximum number of bytes in each addend is stored in register C. The strings of bytes representing the first and second addends start with their least significant bytes at the memory locations pointed to by registers HL and IX, respectively. IY points to the start address (least significant byte) of the string representing the sum.

```
        LD C,08H            ;Eight bytes in each addend
        LD HL,0200H         ;Addend #1
        LD IX,0210H         ;Addend #2
        LD IY, 0220H        ;Sum
        SUB A               ;Clear the accumulator and C flag
ADDB:   LD A,(HL)           ;Get byte from string #1
        ADC A,(IX)          ;Add byte from string #2
        LD (IY),A           ;Store sum in string #3
        INC HL              ;Update memory pointers
        INC IX
        INC IY
        DEC C               ;Have we processed all bytes?
        JR NZ,ADDB          ;If not, add next bytes
        JR C,ERROR          ;If so, check for carry. Overflow if C=1
        RST 38H             ;Return control to operating system
```

Let us discuss how this program operates. Fig. 11-1 shows the addends and sum in their respective memory locations and how the program manipulates them. The initial values for HL, IX, and IY are shown. These registers are updated as successive pairs of memory

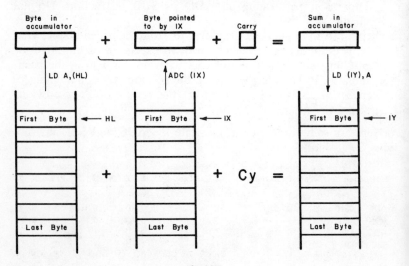

Fig. 11-1.

bytes are added. Notice how the carry, if any, is added in to the next higher order byte by the ADC instruction. The SUB A instruction initially clears or resets the C flag so that the first addition is equivalent to a straightforward ADD. After all the pairs of bytes from string number 1 and string number 2 have been added together, a check is made for the presence of a carry by the JP C,ERROR instruction. The ADC (IX) instruction was the last instruction to affect the C flag so the C flag still represents the existence or non-existence of overflow from addition of the last two (most significant) bytes. *ERROR* represents the memory location of a routine that prints out overflow messages, not shown here.

The preceding program is equally applicable to multibyte two's complement addition, provided that the two addends are n-bit two's complement numbers, where $n = 8 \times$ (length in bytes of the two addends). For two's complement addition the P/V flag should be checked as the overflow indicator, instead of the C flag as above.

DAA INSTRUCTION

For binary coded decimal (bcd) arithmetic a special instruction is required to convert results based on binary operations to results in proper bcd format. The Z-80 only knows one method of addition and subtraction, namely binary. Since two's complement and binary addition and subtraction are essentially the same (except for overflow detection), the Z-80 can also perform two's complement arithmetic. Decimal arithmetic is not the same as binary arithmetic. Consider the following addition problem, solved first as a binary addition and second as a decimal addition of two packed bcd bytes:

```
0 0 0 0 1 0 0 0 =    8 (base 10) or 08 (packed bcd)
0 0 0 0 1 0 0 1 =    9 (base 10) or 09 (packed bcd)
─────────────────
0 0 0 1 0 0 0 1 =   17 (base 10) or 11 (packed bcd)
```

Note that the result, interpreted as a binary number, is correct, but interpreted as a packed bcd number is incorrect. The reason for this is the difference between number base. The Z-80 treats the two digits of a packed bcd number as two *hexadecimal* digits because four bits in binary representation can represent 16 different values. Hence, during an arithmetic operation such as addition, a carry from the right digit to the left digit occurs when the sum is greater than 16. For bcd addition, this carry should occur when the sum is greater than 10. Thus bcd and binary addition do not produce the same result when

    a. The sum of two 4-bit nibbles is between 10 and 15 inclusive, e.g.,

```
  1 0 0 1   9
+ 0 0 1 0   2
  1 0 1 1   B as hex sum, should be 11 as packed bcd sum.
```

In this case, binary produces no carry to the next nibble when decimal addition would.

b. The sum of two 4-bit nibbles is greater than or equal to 16, e.g.,

```
  1 0 0 1   9
+ 1 0 0 1   9
1 0 0 1 0   12 as a hex sum, should be 18 as packed bcd sum.
```

In this case, binary produces a carry to the next nibble but it is six digits "too late."

In both cases presented, the hex answer minus the decimal answer is six. It turns out that when (a) or (b) occurs this is *always* true. Thus, the Z-80 CPU has a special instruction, the *Decimal Adjust Accumulator* instruction, which can detect when either (a) or (b) occurs and add six to a nibble if appropriate. The detection process is quite simple. Any incidence of (a) yields a nibble with a nondecimal hex equivalent such as A, B, C, D, E, or F. Thus, a nibble whose value is greater than nine in a result indicates that six must be added to that nibble. Any incidence of (b) is detected by a carry flag, either C or H, being set. The H flag is set if a carry occurs as a result of adding the two low order nibbles. The C flag is set if a carry occurs as a result of adding the two high order nibbles.

Consider the following sequence of instructions which performs a packed bcd add of the contents of the accumulator and B register:

ADD A,B
DAA

Let's see how these instructions operate on five different sets of data:

	Set 1	Set 2	Set 3	Set 4	Set 5
B register	11	19	91	99	09
Accumulator before ADD A,B	22	18	81	88	05
After ADD, A,B:					
Accumulator	33	31	12	21	0E
H flag	0	1	0	1	0
C flag	0	0	1	1	0
Accumulator After DAA	33	37	72	87	14

The third and fourth set of data values (91 and 81; 99 and 88) represent sums which are greater than 99, the maximum packed bcd value that the accumulator can hold. Thus the final 1 which should be carried as a third digit in the 100's place is dropped. Note that 172 and 187 are the correct answers. The overflow in such cases is indicated by the C flag being set. The last data pair (09 and 05) is an example of an occurrence of the preceding condition (a). Neither H nor C is set but an adjustment to the low order nibble is required since E is not a decimal number.

Thus, to convert our sample program which adds multibyte binary numbers to a program which adds multibyte packed bcd numbers required just one simple change. Merely insert a DAA instruction between the ADC A,(IX) and LD (IY),A instructions.

16-BIT ARITHMETIC INSTRUCTIONS

The 8-bit ADD, ADC, SBC, INC, and DEC instructions have 16-bit analogs which perform essentially the same operation only

Table 11-5. The 16-Bit Arithmetic Group

Mnemonic	Symbolic Operation	C	Z	P/V	S	N	H	Op-Code 76 543 210	No. of Bytes	No. of M Cycles	No. of T States	Comments	
ADD HL, ss	HL ← HL+ss	‡	•	•	•	0	X	00 ss1 001	1	3	11	ss	Reg.
												00	BC
ADC HL, ss	HL←HL+ss+CY	‡	‡	V	‡	0	X	11 101 101	2	4	15	01	DE
								01 ss1 010				10	HL
												11	SP
SBC HL, ss	HL←HL-ss-CY	‡	‡	V	‡	1	X	11 101 101	2	4	15		
								01 ss0 010					
ADD IX, pp	IX ← IX + pp	‡	•	•	•	0	X	11 011 101	2	4	15	pp	Reg.
								00 pp1 001				00	BC
												01	DE
												10	IX
												11	SP
ADD IY, rr	IY←IY+rr	‡	•	•	•	0	X	11 111 101	2	4	15	rr	Reg.
								00 rr1 001				00	BC
												01	DE
												10	IY
												11	SP
INC ss	ss ← ss + 1	•	•	•	•	•	•	00 ss0 011	1	1	6		
INC IX	IX ← IX + 1	•	•	•	•	•	•	11 011 101	2	2	10		
								00 100 011					
INC IY	IY ← IY + 1	•	•	•	•	•	•	11 111 101	2	2	10		
								00 100 011					
DEC ss	ss ← ss - 1	•	•	•	•	•	•	00 ss1 011	1	1	6		
DEC IX	IX ← IX - 1	•	•	•	•	•	•	11 011 101	2	2	10		
								00 101 011					
DEC IY	IY ← IY - 1	•	•	•	•	•	•	11 111 101	2	2	10		
								00 101 011					

Notes: ss is any of the register pairs BC, DE, HL, SP
        pp is any of the register pairs BC, DE, IX, SP
        rr is any of the register pairs BC, DE, IY, SP.

Flag Notation: • = flag not affected, 0 = flag reset, 1 = flag set, X = flag is unknown,
           ‡ = flag is affected according to the result of the operation.

Courtesy Zilog, Inc.

using 16-bit register pairs. The 16-bit instructions treat the flags somewhat differently. These instructions with their associated hex codes appear in Table 11-3. The details of how the 16-bit arithmetic instructions manipulate the flags appear in Table 11-5. As you can see, it contains a great deal of information not appearing in Table 11-3. In Appendix A, we introduce a full set of instruction tables.

CP AND BLOCK SEARCH INSTRUCTIONS:
CPI, CPD, CPIR, and CPDR

The *CP s* instruction compares the contents of the accumulator with a specified 8-bit byte s by computing the difference A−s and setting the C, Z, P/V, as overflow-not parity, S and H flags according to the result. The N flag is set, due to the subtraction. Note that neither the accumulator nor the byte s is changed as a result of the CP operation. The difference, A−s, is stored elsewhere, internal to the CPU, so that the net effect of the CP instruction to the programmer is that the flags are changed. Thus, for example, the CP B instruction has the same effect on the A,B and F registers as the sequence

```
LD C,A    ;Save the accumulator
SUB B     ;Perform the subtraction and set the flags
LD A,C    ;Restore the accumulator
```

You have seen an application of the CP instruction in the experiment which demonstrates jump tables at the end of Chapter 7.

The block search instructions which appear in Table 11-4 operate in a manner similar to the block transfer instructions. The LD operation is the basis for the block transfers while the CP instruction is the basis for the block search group. The *block search instructions* facilitate the process of searching sequential memory locations for a match with a "key byte" contained in the accumulator. As with the block transfer instructions, certain registers must be initialized prior to execution of any block search instruction:

```
BC = number of memory locations to be searched
HL = address of the byte to be compared with the contents of the accumulator
A  = the key value to be matched with successive memory bytes
```

Execution of the CPI, *compare-increment,* instruction causes the following steps to occur:

1. The byte in the location addressed by register pair HL is compared with the contents of the accumulator. The Z, S, and H flags are set according to the result of the compare. (The CP (HL) instruction affects the C flag, while the CPI instruction (as well as the other block search instructions) does not affect

the C flag. So, this step is not identical to the execution of a CP (HL) instruction, strictly speaking.)

2. The contents of the HL register pair are incremented.
3. The contents of the BC register pair are decremented. At this point, the Z-flag is set if A = (HL), reset otherwise. The P/V-flag is reset if register pair BC = 0000, set otherwise.

Execution of the CPIR, *compare-increment-repeat,* instruction causes the following to occur:

1. The byte in the location addressed by register pair HL is compared with the contents of the accumulator. The Z, S, and H flags are set according to the result.
2. The contents of the HL register pair are incremented.
3. The contents of the BC register pair are decremented. At this point the Z-flag has been set if A=(HL), reset otherwise. The P/V flag is reset if register pair BC=0000, set otherwise.
4. If either register pair BC=0000 or A=(HL), then execution proceeds to the next instruction. Otherwise, steps 1, 2, and 3, are repeated.

Execution of the CPD, *compare-decrement,* and the CPDR, *compare-decrement-repeat,* instructions result in very similar sequences of steps. The only difference is that Step 2 decrements HL. Fig. 11-2 illustrates the registers and memory locations before and after execution of the CPIR and CPDR instructions.

INTRODUCTION TO THE EXPERIMENTS

The following experiments are designed to give you an idea of how to program the Z-80 to perform basic arithmetic operations. Some applications of the block search group are also investigated.

The experiments which you will perform may be summarized as follows:

Experiment No.	Comments
1	Demonstrates a method for programming multiple-precision binary multiplication.
2	Demonstrates a method for programming multibyte bcd subtraction.
3	Demonstrates a method for programming a division operation in which a 16-bit binary number is divided by an 8-bit binary number to compute a quotient and remainder.
4	Demonstrates the block search and compare instructions in two useful applications.

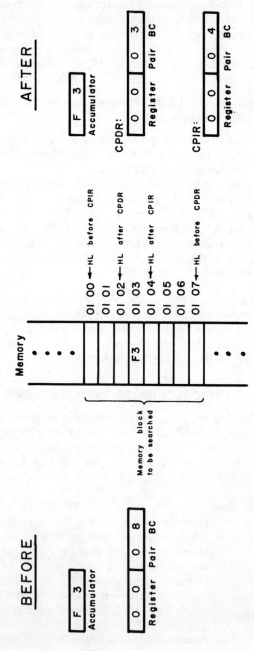

Fig. 11-2.

254

EXPERIMENT NO. 1

Purpose

The purpose of this experiment is to demonstrate a method for programming multiple-precision binary arithmetic. The next program listed multiplies two 16-bit binary numbers stored at locations 0130-0131 and 0132-0133 and places the product in locations 0134-0135. Later we show you a program which multiplies two binary numbers of equal length to produce a product of the same length. Thus, you will see how your Nanocomputer can multiply 64-bit numbers just like large mainframe computers. (It is only fair to mention that the speed is *not* comparable.)

Program No. 32

Memory Location	Object Code	Source Code	Comments
0100	21 00 00	MLT16:LD HL,0000H	;HL = product, initialize at 0
0103	ED 5B 30 01	LD DE,(0130H)	;DE = Multicand
0107	ED 4B 32 01	LD BC,(0132H)	;BC = multiplier
010B	7A	LD A,D	;Check if DE = 0
010C	B3	OR E	
010D	CC 38 00	CALL Z,0038H	;If DE = 0, jump to monitor
0110	CB 38	MLT: SRL B	;BC: shift right, zero fill
0112	CB 19	RR C	;C flag equals current multi- ;plying bit
0114	30 04	JR NC,NCF	;Check the C flag
0116	19	ADD HL,DE	;C flag is set, add DE to HL
0117	DC 38 00	CALL C,0038H	;If ADD causes carry, overflow
011A	78	NCF: LD A,B	;If C flag is reset, check to see
011B	B1	OR C	;if BC = 0
011C	CA 29 01	JP Z,ANS	;If BC = 0 then store answer
011F	CB 23	SLA E	;Otherwise rotate DE left
0121	CB 12	RL D	
0123	DC 38 00	CALL C,0038H	;If C is set, overflow has oc- ;curred so return to monitor
0126	C3 10 01	JP MLT	;Otherwise continue
0129	22 34 01	ANS: LD (0134H),HL	;Store answer
012C	FF	RST 38H	;Return to monitor

Step 1

Let us briefly discuss the methodology used in this program to perform binary multiplication. For convenience, let us multiply two 4-bit binary numbers. The principle shown next for 4-bit multiplication apply equally to 8-bit, 16-bit, or any other precision-binary multiplication. Suppose that we wish to multiply 0011 times 0101. One procedure, quite similar to the usual methods of decimal arithmetic, is as follows:

```
        0 0 1 1   Multiplicand
        0 1 0 1   Multiplier

        0 0 1 1       1 × 0 0 1 1
      0 0 0 0         0 × 0 0 1 1
    0 0 1 1           1 × 0 0 1 1
  0 0 0 0             0 × 0 0 1 1

  0 0 0 1 1 1 1
```

Thus, a clear pattern develops: Each occurrence of a 1 bit in the multiplier causes some shifted version of the multiplicand to be added into a sum which gives the product. The shifts, of course, fill-in zeros from the right. The preceding program implements the technique of shifting and adding as illustrated previously. The HL register pair holds the product; the BC register holds the multiplier; and the DE register pair holds the multiplicand.

Step 2

Load and execute the sample program for several pairs of 16-bit binary numbers. Note that as long as the numbers are kept relatively small the computed product is correct. For example:

$$0400 \times 0020 = 8000$$
$$00FF \times 00FF = FE01$$
$$0100 \times 00FF = FF00$$

What about $\quad 0100 \times 0100 = ?$

We get 0000 in the HL register which is wrong. Let us try the computation by hand. The answer is 1 followed by 16 zeros, or in three hex bytes,

0 1 0 0 0 0.

Unfortunately, we allowed for only two bytes in our answer, so byte three, the most significant byte, cannot appear in the answer. This is an occurrence of *overflow* which is detected in the preceding program by the CALL C,0038H and CALL 0038H instructions. In this program, we just inserted the operating system address for the address of a routine which would somehow report an overflow condition back to the user. Note that overflow is checked for in two places.

Let us look at two 4-bit examples to see why:

```
  1 0 0 0   Multiplicand
  0 1 1 0   Multiplier

  0 0 0 0
  1 0 0 0   Overflow exists because the carry flag is set as a re-
            sult of shifting the multiplicand. A set carry flag indi-
            cates that the product contains more than four bits.
```

```
        0 1 1 0   Multiplicand
        0 0 1 1   Multiplier

        0 1 1 0
      0 1 1 0
Partial sum  1 0 0 1 0   Overflow exists because the shift-add operation causes
                         the carry flag to be set, thus indicating the product
                         contains more than four bits.
```

Thus, to detect overflow in both of the above situations, the carry flag is checked after shifting the multiplicand (register pair DE) and after adding the shifted multiplicand to the HL register pair to form a partial sum.

Step 3

The same techniques used previously for 16-bit or two-byte multiplication can be applied to multiplication of n-byte binary numbers, where n is any positive integer. The following sequence of instructions multiplies two NUM-byte binary numbers that are stored in NUM sequential memory locations with the least significant byte starting at addresses XNUM and YNUM, respectively. The product is stored in NUM sequential memory locations with the least significant bytes starting at address ZNUM.

```
MLTN:    LD B,NUM              ;Load number of bytes per number into reg-
                               ;ister B (NUM=one-byte hex constant)
         LD HL,ZNUM            ;Load HL with address of product (ZNUM=
                               ;two-byte hex constant)
INIT:    LD (HL),00H           ;Initialize product to 0s in each byte
         INC HL
         DJNZ INIT
SHIFTX:  LD B,NUM              ;Shift multiplier XNUM right one bit and
                               ;zero fill: Initialize register B to the number
                               ;of bytes
         LD IX,XNUM+NUM-01H    ;IX=address of most significant byte of
                               ;multiplier (XNUM=two-byte hex constant)
         XOR A
RTX:     RR (IX)
         DEC IX
         DJNZ RTX
         JR NC,ZERO            ;If no carry, current bit in multiplier is zero
                               ;so do not add in multiplicand
         LD B,NUM              ;If carry bit set, current bit in multiplier is
                               ;one so add in multiplicand to partial prod-
                               ;uct residing at location ZNUM
         LD HL,ZNUM
         LD IY,YNUM            ;YNUM=two-byte hex constant
         CCF                   ;Complement the carry flag which was set
                               ;for these instructions. Thus, C flag is now
                               ;zero.
NXTBYT:  LD A,(IY)             ;Add multiplicand to product
         ADC A,(HL)
```

```
          LD (HL),A              ;Store sum in product string
          INC IY                 ;Update byte pointers
          INC HL
          DJNZ NXTBYT
ZERO:     LD B,NUM               ;Check if multiplier is zero. If so, we are
                                 ;done
          LD IX,XNUM
          XOR A                  ;Clear A for zero check
ZCHK:     OR (IX)                ;Check to see if multiplier=0
          JR NZ,SHIFTY           ;If multiplier not zero, then shift multipli-
                                 ;cand again
          INC IX
          DJNZ ZCHK
          RST 38H                ;Return to monitor if multiplier is zero.
SHIFTY:   LD B,NUM               ;Shift multiplicand YNUM right one bit, zero
                                 ;fill vacated bit
          LD IY,YNUM
          XOR A                  ;Clear carry bit
LFTY:     RL (IY)                ;Start shifting
          INC IY
          DJNZ LFTY
          JP SHIFTX
          RST 38H                ;Multiplier=0, hence we are done.
```

Go over this routine carefully to make sure that you understand it thoroughly. For the first time we have used variables like NUM, XNUM, YNUM, and ZNUM for one-byte and two-byte hex constants. This is a very common practice in the literature on software development, so you should become used to it.

Step 4

Hand assemble the NUM-byte multiply program substituting your own values for NUM, XNUM, YNUM, and ZNUM. See if you can execute some sample programs.

Step 5

Note that the NUM-byte multiply program does not check for overflow. Put in your own checks and see if they work.

EXPERIMENT NO. 2

Purpose

The purpose of this experiment is to demonstrate a method for programming multibyte bcd subtraction. The following program inputs two NUM-byte bcd numbers whose least significant bytes are at locations XNUM and YNUM, respectively, computes their difference (the string starting at address YNUM is subtracted from the string starting at address XNUM), and stores the difference starting at location ZNUM.

Program No. 33

Memory Location	Object Code	Source Code	Comments
0200	06 N	SUBN: LD B,NUM	;Register B counts the num- ;ber of bytes
0202	DD 21 X2 X1	LD IX,XNUM	
0206	FD 21 Y2 Y1	LD IY,YNUM	
020A	21 Z2 Z1	LD HL,ZNUM	
020D	37	SCF	;Set carry flag: 100's com- ;plement for first subtract
020E	3E 99	NXTBYT: LD A,99H	;Find 99 or 100's comple- ;ment of subtrahend
0210	CE 00	ADC A,00H	
0212	FD 96 00	SUB (IY)	
0215	DD 86 00	ADD A,(IX)	;Add minuend byte
0218	27	DAA	;Adjust for decimal arith- ;metic
0219	77	LD (HL),A	
021A	DD 23	INC IX	;Update pointers
021C	FD 23	INC IY	
021E	23	INC HL	
021F	10 ED	DJNZ NXTBYT	;Keep subtracting until all ;bytes processed ;No carry after last byte ;indicates overflow!
0221	FF	RST 38H	

Step 1

Let us discuss how this program works. Recall that in our discussion on subtraction of two's complement numbers, we said that subtraction of a two's complement number is equivalent to forming its two's complement and then adding it. The same is true for packed bcd subtraction, only instead of forming a two's complement, you form a 100's complement. Let us look at some examples:

Packed BCD byte	03	94	30	01	50
100's complement	97	06	70	99	50

Hence, to find the 100's complement of a packed bcd byte, merely subtract the byte from 100 as a decimal two digit number. Similarly, you can compute the 10's complement of a bcd nibble, but we do not need to use this fact here. Let us now perform a three-byte bcd subtraction using the *complement and add* technique.

Find the difference: 256925−133639

Step 1: Form 100's complement of least significant byte of subtrahend

$$100-39=61$$

Step 2: Add 61 to least significant byte of minuend (decimal addition)

$$25 + 61 = 86$$

No carry occurred

Step 3: Since Step 2 resulted in no carry, form the *99's complement* of the next least significant byte of the subtrahend

$$99-36=63$$

Step 4: Add 63 to the next least significant byte of the minuend

$$69 + 63 = 32$$
Carry Occurred

Step 5: Since Step 4 resulted in a carry, form the 100's complement of the most significant byte of the subtrahend

$$100-13=87$$

Step 6: Add 87 to the most significant byte of the minuend

$$25 + 87 = 12$$
Carry Occurred

Step 7: Answer is 123286 which is correct. The correctness is assured because a carry occurred. Had there been no carry, the answer would have been wrong, and overflow would have occurred. Since bcd numbers are always greater than or equal to zero, overflow occurs whenever the subtrahend is greater than the minuend.

We will not dwell on a mathematical proof of the preceding technique. Suffice it to say that the 100's complement is formed when a borrow from the next higher byte has not occurred, while the 99's complement is formed when a borrow has occurred in order to perform the subtraction of one packed bcd byte from another. In terms of the complement and add technique:

A borrow in the subtraction process is equivalent to no carry in the complement and add process.

Thus, if the carry flag is SET at the end of the bcd subtraction, there is *no* overflow. This may at first seem somewhat "unintuitive," but it will become more natural as you think about it.

Step 2

Load and execute the above program with several sample bcd strings to subtract. Be sure to supply values for:

NUM =1 byte hex constant representing the number of packed bcd bytes

XNUM=2 byte address of minuend (hex)

YNUM=2 byte address of subtrahend (hex)
ZNUM=2 byte address of difference (hex)

EXPERIMENT NO. 3

Purpose

The purpose of this experiment is to demonstrate a method for programming a division operation in which a 16-bit binary number is divided by an 8-bit binary number to compute a quotient and a remainder. In the program listed next, it is assumed that initially register HL contains the 16-bit binary dividend and register D contains the 8-bit binary divisor. At the completion of execution, the 8-bit quotient is in register L and the 8-bit remainder is in register H. For the division algorithm implemented in Program No. 34 to function properly, we must assume that the divisor and dividend are in *normalized form*. That is:

    a. The most significant bit of the 16-bit dividend is zero, and

    b. The most significant byte of the dividend is less than the divisor to ensure that the quotient will fit into the 8 bits allotted for it.

Program No. 34

Memory Location	Object Code	Source Code		Comments
0300	06 08	DIV:	LD B,08H	;# bits in divisor
0302	1E 00		LD E,00H	;Divisor in DE
0304	29	NXTBIT:	ADD HL,HL	;Shift HL left, zero fill
0305	AF		XOR A	;Reset the carry flag
0306	ED 52		SBC HL,DE	;Will DE go?
0308	23		INC HL	;Assume, yes
0309	30 02		JR NC,NXT	;If not, undo the damage
030B	19		ADD HL,DE	;Add DE back in
030C	2B		DEC HL	;Set quotient bit to zero
030D	10 F5	NXT:	DJNZ NXTBIT	
030F	FF		RST 38H	

Step 1

Let us first look into how this program operates. The algorithm used is quite similar to the method used for hand calculating decimal long division problems. However, it is easier because only 0s and 1s are involved. Let us look at an example in which the 4-bit binary number 8 is divided into the 8-bit binary number 6E. Set up the problem as you would a normal long-division problem, writing all numbers in binary:

$$1\ 0\ 0\ 0\,\overline{\big)\,0\ 1\ 1\ 0\ 1\ 1\ 1\ 0}$$

To determine successive bits in the quotient, merely enter a 1 if the divisor "will go" or a 0 if it "won't go" into the most significant bits of the residue of successive subtractions of the divisor from the dividend:

```
                    1 1 0 1
        1 0 0 0 | 0 1 1 0 1 1 1 0
                  1 0 0 0
                  _____
                  1 0 1 1
                  1 0 0 0
                  _____
                    0 1 1 1 0
                    1 0 0 0
                    _____
                      1 1 0
```

Hence the quotient is 1101=D (base 16) and the remainder is $0110 = 6$ (base 16).

In the preceding program, the registers are initialized as follows:

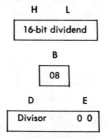

Since the most significant bit of HL is zero and the contents of D are greater than the contents of H (see assumptions about normalized dividend and divisor), the first step in the program is to shift left, zero fill HL by one bit (ADD HL,HL) and then compare the contents of DE and HL. If DE is less than or equal to HL, the quotient is set to one, otherwise it is zero. Notice how the quotient is rotated into the lower four bits of register pair HL. This is possible because as each quotient bit is added, an old dividend bit is discarded. The method for determining whether the new quotient bit (which is always the least significant bit of register L) should be zero or one, DE is subtracted from HL. A carry indicates the quotient bit should be zero, while no carry implies DE "went into" HL so the quotient bit should be 1 (INC HL). Note that the HL−DE subtraction must use the SBC instruction since there is no 16-bit SUB instruction. This necessitates the XOR A instruction just before the SBC instruction to ensure a zero carry flag. If DE "will not go" into HL, the value of the last residue in HL must be restored by adding DE back and decrementing HL.

Step 2

Load and execute the preceding program in single-step mode for several sample problems.

EXPERIMENT NO. 4

Purpose

The purpose of this experiment is to demonstrate the block search and compare instructions in two useful applications. We present two programs which utilize these instructions to perform often required programming tasks.

Program No. 35

SEARCH a string of characters for a particular character.

Memory Location	Object Code	Source Code	Comments
0400	21 00 0A	LD HL,0A00H	;Start address of character ;string
0403	01 20 00	LD BC,0020H	;Number of characters in ;string
0406	3E 24	LD A,24H	;Character to locate: 24 is an ;ASCII '$'.
0408	ED B1	CPIR	;Find the $
040A	C2 0F 04	JP NZ,NOFIND	;If Z flag=0, the character ;was not found
040D	2B	DEC HL	;Subtract 1 from HL so it ;points to the character
040E	03	INC BC	;Increment BC so it gives
040F	FF	NOFIND: RST 38H	;character number in string

Program No. 36

Search a table of records for a particular record identified by a three-character string.

Memory Location	Object Code	Source Code	Comments
0412	31 00 0F	LD SP,0F00H	;Locate the stack
0415	21 00 0C	LD HL,0C00H	;Address of last record in table
0418	01 06 00	LD BC,0006H	;Number of records in table
041B	3A 00 0B	LD A,(0B00H)	;First character in identifying ;3 character string
041E	11 F9 FF	LD DE,FFF9H	;−(record length −1): 16−bit ;two's complement
0421	ED A9	NREC: CPD	;Match?
0423	28 09	JR Z,CHECK	
0425	E2 42 04	JP PO,NOFIND	;All records examined?
0428	19	UPD: ADD HL,DE	;Update HL to beginning of ;next record
0429	3A 00 0B	LD A,(0B00H)	;Reset accumulator

```
042C    18 F3                JR  NREC        ;Look at next record
042E    3A 01 0B    CHECK:   LD  A,(0B01H)   ;Compare second bytes
0431    E5                   PUSH HL         ;HL now points to last byte
                                             ;of record immediatetly pre-
                                             ;ceding record to be checked
0432    DD E1                POP  IX         ;Load IX with HL
0434    DD BE 02             CP  (IX+02H)
0437    20 EF                JR  NZ,UPD      ;Go back to search if no match
0439    3A 02 0B             LD  A,(0B02H)   ;Compare third bytes
043C    DD BE 03             CP  (IX+03H)    .
043F    20 E7                JR  NZ,UPD      ;Go back to search if no match
0441    23                   INC HL          ;HL now points to first byte of
                                             ;matching record. Z-flag is set
0442    FF          NOFIND:  RST 38H
```

Step 1

Let us examine Program No. 35. This program begins by loading register pair HL with the address of byte 1 of a string of bytes, register pair BC with the number of bytes in this string, and the accumulator with the key byte, i.e., the byte to match in the search. The CPIR instruction sequentially checks each byte in the string until a match is found or there are no more bytes to check. If a match is found, the CPIR instruction sets the Z-flag which causes the DEC HL and INC BC instructions to be executed so that HL does indeed point to the matching string byte, and BC does represent the byte number in the string of the matching byte. If no match is found, control returns to the operating system with the Z-flag reset, the P/V-flag reset, and BC=0000.

This program, set up as a subroutine, could be used in implementing jump tables much like the one demonstrated in Chapter 7. The values to be searched can be stored in a separate block of memory away from their associated jump addresses. Program No. 35 would be called on to search the values for a match and return the index of the matched value in register pair BC. The index would then be used to find the proper jump address for subsequent transfer of control.

Step 2

Load and execute Program No. 35. Use several sample strings and key values to thoroughly test the logic of the program.

Step 3

Let us examine Program No. 36. Suppose we have a table located in memory as follows:

	Byte No.							
	1	2	3	4	5	6	7	8
Location								
0BD8	41	51	46	31	32	33	30	36	Record 1
0BE0	42	46	47	33	36	30	30	34	Record 2

0BE8	41	42	43	36	35	34	32	31	**Record 3**
0BF0	43	42	41	36	36	36	36	36	**Record 4**
0BF8	43	41	42	34	33	34	33	34	**Record 5**
0C00	42	42	42	31	32	33	32	31	**Record 6**
	Identifying Initials			**Telephone Extension**					

The table consists of six records with each record containing eight bytes. For each record:

> Bytes 1-3 are a three-character identification code
> Bytes 4-8 represent a five-digit telephone extension

Hence, we have a telephone directory for a six person office. To look up a person's telephone number, merely match the ASCII representation of his initials with the first three bytes of some record in the table, and the next five bytes are the phone number. Here is an ASCII-HEX table of equivalent representations for the alphabet.

A	41	J	4A	S	53
B	42	K	4B	T	54
C	43	L	4C	U	55
D	44	M	4D	V	56
E	45	N	4E	W	57
F	46	O	4F	X	58
G	47	P	50	Y	59
H	48	Q	51	Z	5A
I	49	R	52		

Recall that from an earlier experiment, the ASCII representation for characters 0 through 9 runs from 30 through 39. Hence "AQF" has the phone number 12306.

Program No. 36 reads a table such as the one presented earlier and returns a pointer to the record whose first three characters match a key string, stored at memory locations 0B00, 0B01, and 0B02. The program starts out by loading the HL register pair with the address of the last record, the BC register pair with the number of records in the table, and the accumulator with the first byte of the key string. The CPD in combination with successive adds of −7 to the HL register pair checks first bytes of each record, from record number 6 to record number 35, for a match with byte 1 of the three-byte key. (Note that −7 is added to HL instead of −8 because the CPD instruction decrements HL.) When a match is found, bytes two and three must be checked. This is accomplished by the instruction sequence beginning at statement CHECK. This sequence can be easily changed to accommodate a need to check more bytes by introducing a loop, but for just two bytes, a loop is not necessary.

Summary of Z-80 Op Codes and Execution Times

The following tables summarize the Z-80 instruction set. The instructions are arranged into groups as shown earlier in the instruction tables appearing in Chapters 6 through 12. Each table shows the assembly language mnemonic, a symbolic shorthand description of the operation of the instruction, the contents of the flag register after the instruction execution, the binary op code, the number of bytes, as well as the number of memory cycles and total number of T-states (external clock periods) required for fetching and executing of the instruction. Where applicable, additional comments are included.

Table A-1. The 8-Bit Load Group

Mnemonic	Symbolic Operation	C	Z	P/V	S	N	H	OP-Code 76 543 210	No. of Bytes	No. of M Cycles	No. of T Cycles	Comments
LD r, r′	r ← r′	•	•	•	•	•	•	01 r r′	1	1	4	r, r′ Reg.
LD r, n	r ← n	•	•	•	•	•	•	00 r 110	2	2	7	000 B
								← n →				001 C
LD r, (HL)	r ← (HL)	•	•	•	•	•	•	01 r 110	1	2	7	010 D
LD r, (IX+d)	r ← (IX+d)	•	•	•	•	•	•	11 011 101	3	5	19	011 E
								01 r 110				100 H
								← d →				101 L
LD r, (IY+d)	r ← (IY+d)	•	•	•	•	•	•	11 111 101	3	5	19	111 A
								01 r 110				
								← d →				
LD (HL), r	(HL) ← r	•	•	•	•	•	•	01 110 r	1	2	7	
LD (IX+d), r	(IX+d) ← r	•	•	•	•	•	•	11 011 101	3	5	19	
								01 110 r				
								← d →				
LD (IY+d), r	(IY+d) ← r	•	•	•	•	•	•	11 111 101	3	5	19	
								01 110 r				
								← d →				
LD (HL), n	(HL) ← n	•	•	•	•	•	•	00 110 110	2	3	10	
								← n →				
LD (IX+d), n	(IX+d) ← n	•	•	•	•	•	•	11 011 101	4	5	19	
								00 110 110				
								← d →				
								← n →				
LD (IY+d), n	(IY+d) ← n	•	•	•	•	•	•	11 111 101	4	5	19	
								00 110 110				
								← d →				
								← n →				
LD A, (BC)	A ← (BC)	•	•	•	•	•	•	00 001 010	1	2	7	
LD A, (DE)	A ← (DE)	•	•	•	•	•	•	00 011 010	1	2	7	
LD A, (nn)	A ← (nn)	•	•	•	•	•	•	00 111 010	3	4	13	
								← n →				
								← n →				
LD (BC), A	(BC) ← A	•	•	•	•	•	•	00 000 010	1	2	7	
LD (DE), A	(DE) ← A	•	•	•	•	•	•	00 010 010	1	2	7	
LD (nn), A	(nn) ← A	•	•	•	•	•	•	00 110 010	3	4	13	
								← n →				
								← n →				
LD A, I	A ← I	•	‡	IFF	‡	0	0	11 101 101	2	2	9	
								01 010 111				
LD A, R	A ← R	•	‡	IFF	‡	0	0	11 101 101	2	2	9	
								01 011 111				
LD I, A	I ← A	•	•	•	•	•	•	11 101 101	2	2	9	
								01 000 111				
LD R, A	R ← A	•	•	•	•	•	•	11 101 101	2	2	9	
								01 001 111				

Notes: r, r′ means any of the registers A, B, C, D, E, H, L

IFF the content of the interrupt enable flip-flop (IFF) is copied into the P/V flag

Flag Notation: • = flag not affected, 0 = flag reset, 1 = flag set, X = flag is unknown,

‡ = flag is affected according to the result of the operation.

Table A-2. The 16-Bit Load Group

Mnemonic	Symbolic Operation	C	Z	P/V	S	N	H	76 543 210	No. of Bytes	No. of M Cycles	No. of T States	Comments	
LD dd, nn	dd ← nn	•	•	•	•	•	•	00 dd0 001 / ← n → / ← n →	3	3	10	dd	Pair
												00	BC
												01	DE
LD IX, nn	IX ← nn	•	•	•	•	•	•	11 011 101 / 00 100 001 / ← n → / ← n →	4	4	14	10	HL
												11	SP
LD IY, nn	IY ← nn	•	•	•	•	•	•	11 111 101 / 00 100 001 / ← n → / ← n →	4	4	14		
LD HL, (nn)	H ← (nn+1) / L ← (nn)	•	•	•	•	•	•	00 101 010 / ← n → / ← n →	3	5	16		
LD dd, (nn)	dd_H ← (nn+1) / dd_L ← (nn)	•	•	•	•	•	•	11 101 101 / 01 dd1 011 / ← n → / ← n →	4	6	20		
LD IX, (nn)	IX_H ← (nn+1) / IX_L ← (nn)	•	•	•	•	•	•	11 011 101 / 00 101 010 / ← n → / ← n →	4	6	20		
LD IY, (nn)	IY_H ← (nn+1) / IY_L ← (nn)	•	•	•	•	•	•	11 111 101 / 00 101 010 / ← n → / ← n →	4	6	20		
LD (nn), HL	(nn+1) ← H / (nn) ← L	•	•	•	•	•	•	00 100 010 / ← n → / ← n →	3	5	16		
LD (nn), dd	(nn+1) ← dd_H / (nn) ← dd_L	•	•	•	•	•	•	11 101 101 / 01 dd0 011 / ← n → / ← n →	4	6	20		
LD (nn), IX	(nn+1) ← IX_H / (nn) ← IX_L	•	•	•	•	•	•	11 011 101 / 00 100 010 / ← n → / ← n →	4	6	20		
LD (nn), IY	(nn+1) ← IY_H / (nn) ← IY_L	•	•	•	•	•	•	11 111 101 / 00 100 010 / ← n → / ← n →	4	6	20		
LD SP, HL	SP ← HL	•	•	•	•	•	•	11 111 001	1	1	6		
LD SP, IX	SP ← IX	•	•	•	•	•	•	11 011 101 / 11 111 001	2	2	10		
LD SP, IY	SP ← IY	•	•	•	•	•	•	11 111 101 / 11 111 001	2	2	10	qq	Pair
PUSH qq	(SP-2) ← qq_L / (SP-1) ← qq_H	•	•	•	•	•	•	11 qq0 101	1	3	11	00	BC
												01	DE
PUSH IX	(SP-2) ← IX_L / (SP-1) ← IX_H	•	•	•	•	•	•	11 011 101 / 11 100 101	2	4	15	10	HL
PUSH IY	(SP-2) ← IY_L / (SP-1) ← IY_H	•	•	•	•	•	•	11 111 101 / 11 100 101	2	4	15	11	AF
POP qq	qq_H ← (SP+1) / qq_L ← (SP)	•	•	•	•	•	•	11 qq0 001	1	3	10		
POP IX	IX_H ← (SP+1) / IX_L ← (SP)	•	•	•	•	•	•	11 011 101 / 11 100 001	2	4	14		
POP IY	IY_H ← (SP+1) / IY_L ← (SP)	•	•	•	•	•	•	11 111 101 / 11 100 001	2	4	14		

Notes: dd is any of the register pairs BC, DE, HL, SP
qq is any of the register pairs AF, BC, DE, HL
$(PAIR)_H$, $(PAIR)_L$ refer to high order and low order eight bits of the register pair respectively.
E.g. BC_L = C, AF_H = A

Flag Notation: • = flag not affected, 0 = flag reset, 1 = flag set, X = flag is unknown,
‡ flag is affected according to the result of the operation.

Courtesy Zilog, Inc.

Table A-3. Exchange Group and Block Transfer and Search Group

Mnemonic	Symbolic Operation	Flags						Op-Code 76 543 210	No. of Bytes	No. of M Cycles	No. of T States	Comments
		C	Z	P/V	S	N	H					
EX DE, HL	DE ·· HL	•	•	•	•	•	•	11 101 011	1	1	4	
EX AF, AF'	AF ·· AF'	•	•	•	•	•	•	00 001 000	1	1	4	
EXX	(BC)↔(BC') (DE)↔(DE') (HL)↔(HL')	•	•	•	•	•	•	11 011 001	1	1	4	Register bank and auxiliary register bank exchange
EX (SP), HL	H ↔ (SP+1) L ↔ (SP)	•	•	•	•	•	•	11 100 011	1	5	19	
EX (SP), IX	IX$_H$↔(SP+1) IX$_L$ ↔ (SP)	•	•	•	•	•	•	11 011 101 11 100 011	2	6	23	
EX (SP), IY	IY$_H$↔(SP+1) IY$_L$ ↔ (SP)	•	•	•	•	•	•	11 111 101 11 100 011	2	6	23	
LDI	(DE) ← (HL) DE ← DE+1 HL ← HL+1 BC ← BC-1	•	•	① ‡	•	0	0	11 101 101 10 100 000	2	4	16	Load (HL) into (DE), increment the pointers and decrement the byte counter (BC)
LDIR	(DE) ← (HL) DE ← DE+1 HL ← HL+1 BC ← BC-1 Repeat until BC = 0	•	•	0	•	0	0	11 101 101 10 110 000	2 2	5 4	21 16	If BC ≠ 0 If BC = 0
LDD	(DE) ← (HL) DE ← DE-1 HL ← HL-1 BC ← BC-1	•	•	① ‡	•	0	0	11 101 101 10 101 000	2	4	16	
LDDR	(DE) ← (HL) DE ← DE-1 HL ← HL-1 BC ← BC-1 Repeat until BC = 0	•	•	0	•	0	0	11 101 101 10 111 000	2 2	5 4	21 16	If BC ≠ 0 If BC = 0
CPI	A – (HL) HL ← HL+1 BC ← BC-1	•	② ‡	① ‡	‡	1	‡	11 101 101 10 100 001	2	4	16	
CPIR	A – (HL) HL ← HL+1 BC ← BC-1 Repeat until A = (HL) or BC = 0	•	② ‡	① ‡	‡	1	‡	11 101 101 10 110 001	2 2	5 4	21 16	If BC ≠ 0 and A ≠ (HL) If BC = 0 or A = (HL)
CPD	A – (HL) HL ← HL-1 BC ← BC-1	•	② ‡	① ‡	‡	1	‡	11 101 101 10 101 001	2	4	16	
CPDR	A – (HL) HL ← HL-1 BC ← BC-1 Repeat until A = (HL) or BC = 0	•	② ‡	① ‡	‡	1	‡	11 101 101 10 111 001	2 2	5 4	21 16	If BC ≠ 0 and A ≠ (HL) If BC = 0 or A = (HL)

Notes: ① P/V flag is 0 if the result of BC-1 = 0, otherwise P/V = 1
 ② Z flag is 1 if A = (HL), otherwise Z = 0.

Flag Notation: • = flag not affected, 0 = flag reset, 1 = flag set, X = flag is unknown,
‡ = flag is affected according to the result of the operation.

Table A-4. The 8-Bit Arithmetic and Logical Group

Mnemonic	Symbolic Operation	C	Z	P/V	S	N	H	Op-Code 76 543 210	No. of Bytes	No. of M Cycles	No. of T States	Comments
ADD r	A ← A + r	↕	↕	V	↕	0	↕	10 [000] r	1	1	4	r Reg.
ADD n	A ← A + n	↕	↕	V	↕	0	↕	11 [000] 110	2	2	7	000 B
								← n →				001 C
												010 D
ADD (HL)	A ← A + (HL)	↕	↕	V	↕	0	↕	10 [000] 110	1	2	7	011 E
ADD (IX+d)	A ← A + (IX+d)	↕	↕	V	↕	0	↕	11 011 101	3	5	19	100 H
								10 [000] 110				101 L
								← d →				111 A
ADD (IY+d)	A ← A+(IY+d)	↕	↕	V	↕	0	↕	11 111 101	3	5	19	
								10 [000] 110				
								← d →				
ADC s	A ← A + s + CY	↕	↕	V	↕	0	↕	[001]				s is any of r, n,
SUB s	A ← A - s	↕	↕	V	↕	1	↕	[010]				(HL), (IX+d),
SBC s	A ← A - s - CY	↕	↕	V	↕	1	↕	[011]				(IY+d) as shown for
AND s	A ← A ∧ s	0	↕	P	↕	0	↕	[100]				ADD instruction
OR s	A ← A ∨ s	0	↕	P	↕	0	↕	[110]				
XOR s	A ← A ⊕ s	0	↕	P	↕	0	↕	[101]				The indicated bits
CP s	A - s	↕	↕	V	↕	1	↕	[111]				replace the 000 in the ADD set above.
INC r	r ← r + 1	●	↕	V	↕	0	↕	00 r [100]	1	1	4	
INC (HL)	(HL) ← (HL)+1	●	↕	V	↕	0	↕	00 110 [100]	1	3	11	
INC (IX+d)	(IX+d) ← (IX+d)+1	●	↕	V	↕	0	↕	11 011 101	3	6	23	
								00 110 [100]				
								← d →				
INC (IY+d)	(IY+d) ← (IY+d) + 1	●	↕	V	↕	0	↕	11 111 101	3	6	23	
								00 110 [100]				
								← d →				
DEC d	d ← d - 1	●	↕	V	↕	1	↕	[101]				d is any of r. (HL), (IX+d), (IY+d) as shown for INC Same format and states as INC Replace 100 with 101 in OP code.

Notes: The V symbol in the P/V flag column indicates that the P/V flag contains the overflow of the result of the operation. Similarly the P symbol indicates parity. V = 1 means overflow. V = 0 means not overflow. P = 1 means parity of the result is even, P = 0 means parity of the result is odd.

Flag Notation: ● = flag not affected. 0 = flag reset, 1 = flag set. X = flag is unknown.
        ↕ = flag is affected according to the result of the operation.

Courtesy Zilog, Inc.

Table A-5. General-Purpose Arithmetic and CPU Control Group

Mnemonic	Symbolic Operation	Flags						Op-Code			No. of Bytes	No. of M Cycles	No. of T States	Comments
		C	Z	P/V	S	N	H	76	543	210				
DAA	Converts acc. content into packed BCD following add or subtract with packed BCD operands	‡	‡	P	‡	•	‡	00	100	111	1	1	4	Decimal adjust accumulator
CPL	A ← Ā	•	•	•	•	1	1	00	101	111	1	1	4	Complement accumulator (one's complement)
NEG	A ← 0 − A	‡	‡	V	‡	1	‡	11	101	101	2	2	8	Negate acc. (two's complement)
								01	000	100				
CCF	CY ← $\overline{CY}$	‡	•	•	•	0	X	00	111	111	1	1	4	Complement carry flag
SCF	CY ← 1	1	•	•	•	0	0	00	110	111	1	1	4	Set carry flag
NOP	No operation	•	•	•	•	•	•	00	000	000	1	1	4	
HALT	CPU halted	•	•	•	•	•	•	01	110	110	1	1	4	
DI	IFF ← 0	•	•	•	•	•	•	11	110	011	1	1	4	
EI	IFF ← 1	•	•	•	•	•	•	11	111	011	1	1	4	
IM 0	Set interrupt mode 0	•	•	•	•	•	•	11	101	101	2	2	8	
								01	000	110				
IM 1	Set interrupt mode 1	•	•	•	•	•	•	11	101	101	2	2	8	
								01	010	110				
IM2	Set interrupt mode 2	•	•	•	•	•	•	11	101	101	2	2	8	
								01	011	110				

Notes: IFF indicates the interrupt enable flip-flop
CY indicates the carry flip-flop.

Flag Notation: • = flag not affected, 0 = flag reset, 1 = flag set, X = flag is unknown,
‡ = flag is affected according to the result of the operation.

Courtesy Zilog, Inc.

Table A-6. The 16-Bit Arithmetic Group

Mnemonic	Symbolic Operation	C	Z	P/V	S	N	H	Op-Code 76 543 210	No. of Bytes	No. of M Cycles	No. of T States	Comments	
ADD HL, ss	HL ← HL+ss	‡	•	•	•	0	X	00 ss1 001	1	3	11	ss	Reg.
												00	BC
ADC HL, ss	HL←HL+ss+CY	‡	‡	V	‡	0	X	11 101 101	2	4	15	01	DE
								01 ss1 010				10	HL
SBC HL, ss	HL←HL-ss-CY	‡	‡	V	‡	1	X	11 101 101	2	4	15	11	SP
								01 ss0 010					
ADD IX, pp	IX ← IX + pp	‡	•	•	•	0	X	11 011 101	2	4	15	PP	Reg.
								00 pp1 001				00	BC
												01	DE
												10	IX
												11	SP
ADD IY, rr	IY←IY+rr	‡	•	•	•	0	X	11 111 101	2	4	15	rr	Reg.
								00 rr1 001				00	BC
												01	DE
												10	IY
												11	SP
INC ss	ss ← ss + 1	•	•	•	•	•	•	00 ss0 011	1	1	6		
INC IX	IX ← IX + 1	•	•	•	•	•	•	11 011 101	2	2	10		
								00 100 011					
INC IY	IY ← IY + 1	•	•	•	•	•	•	11 111 101	2	2	10		
								00 100 011					
DEC ss	ss ← ss - 1	•	•	•	•	•	•	00 ss1 011	1	1	6		
DEC IX	IX ← IX - 1	•	•	•	•	•	•	11 011 101	2	2	10		
								00 101 011					
DEC IY	IY ← IY - 1	•	•	•	•	•	•	11 111 101	2	2	10		
								00 101 011					

Notes: ss is any of the register pairs BC, DE, HL, SP
pp is any of the register pairs BC, DE, IX, SP
rr is any of the register pairs BC, DE, IY, SP.

Flag Notation: • = flag not affected, 0 = flag reset, 1 = flag set, X = flag is unknown,
‡ = flag is affected according to the result of the operation.

Courtesy Zilog, Inc.

Table A-7. Rotate and Shift Group

Mnemonic	Symbolic Operation	Flags C	Z	P/V	S	N	H	Op-Code 76 543 210	No. of Bytes	No. of M Cycles	No. of T States	Comments
RLCA		‡	•	•	•	0	0	00 000 111	1	1	4	Rotate left circular accumulator
RLA		‡	•	•	•	0	0	00 010 111	1	1	4	Rotate left accumulator
RRCA		‡	•	•	•	0	0	00 001 111	1	1	4	Rotate right circular accumulator
RRA		‡	•	•	•	0	0	00 011 111	1	1	4	Rotate right accumulator
RLC r		‡	‡	P	‡	0	0	11 001 011 / 00 [000] r	2	2	8	Rotate left circular register r
RLC (HL)		‡	‡	P	‡	0	0	11 001 011 / 00 [000] 110	2	4	15	
RLC (IX+d)	r, (HL), (IX+d), (IY+d)	‡	‡	P	‡	0	0	11 011 101 / 11 001 011 / ← d → / 00 [000] 110	4	6	23	
RLC (IY+d)		‡	‡	P	‡	0	0	11 111 101 / 11 001 011 / ← d → / 00 [000] 110	4	6	23	
RL s	S = r, (HL), (IX+d), (IY+d)	‡	‡	P	‡	0	0	[010]				Instruction format and states are as shown for RLC,s. To form new OP-code replace [000] of RLC,s with shown code
RRC s	S = r, (HL), (IX+d), (IY+d)	‡	‡	P	‡	0	0	[001]				
RR s	S = r, (HL), (IX+d), (IY+d)	‡	‡	P	‡	0	0	[011]				
SLA s	S = r, (HL), (IX+d), (IY+d)	‡	‡	P	‡	0	0	[100]				
SRA s	S = r, (HL), (IX+d), (IY+d)	‡	‡	P	‡	0	0	[101]				
SRL s	S = r, (HL), (IX+d), (IY+d)	‡	‡	P	‡	0	0	[111]				
RLD		•	‡	P	‡	0	0	11 101 101 / 01 101 111	2	5	18	Rotate digit left and right between the accumulator and location (HL). The content of the upper half of the accumulator is unaffected
RRD		•	‡	P	‡	0	0	11 101 101 / 01 100 111	2	5	18	

Register table for RLC group:

r	Reg.
000	B
001	C
010	D
011	E
100	H
101	L
111	A

Flag Notation: • = flag not affected, 0 = flag reset, 1 = flag set, X = flag is unknown, ‡ = flag is affected according to the result of the operation.

Courtesy Zilog, Inc.

Table A-8. Bit SET, RESET, and TEST Group

Mnemonic	Symbolic Operation	Flags						Op-Code			No. of Bytes	No. of M Cycles	No. of T States	Comments	
		C	Z	P/V	S	N	H	76	543	210					
BIT b, r	$Z \leftarrow \overline{r_b}$	•	‡	X	X	0	1	11	001	011	2	2	8	r	Reg.
								01	b	r				000	B
BIT b, (HL)	$Z \leftarrow \overline{(HL)_b}$	•	‡	X	X	0	1	11	001	011	2	3	12	001	C
								01	b	110				010	D
														011	E
BIT b, (IX+d)	$Z \leftarrow \overline{(IX+d)_b}$	•	‡	X	X	0	1	11	011	101	4	5	20	100	H
								11	001	011				101	L
								←	d	→				111	A
								01	b	110					
														b	Bit Tested
BIT b, (IY+d)	$Z \leftarrow \overline{(IY+d)_b}$	•	‡	X	X	0	1	11	111	101	4	5	20	000	0
								11	001	011				001	1
								←	d	→				010	2
								01	b	110				011	3
														100	4
														101	5
														110	6
														111	7
SET b, r	$r_b \leftarrow 1$	•	•	•	•	•	•	11	001	011	2	2	8		
								[11]	b	r					
SET b, (HL)	$(HL)_b \leftarrow 1$	•	•	•	•	•	•	11	001	011	2	4	15		
								[11]	b	110					
SET b, (IX+d)	$(IX+d)_b \leftarrow 1$	•	•	•	•	•	•	11	011	101	4	6	23		
								11	001	011					
								←	d	→					
								[11]	b	110					
SET b, (IY+d)	$(IY+d)_b \leftarrow 1$	•	•	•	•	•	•	11	111	101	4	6	23		
								11	001	011					
								←	d	→					
								[11]	b	110					
RES b, s	$s_b \leftarrow 0$ $s \equiv r, (HL),$ $(IX+d),$ $(IY+d)$							[10]						To form new OP-code replace [11] of SET b,s with [10]. Flags and time states for SET instruction	

Notes: The notation s_b indicates bit b (0 to 7) or location s.

Flag Notation: • = flag not affected, 0 = flag reset, 1 = flag set, X = flag is unknown,
‡ = flag is affected according to the result of the operation.

Courtesy Zilog, Inc.

Mnemonic	Symbolic Operation	C	Z	P/V	S	N	H	76	543	210	No. of Bytes	No. of M Cycles	No. of T States	Comments
JP nn	PC ← nn	•	•	•	•	•	•	11	000	011	3	3	10	
								← n →						
								← n →						
JP cc, nn	If condition cc is true PC ← nn, otherwise continue	•	•	•	•	•	•	11	cc	010	3	3	10	
								← n →						
								← n →						
JR e	PC ← PC + e	•	•	•	•	•	•	00	011	000	2	3	12	
								← e-2 →						
JR C, e	If C = 0, continue	•	•	•	•	•	•	00	111	000	2	2	7	If condition not met
								← e-2 →						
	If C = 1, PC ← PC+e										2	3	12	If condition is met
JR NC, e	If C = 1, continue	•	•	•	•	•	•	00	110	000	2	2	7	If condition not met
								← e-2 →						
	If C = 0, PC ← PC + e										2	3	12	If condition is met
JR Z, e	If Z = 0 continue	•	•	•	•	•	•	00	101	000	2	2	7	If condition not met
								← e-2 →						
	If Z = 1, PC ← PC + e										2	3	12	If condition is met
JR NZ, e	If Z = 1, continue	•	•	•	•	•	•	00	100	000	2	2	7	If condition not met
								← e-2 →						
	If Z = 0, PC ← PC + e										2	3	12	If condition met
JP (HL)	PC ← HL	•	•	•	•	•	•	11	101	001	1	1	4	
JP (IX)	PC ← IX	•	•	•	•	•	•	11	011	101	2	2	8	
								11	101	001				
JP (IY)	PC ← IY	•	•	•	•	•	•	11	111	101	2	2	8	
								11	101	001				
DJNZ,e	B ← B-1 If B = 0, continue	•	•	•	•	•	•	00	010	000	2	2	8	If B = 0
								← e-2 →						
	If B ≠ 0, PC ← PC + e										2	3	13	IF B ≠ 0

cc	Condition
000	NZ non zero
001	Z zero
010	NC non carry
011	C carry
100	PO parity odd
101	PE parity even
110	P sign positive
111	M sign negative

Notes: e represents the extension in the relative addressing mode.

e is a signed two's complement number in the range <-126, 129>

e-2 in the op-code provides an effective address of pc +e as PC is incremented by 2 prior to the addition of e.

Flag Notation: • = flag not affected, 0 = flag reset, 1 = flag set, X = flag is unknown,

‡ = flag is affected according to the result of the operation.

Courtesy Zilog, Inc.

Table A-10. CALL and RETURN Group

Mnemonic	Symbolic Operation	Flags C	Z	P/V	S	N	H	Op-Code 76 543 210	No. of Bytes	No. of M Cycles	No. of T States	Comments
CALL nn	$(SP-1) \leftarrow PC_H$ $(SP-2) \leftarrow PC_L$ $PC \leftarrow nn$	•	•	•	•	•	•	11 001 101 ← n → ← n →	3	5	17	
CALL cc, nn	If condition cc is false continue, otherwise same as CALL nn	•	•	•	•	•	•	11 cc 100 ← n → ← n →	3 3	3 5	10 17	If cc is false If cc is true
RET	$PC_L \leftarrow (SP)$ $PC_H \leftarrow (SP+1)$	•	•	•	•	•	•	11 001 001	1	3	10	
RET cc	If condition cc is false continue, otherwise same as RET	•	•	•	•	•	•	11 cc 000	1 1	1 3	5 11	If cc is false If cc is true
RETI	Return from interrupt	•	•	•	•	•	•	11 101 101 01 001 101	2	4	14	
RETN	Return from non maskable interrupt	•	•	•	•	•	•	11 101 101 01 000 101	2	4	14	
RST p	$(SP-1) \leftarrow PC_H$ $(SP-2) \leftarrow PC_L$ $PC_H \leftarrow 0$ $PC_L \leftarrow P$	•	•	•	•	•	•	11 t 111	1	3	11	

cc	Condition	
000	NZ	non zero
001	Z	zero
010	NC	non carry
011	C	carry
100	PO	parity odd
101	PE	parity even
110	P	sign positive
111	M	sign negative

t	P
000	00H
001	08H
010	10H
011	18H
100	20H
101	28H
110	30H
111	38H

Flag Notation: • = flag not affected, 0 = flag reset, 1 = flag set, X = flag is unknown
‡ = flag is affected according to the result of the operation.

Courtesy Zilog, Inc.

Mnemonic	Symbolic Operation	C	Z	P/V	S	N	H	Op-Code 76 543 210	No. of Bytes	No. of M Cycles	No. of T States	Comments
IN A, (n)	A ← (n)	•	•	•	•	•	•	11 011 011 ← n →	2	3	10	n to $A_0 \sim A_7$ Acc to $A_8 \sim A_{15}$
IN r, (C)	r ← (C) if r = 110 only the flags will be affected	•	↕	P	↕	0	↕	11 101 101 01 r 000	2	3	11	C to $A_0 \sim A_7$ B to $A_8 \sim A_{15}$
INI	(HL) ← (C)① B ← B - 1 HL ← HL + 1	•	↕	X	X	1	X	11 101 101 10 100 010	2	4	15	C to $A_0 \sim A_7$ B to $A_8 \sim A_{15}$
INIR	(HL) ← (C) B ← B - 1 HL ← HL + 1 Repeat until B = 0	•	1	X	X	1	X	11 101 101 10 110 010	2 2	5 (If B ≠ 0) 4 (If B = 0)	20 15	C to $A_0 \sim A_7$ B to $A_8 \sim A_{15}$
IND	(HL) ← (C)① B ← B - 1 HL ← HL - 1	•	↕	X	X	1	X	11 101 101 10 101 010	2	4	15	C to $A_0 \sim A_7$ B to $A_8 \sim A_{15}$
INDR	(HL) ← (C) B ← B - 1 HL ← HL - 1 Repeat until B = 0	•	1	X	X	1	X	11 101 101 10 111 010	2 2	5 (If B ≠ 0) 4 (If B = 0)	20 15	C to $A_0 \sim A_7$ B to $A_8 \sim A_{15}$
OUT (n), A	(n) ← A	•	•	•	•	•	•	11 010 011	2	3	11	n to $A_0 \sim A_7$ Acc to $A_8 \sim A_{15}$
OUT (C), r	(C) ← r	•	•	•	•	•	•	11 101 101 01 r 001	2	3	12	C to $A_0 \sim A_7$ B to $A_8 \sim A_{15}$
OUTI	(C) ← (HL)① B ← B - 1 HL ← HL + 1	•	↕	X	X	1	X	11 101 101 10 100 011	2	4	15	C to $A_0 \sim A_7$ B to $A_8 \sim A_{15}$
OTIR	(C) ∼ (HL) B ← B - 1 HL ← HL + 1 Repeat until B = 0	•	1	X	X	1	X	11 101 101 10 110 011	2 2	5 (If B ≠ 0) 4 (If B = 0)	20 15	C to $A_0 \sim A_7$ B to $A_8 \sim A_{15}$
OUTD	(C) ← (HL)① B ← B - 1 HL ← HL - 1	•	↕	X	X	1	X	11 101 101 10 101 011	2	4	15	C to $A_0 \sim A_7$ B to $A_8 \sim A_{15}$
OTDR	(C) ← (HL) B ← B - 1 HL ← HL - 1 Repeat until B = 0	•	1	X	X	1	X	11 101 101 10 111 011	2 2	5 (If B ≠ 0) 4 (If B = 0)	20 15	C to $A_0 \sim A_7$ B to $A_8 \sim A_{15}$

Notes: ① If the result of B - 1 is zero the Z flag is set, otherwise it is reset.

Flag Notation: • = flag not affected, 0 = flag reset, 1 = flag set, X = flag is unknown,
↕ = flag is affected according to the result of the operation.

Z-80 CPU Instructions Sorted by Mnemonic

OBJ CODE	SOURCE STATEMENT	OBJ CODE	SOURCE STATEMENT	OBJ CODE	SOURCE STATEMENT
00	NOP	218405	LD HL, NN	42	LD B, D
018405	LD BC, NN	228405	LD (NN), HL	43	LD B, E
02	LD (BC), A	23	INC HL	44	LD B, H, NN
03	INC BC	24	INC H	45	LD B, L
04	INC B	25	DEC H	46	LD B, (HL)
05	DEC B	2620	LD H, N	47	LD B, A
0620	LD B, N	27	DAA	48	LD C, B
07	RLCA	282E	JR Z, DIS	49	LD C, C
08	EX AF, AF'	29	ADD HL, HL	4A	LD C, D
09	ADD HL, BC	2A8405	LD (HL), (NN)	4B	LD C, E
0A	LD A, (BC)	2B	DEC HL	4C	LD C, H
0B	DEC BC	2C	INC L	4D	LD C, L
0C	INC C	2D	DEC L	4E	LD C, (HL)
0D	DEC C	2E20	LD L, N	4F	LD C, A
0E20	LD C, N	2F	CPL	50	LD D, B
0F	RRCA	302E	JR NC, DIS	51	LD D, C
102E	DJNZ DIS	318405	LD SP, NN	52	LD D, D
118405	LD DE, NN	328405	LD (NN), A	53	LD D, E
12	LD (DE), A	33	INC SP	54	LD D, H
13	INC DE	34	INC (HL)	55	LD D, L
14	INC D	35	DEC (HL)	56	LD D, (HL)
15	DEC D	3620	LD (HL), N	57	LD D, A
1620	LD D, N	37	SCF	58	LD E, B
17	RLA	382E	JR C, DIS	59	LD E, C
182E	JR DIS	39	ADD HL, SP	5A	LD E, D
19	ADD HL, DE	3A8405	LD A, (NN)	5B	LD E, E
1A	LD A, (DE)	3B	DEC SP	5C	LD E, H
1B	DEC DE	3C	INC A	5D	LD E, L
1C	INC E	3D	DEC A	5E	LD E, (HL)
1D	DEC E	3E20	LD A, N	5F	LD E, A
1E20	LD E, N	3F	CCF	60	LD H, B
1F	RRA	40	LD B, B	61	LD H, C
202E	JR NZ, DIS	41	LD B, C	62	LD H, D

Courtesy Zilog, Inc.

OBJ CODE	SOURCE STATEMENT	OBJ CODE	SOURCE STATEMENT	OBJ CODE	SOURCE STATEMENT
63	LD H, E	A5	AND L	E9	JP (HL)
64	LD H, H	A6	AND (HL)	EA8405	JE PE NN
65	LD H, L	A7	AND A	EB	EX DE, HL
66	LD H, (HL)	A8	XOR B	EC8405	CALL PE, NN
67	LD H, A	A9	XOR C	EE20	XOR N
68	LD L, B	AA	XOR D	EF	RST 28H
69	LD L, C	AB	XOR E	F0	RET P
6A	LD L, D	AC	XOR H	F1	POP AF
6B	LD L, E	AD	XOR L	F28405	JP P, NN
6C	LD L, H	AE	XOR (HL)	F3	DI
6D	LD L, L	AF	XOR A	F48405	CALL P, NN
6E	LD L, (HL)	B0	OR B	F5	PUSH AF
6F	LD L, A	B1	OR C	F620	OR N
70	LD (HL), B	B2	OR D	F7	RST 30H
71	LD (HL), C	B3	OR E	F8	RET M
72	LD (HL), D	B4	OR H	F9	LD SP, HL
73	LD (HL), E	B5	OR L	FA8405	JP M, NN
74	LD (HL), H	B6	OR (HL)	FB	EI
75	LD (HL), L	B7	OR A	FC8405	CALL M, NN
76	HALT	B8	CP B	FE20	CP N
77	LD (HL), A	B9	CP C	FF	RST 38H
78	LD A, B	BA	CP D	CB00	RLC B
79	LD A, C	BB	CP E	CB01	RLC C
7A	LD A, D	BC	CP H	CB02	RLC D
7B	LD A, E	BD	CP L	CB03	RLC E
7C	LD A, H	BE	CP (HL)	CB04	RLC H
7D	LD A, L	BF	CP A	CB05	RLC L
7E	LD A, (HL)	C0	RET NZ	CB06	RLC (HL)
7F	LD A, A	C1	POP BC	CB07	RLC A
80	ADD A, B	C28405	JP NZ, NN	CB08	RRC B
81	ADD A, C	C38405	JP NN	CB09	RRC C
82	ADD A, D	C48405	CALL NZ, NN	CB0A	RRC D
83	ADD A, E	C5	PUSH BC	CB0B	RRC E
84	ADD A, H	C620	ADD A, N	CB0C	RRC H
85	ADD A, L	C7	RST 0	CB0D	RRC L
86	ADD A, (HL)	C8	RET Z	CB0E	RRC (HL)
87	ADD A, A	C9	RET	CB0F	RRC A
88	ADC A, B	CA8405	JP Z, NN	CB10	RL B
89	ADC A, C	CC8405	CALL Z, NN	CB11	RL C
8A	ADC A, D	CD8405	CALL NN	CB12	RL D
8B	ADC A, E	CE20	ADC A, N	CB13	RL E
8C	ADC A, H	CF	RST 8	CB14	RL H
8D	ADC A, L	D0	RET NC	CB15	RL L
8E	ADC A, (HL)	D1	POP DE	CB16	RL (HL)
8F	ADC A, A	D28405	JP NC, NN	CB17	RL A
90	SUB B	D320	OUT (N), A	CB18	RR B
91	SUB C	D48405	CALL NC, NN	CB19	RR C
92	SUB D	D5	PUSH DE	CB1A	RR D
93	SUB E	D620	SUB N	CB1B	RR E
94	SUB H	D7	RST 10H	CB1C	RR H
95	SUB L	D8	RET C	CB1D	RR L
96	SUB (HL)	D9	EXX	CB1E	RR (HL)
97	SUB A	DA8405	JP C, NN	CB1F	RR A
98	SBC A, B	DB20	IN A, (N)	CB20	SLA B
99	SBC A, C	DC8405	CALL C, N	CB21	SLA C
9A	SBC A, D	DE20	SBC A, N	CB22	SLA D
9B	SBC A, E	DF	RST 18H	CB23	SLA E
9C	SBC A, H	E0	RET PO	CB24	SLA H
9D	SBC A, L	E1	POP HL	CB25	SLA L
9E	SBC A, (HL)	E28405	JP PO, NN	CB26	SLA (HL)
9F	SBC A, A	E3	EX (SP), HL	CB27	SLA A
A0	AND B	E48405	CALL PO, NN	CB28	SRA B
A1	AND C	E5	PUSH HL	CB29	SRA C
A2	AND D	E620	AND N	CB2A	SRA D
A3	AND E	E7	RST 20 H	CB2B	SRA E
A4	AND H	E8	RET PE	CB2C	SRA H

Courtesy Zilog, Inc.

OBJ CODE	SOURCE STATEMENT	OBJ CODE	SOURCE STATEMENT	OBJ CODE	SOURCE STATEMENT
CB2D	SRA L	CB77	BIT 6, A	CBB9	RES 7, C
CB2E	SRA (HL)	CB78	BIT 7, B	CBBA	RES 7, D
CB2F	SRA A	CB79	BIT 7, C	CBBB	RES 7, E
CB38	SRL B	CB7A	BIT 7, D	CBBC	RES 7, H
CB39	SRL C	CB7B	BIT 7, E	CBBD	RES 7, L
CB3A	SRL D	CB7C	BIT 7, H	CBBE	RES 7, (HL)
CB3B	SRL E	CB7D	BIT 7, L	CBBF	RES 7, A
CB3C	SRL H	CB7E	BIT 7, (HL)	CBC0	SET 0, B
CB3D	SRL L	CB7F	BIT 7, A	CBC1	SET 0, C
CB3E	SRL (HL)	CB80	RES 0, B	CBC2	SET 0, D
CB3F	SRL A	CB81	RES 0, C	CBC3	SET 0, E
CB40	BIT 0, B	CB82	RES 0, D	CBC4	SET 0, H
CB41	BIT 0, C	CB83	RES 0, E	CBC5	SET 0, L
CB42	BIT 0, D	CB84	RES 0, H	CBC6	SET 0, (HL)
CB43	BIT 0, E	CB85	RES 0, L	CBC7	SET 0, A
CB44	BIT 0, H	CB86	RES 0, (HL)	CBC8	SET 1, B
CB45	BIT 0, L	CB87	RES 0, A	CBC9	SET 1, C
CB46	BIT 0, (HL)	CB88	RES 1, B	CBCA	SET 1, D
CB47	BIT 0, A	CB89	RES 1, C	CBCB	SET 1, E
CB48	BIT 1, B	CB8A	RES 1, D	CBCC	SET 1, H
CB49	BIT 1, C	CB8B	RES 1, E	CBCD	SET 1, L
CB4A	BIT 1, D	CB8C	RES 1, H	CBCE	SET 1, (HL)
CB4B	BIT 1, E	CB8D	RES 1, L	CBCF	SET 1, A
CB4C	BIT 1, H	CB8E	RES 1, (HL)	CBD0	SET 2, B
CB4D	BIT 1, L	CB8F	RES 1, A	CBD1	SET 2, C
CB4E	BIT 1, (HL)	CB90	RES 2, B	CBD2	SET 2, D
CB4F	BIT 1, A	CB91	RES 2, C	CBD3	SET 2, E
CB50	BIT 2, B	CB92	RES 2, D	CBD4	SET 2, H
CB51	BIT 2, C	CB93	RES 2, E	CBD5	SET 2, L
CB52	BIT 2, D	CB94	RES 2, H	CBD6	SET 2, (HL)
CB53	BIT 2, E	CB95	RES 2, L	CBD7	SET 2, A
CB54	BIT 2, H	CB96	RES 2, (HL)	CBD8	SET 3, B
CB55	BIT 2, L	CB97	RES 2, A	CBD9	SET 3, C
CB56	BIT 2, (HL)	CB98	RES 3, B	CBDA	SET 3, D
CB57	BIT 2, A	CB99	RES 3, C	CBDB	SET 3, E
CB58	BIT 3, B	CB9A	RES 3, D	CBDC	SET 3, H
CB59	BIT 3, C	CB9B	RES 3, E	CBDD	SET 3, L
CB5A	BIT 3, D	CB9C	RES 3, H	CBDE	SET 3, (HL)
CB5B	BIT 3, E	CB9D	RES 3, L	CBDF	SET 3, A
CB5C	BIT 3, H	CB9E	RES 3, (HL)	CBE0	SET 4, B
CB5D	BIT 3, L	CB9F	RES 3, A	CBE1	SET 4, C
CB5E	BIT 3, (HL)	CBA0	RES 4, B	CBE2	SET 4, D
CB5F	BIT 3, A	CBA1	RES 4, C	CBE3	SET 4, E
CB60	BIT 4, B	CBA2	RES 4, D	CBE4	SET 4, H
CB61	BIT 4, C	CBA3	RES 4, E	CBE5	SET 4, L
CB62	BIT 4, D	CBA4	RES 4, H	CBE6	SET 4, (HL)
CB63	BIT 4, E	CBA5	RES 4, L	CBE7	SET 4, A
CB64	BIT 4, H	CBA6	RES 4, (HL)	CBE8	SET 5, B
CB65	BIT 4, L	CBA7	RES 4, A	CBE9	SET 5, C
CB66	BIT 4, (HL)	CBA8	RES 5, B	CBEA	SET 5, D
CB67	BIT 4, A	CBA9	RES 5, C	CBEB	SET 5, E
CB68	BIT 5, B	CBAA	RES 5, D	CBEC	SET 5, H
CB69	BIT 5, C	CBAB	RES 5, E	CBED	SET 5, L
CB6A	BIT 5, D	CBAC	RES 5, H	CBEE	SET 5, (HL)
CB6B	BIT 5, E	CBAD	RES 5, L	CBEF	SET 5, A
CB6C	BIT 5, H	CBAE	RES 5, (HL)	CBF0	SET 6, B
CB6D	BIT 5, L	CBAF	RES 5, A	CBF1	SET 6, C
CB6E	BIT 5, (HL)	CBB0	RES 6, B	CBF2	SET 6, D
CB6F	BIT 5, A	CBB1	RES 6, C	CBF3	SET 6, E
CB70	BIT 6, B	CBB2	RES 6, D	CBF4	SET 6, H
CB71	BIT 6, C	CBB3	RES 6, E	CBF5	SET 6, L
CB72	BIT 6, D	CBB4	RES 6, H	CBF6	SET 6, (HL)
CB73	BIT 6, E	CBB5	RES 6, L	CBF7	SET 6, A
CB74	BIT 6, H	CBB6	RES 6, (HL)	CBF8	SET 7, B
CB75	BIT 6, L	CBB7	RES 6, A	CBF9	SET 7, C
CB76	BIT 6, (HL)	CBB8	RES 7, B	CBFA	SET 7, D

Courtesy Zilog, Inc.

OBJ CODE	SOURCE STATEMENT	OBJ CODE	SOURCE STATEMENT	OBJ CODE	SOURCE STATEMENT
CBFB	SET 7, E	DDCB05BE	RES 7, (IX + d)	FD23	INC IY
CBFC	SET 7, H	DDCB05C6	SET 0, (IX + d)	FD29	ADD IY, IY
CBFD	SET 7, L	DDCB05CE	SET 1, (IX + d)	FD2A8405	LD IY, (NN)
CBFE	SET 7, (HL)	DDCB05D6	SET 2, (IX + d)	FD2B	DEC IY
CBFF	SET 7, A	DDCB05DE	SET 3, (IX + d)	FD3405	INC (IY + d)
DD09	ADD IX, BC	DDCB05E6	SET 4, (IX + d)	FD3505	DEC (IY + d)
DD19	ADD IX' DE	DDCB05EE	SET 5, (IX + d)	FD360520	LD (IY + d), N
DD218405	LD IX, NN	DDCB05F6	SET 6, (IX + d)	FD39	ADD IY, SP
DD228405	LD (NN), IX	DDCB05FE	SET 7, (IX + d)	FD4605	LD B, (IY + d)
DD23	INC IX	ED40	IN B, (C)	FD4E05	LD C, (IY + d)
DD29	ADD IX, IX	ED41	OUT (C), B	FD5605	LD D, (IY + d)
DD2A8405	LD IX, (NN)	ED42	SBC HL, BC	FD5E05	LD E, (IY + d)
DD2B	DEC IX	ED438405	LD (NN), BC	FD6605	LD H, (IY + d)
DD3405	INC (IX + d)	ED44	NEG	FD6E05	LD L, (IY + d)
DD3505	DEC (IX + d)	ED45	RETN	FD7005	LD (IY + d), B
DD360520	LD (IX + d), N	ED46	IM 0	FD7105	LD (IY + d), C
DD39	ADD IX, SP	ED47	LD I, A	FD7205	LD (IY + d), D
DD4605	LD B, (IX + d)	ED48	IN C, (C)	FD7305	LD (IY + d), E
DD4E05	LD C, (IX + d)	ED49	OUT (C), C	FD7405	LD (IY + d), H
DD5605	LD D, (IX + d)	ED4A	ADC HL, BC	FD7505	LD (IY + d), L
DD5E05	LD E, (IX + d)	ED4B8405	LD BC, (NN)	FD7705	LD (IY + d), A
DD6605	LD H, (IX + d)	ED4D	RETI	FD7E05	LD A, (IY + d)
DD6E05	LD L, (IX + d)	ED50	IN D, (C)	FD8605	ADD A, (IY + d)
DD7005	LD (IX + d), B	ED51	OUT (C), D	FD8E05	ADC A, (IY + d)
DD7105	LD (IX + d), C	ED52	SBC HL, DE	FD9605	SUB (IY + d)
DD7205	LD (IX + d), D	ED538405	LD (NN), DE	FD9E05	SBC A, (IY + d)
DD7305	LD (IX + d), E	ED56	IM 1	FDA605	AND (IY + d)
DD7405	LD (IX + d), H	ED57	LD A, I	FDAE05	XOR (IY + d)
DD7505	LD (IX + d), L	ED58	IN E, (C)	FDB605	OR (IY + d)
DD7705	LD (IX + d), A	ED59	OUT (C), E	FDBE05	CP (IY + d)
DD7E05	LD A, (IX + d)	ED5A	ADC HL, DE	FDE1	POP IY
DD8605	ADD A, (IX + d)	ED5B8405	LD DE, (NN)	FDE3	EX (SP), IY
DD8E05	ADC A, (IX + d)	ED5E	IM 2	FDE5	PUSH IY
DD9605	SUB (IX + d)	ED60	IN H, (C)	FDE9	JP (IY)
DD9E05	SBC A, (IX + d)	ED61	OUT (C), H	FDF9	LD SP, IY
DDA605	AND (IX + d)	ED62	SBC HL, HL	FDCB0506	RLC (IY + d)
DDAE05	XOR (IX + d)	ED67	RRD	FDCB050E	RRC (IY + d)
DDB605	OR (IX + d)	ED68	IN L, (C)	FDCB0516	RL (IY + d)
DDBE05	CP (IX + d)	ED69	OUT (C), L	FDCB051E	RR (IY + d)
DDE1	POP IX	ED6A	ADC HL, HL	FDCB0526	SLA (IY + d)
DDE3	EX (SP), IX	ED6F	RLD	FDCB052E	SRA (IY + d)
DDE5	PUSH IX	ED72	SBC HL, SP	FDCB053E	SRL (IY + d)
DDE9	JP (IX)	ED738405	LD (NN), SP	FDCB0546	BIT 0, (IY + d)
DDF9	LD SP, IX	ED78	IN A, (C)	FDCB054E	BIT 1, (IY + d)
DDCB0506	RLC (IX + d)	ED79	OUT (C), A	FDCB0556	BIT 2, (IY + d)
DDCB050E	RRC (IX + d)	ED7A	ADC HL, SP	FDCB055E	BIT 3, (IY + d)
DDCB0516	RL (IX + d)	ED7B8405	LD SP, (NN)	FDCB0566	BIT 4, (IY + d)
DDCB051E	RR (IX + d)	EDA0	LDI	FDCB056E	BIT 5, (IY + d)
DDCB0526	SLA (IX + d)	EDA1	CPI	FDCB0576	BIT 6, (IY + d)
DDCB052E	SRA (IX + d)	EDA2	INI	FDCB057E	BIT 7, (IY + d)
DDCB053E	SRL (IX + d)	EDA3	OUTI	FDCB0586	RES 0, (IY + d)
DDCB0546	BIT 0, (IX + d)	EDA8	LDD	FDCB058E	RES 1, (IY + d)
DDCB054E	BIT 1, (IX + d)	EDA9	CPD	FDCB0596	RES 2, (IY + d)
DDCB0556	BIT 2, (IX + d)	EDAA	IND	FDCB059E	RES 3, (IY + d)
DDCB055E	BIT 3, (IX + d)	EDAB	OUTD	FDCB05A6	RES 4, (IY + d)
DDCB0566	BIT 4, (IX + d)	EDB0	LDIR	FDCB05AE	RES 5, (IY + d)
DDCB056E	BIT 5, (IX + d)	EDB1	CPIR	FDCB05B6	RES 6, (IY + d)
DDCB0576	BIT 6, (IX + d)	EDB2	INIR	FDCB05BE	RES 7, (IY + d)
DDCB057E	BIT 7, (IX + d)	EDB3	OTIR	FDCB05C6	SET 0, (IY + d)
DDCB0586	RES 0, (IX + d)	EDB8	LDDR	FDCB05CE	SET 1, (IY + d)
DDCB058E	RES 1, (IX + d)	EDB9	CPDR	FDCB05D6	SET 2, (IY + d)
DDCB0596	RES 2, (IX + d)	EDBA	INDR	FDCB05DE	SET 3, (IY + d)
DDCB059E	RES 3, (IX + d)	EDBB	OTDR	FDCB05E6	SET 4, (IY + d)
DDCB05A6	RES 4, (IX + d)	FD09	ADD IY, BC	FDCB05EE	SET 5, (IY + d)
DDCB05AE	RES 5, (IX + d)	FD19	ADD IY, DE	FDCB05F6	SET 6, (IY + d)
DDCB05B6	RES 6, (IX + d)	FD218405	LD IY, NN	FDCB05FE	SET 7, (IY + d)
		FD228405	LD (NN), IY		

Courtesy Zilog, Inc.

APPENDIX **C**

Z-80 CPU Instructions
Sorted by Op Code

OBJ CODE	SOURCE STATEMENT	OBJ CODE	SOURCE STATEMENT	OBJ CODE	SOURCE STATEMENT
8E	ADC A, (HL)	FD09	ADD IY, BC	CB4D	BIT 1, L
DD8E05	ADC A, (IX + d)	FD19	ADD IY, DE	CB56	BIT 2, (HL)
FD8E05	ADC A, (IY + d)	FD29	ADD IY, IY	DDCB0556	BIT 2, (IX + d)
8F	ADC A, A	FD39	ADD IY, SP	FDCB0556	BIT 2, (IY + d)
88	ADC A, B	A6	AND (HL)	CB57	BIT 2, A
89	ADC A, C	DDA605	AND (IX + d)	CB50	BIT 2, B
8A	ADC A, D	FDA605	AND (IY + d)	CB51	BIT 2, C
8B	ADC A, E	A7	AND A	CB52	BIT 2, D
8C	ADC A, H	A0	AND B	CB53	BIT 2, E
8D	ADC A, L	A1	AND C	CB54	BIT 2, H
CE20	ADC A, N	A2	AND D	CB55	BIT 2, L
ED4A	ADC HL, BC	A3	AND E	CB5E	BIT 3, (HL)
ED5A	ADC HL, DE	A4	AND H	DDCB055E	BIT 3, (IX + d)
ED6A	ADC HL, HL	A5	AND L	FDCB055E	BIT 3, (IY + d)
ED7A	ADC HL, SP	E620	AND N	CB5F	BIT 3, A
86	ADD A, (HL)	CB46	BIT 0, (HL)	CB58	BIT 3, B
DD8605	ADD A, (IX + d)	DDCB0546	BIT 0, (IX + d)	CB59	BIT 3, C
FD8605	ADD A, (IY + d)	FDCB0546	BIT 0, (IY + d)	CB5A	BIT 3, D
87	ADD A, A	CB47	BIT 0, A	CB5B	BIT 3, E
80	ADD A, B	CB40	BIT 0, B	CB5C	BIT 3, H
81	ADD A, C	CB41	BIT 0, C	CB5D	BIT 3, L
82	ADD A, D	CB42	BIT 0, D	CB66	BIT 4, (HL)
83	ADD A, E	CB43	BIT 0, E	DDCB0566	BIT 4, (IX + d)
84	ADD A, H	CB44	BIT 0, H	FDCB0566	BIT 4, (IY + d)
85	ADD A, L	CB45	BIT 0, L	CB67	BIT 4, A
C620	ADD A, N	CB4E	BIT 1, (HL)	CB60	BIT 4, B
09	ADD HL, BC	DDCB054E	BIT 1, (IX + d)	CB61	BIT 4, C
19	ADD HL, DE	FDCB054E	BIT 1, (IY + d)	CB62	BIT 4, D
29	ADD HL, HL	CB4F	BIT 1, A	CB63	BIT 4, E
39	ADD HL, SP	BC48	BIT 1, B	CB64	BIT 4, H
DD09	ADD IX, BC	CB49	BIT 1, C	CB65	BIT 4, L
DD19	ADD IX, DE	CB4A	BIT 1, D	CB6E	BIT 5, (HL)
DD29	ADD IX, IX	CB4B	BIT 1, E	DDCB056E	BIT 5, (IX + d)
DD39	ADD IX, SP	CB4C	BIT 1, H	FDCB056E	BIT 5, (IY + d)

Courtesy Zilog, Inc.

OBJ CODE	SOURCE STATEMENT	OBJ CODE	SOURCE STATEMENT	OBJ CODE	SOURCE STATEMENT
CB6F	BIT 5, A	DD2B	DEC IX	71	LD (HL), C
CB68	BIT 5, B	FD2B	DEC IY	72	LD (HL), D
CB69	BIT 5, C	2D	DEC L	73	LD (HL), E
CB6A	BIT 5, D	3B	DEC SP	74	LD (HL), H
CB6B	BIT 5, E	F3	DI	75	LD (HL), L
CB6C	BIT 5, H	102E	DJNZ DIS	3620	LD (HL), N
CB6D	BIT 5, L	FB	EI	DD7705	LD (IX + d), A
CB76	BIT 6, (HL)	E3	EX (SP), HL	DD7005	LD (IX + d), B
DDCB0576	BIT 6, (IX + d)	DDE3	EX (SP), IX	DD7105	LD (IX + d), C
FDCB0576	BIT 6, (IY + d)	FDE3	EX (SP), IY	DD7205	LD (IX + d), D
CB77	BIT 6, A	08	EX AF, AF'	DD7305	LD (IX + d), E
CB70	BIT 6, B	EB	EX DE, HL	DD7405	LD (IX + d), H
CB71	BIT 6, C	D9	EXX	DD7505	LD (IX + d), L
CB72	BIT 6, D	76	HALT	DD360520	LD (IX + d), N
CB73	BIT 6, E	ED46	IM 0	FD7705	LD (IY + d), A
CB74	BIT 6, H	ED56	IM 1	FD7005	LD (IY + d), B
CB75	BIT 6, L	ED5E	IM 2	FD7105	LD (IY + d), C
CB7E	BIT 7, (HL)	ED78	IN A, (C)	FD7205	LD (IY + d), D
DDCB057E	BIT 7, (IX + d)	DB20	IN A, (N)	FD7305	LD (IY + d), E
FDCB057E	BIT 7, (IY + d)	ED40	IN B, (C)	FD7405	LD (IY + d), H
CB7F	BIT 7, A	ED48	IN C, (C)	FD7505	LD (IY + d), L
CB78	BIT 7, B	ED50	IN D, (C)	FD360520	LD (IY + d), N
CB79	BIT 7, C	ED58	IN E, (C)	328405	LD (NN), A
CB7A	BIT 7, D	ED60	IN H, (C)	ED438405	LD (NN), BC
CB7B	BIT 7, E	ED68	IN L, (C)	ED538405	LD (NN), DE
CB7C	BIT 7, H	34	INC (HL)	228405	LD (NN), HL
CB7D	BIT 7, L	DD3405	INC (IX + d)	DD228405	LD (NN), IX
DC8405	CALL C, NN	FD3405	INC (IY + d)	FD228405	LD (NN), IY
FC8405	CALL M, NN	3C	INC A	ED738405	LD (NN), SP
D48405	CALL NC, NN	04	INC B	0A	LD A, (BC)
CD8405	CALL NN	03	INC BC	1A	LD A, (DE)
C48405	CALL NZ, NN	0C	INC C	7E	LD A, (HL)
F48405	CALL P, NN	14	INC D	DD7E05	LD A, (IX + d)
EC8405	CALL PE, NN	13	INC DE	FD7E05	LD A, (IY + d)
E48405	CALL PO, NN	1C	INC E	3A8405	LD A, (NN)
CC8405	CALL Z, NN	24	INC H	7F	LD A, A
3F	CCF	23	INC HL	78	LD A, B
BE	CP (HL)	DD23	INC IX	79	LD A, C
DDBE05	CP (IX + d)	FD23	INC IY	7A	LD A, D
FDBE05	CP (IY + d)	2C	INC L	7B	LD A, E
BF	CP A	33	INC SP	7C	LD A, H
B8	CP B	EDAA	IND	ED57	LD A, I
B9	CP C	EDBA	INDR	7D	LD A, L
BA	CP D	EDA2	INI	3E20	LD A, N
BB	CP E	EDB2	INIR	46	LD B, (HL)
BC	CP H	E9	JP (HL)	DD4605	LD B, (IX + d)
BD	CP L	DDE9	JP (IX)	FD4605	LD B, (IY + d)
FE20	CP N	FDE9	JP (IY)	47	LD B, A
EDA9	CPD	DA8405	JP C, NN	40	LD B, B
EDB9	CPDR	FA8405	JP M, NN	41	LD B, C
EDA1	CPI	D28405	JP NC, NN	42	LD B, D
EDB1	CPIR	C38405	JP NN	43	LD B, E
2F	CPL	C28405	JP NZ, NN	44	LD B, H, NN
27	DAA	F28405	JP P, NN	45	LD B, L
35	DEC (HL)	EA8405	JP PE, NN	0620	LD B, N
DD3505	DEC (IX + d)	E28405	JP PO, NN	ED4B8405	LD BC, (NN)
FD3505	DEC (IY + d)	CA8405	JP Z, NN	018405	LD BC, NN
3D	DEC A	382E	JR C, DIS	4E	LD C, (HL)
05	DEC B	182E	JR DIS	DD4E05	LD C, (IX + d)
0B	DEC BC	302E	JR NC, DIS	FD4E05	LD C, (IY + d)
0D	DEC C	202E	JR NZ, DIS	4F	LD C, A
15	DEC D	282E	JR Z, DIS	48	LD C, B
1B	DEC DE	02	LD (BC), A	49	LD C, C
1D	DEC E	12	LD (DE), A	4A	LD C, D
25	DEC H	77	LD (HL), A	4B	LD C, E
2B	DEC HL	70	LD (HL), B	4C	LD C, H

Courtesy Zilog, Inc.

OBJ CODE	SOURCE STATEMENT	OBJ CODE	SOURCE STATEMENT	OBJ CODE	SOURCE STATEMENT
4D	LD C, L	DDB605	OR (IX + d)	CB9F	RES 3, A
0E20	LD C, N	FDB605	OR (IY + d)	CB98	RES 3, B
56	LD D, (HL)	B7	OR A	CB99	RES 3, C
DD5605	LD D, (IX + d)	B0	OR B	CB9A	RES 3, D
FD5605	LD D, (IY + d)	B1	OR C	CB9B	RES 3, E
57	LD D, A	B2	OR D	CB9C	RES 3, H
50	LD D, B	B3	OR E	CB9D	RES 3, L
51	LD D, C	B4	OR H	CBA6	RES 4, (HL)
52	LD D, D	B5	OR L	DDCB05A6	RES 4, (IX + d)
53	LD D, E	F620	OR N	FDCB05A6	RES 4, (IY + d)
54	LD D, H	EDBB	OTDR	CBA7	RES 4, A
55	LD D, L	EDB3	OTIR	CBA0	RES 4, B
1620	LD D, N	ED79	OUT (C), A	CBA1	RES 4, C
ED5B8405	LD DE, (NN)	ED41	OUT (C), B	CBA2	RES 4, D
118405	LD DE, NN	ED49	OUT (C), C	CBA3	RES 4, E
5E	LD E, (HL)	ED51	OUT (C), D	CBA4	RES 4, H
DD5E05	LD E, (IX + d)	ED59	OUT (C), E	CBA5	RES 4, L
FD5E05	LD E, (IY + d)	ED61	OUT (C), H	CBAE	RES 5, (HL)
5F	LD E, A	ED69	OUT (C), L	DDCB05AE	RES 5, (IX + d)
58	LD E, B	D320	OUT (N), A	FDCB05AE	RES 5, (IY + d)
59	LD E, C	EDAB	OUTD	CBAF	RES 5, A
5A	LD E, D	EDA3	OUTI	CBA8	RES 5, B
5B	LD E, E	F1	POP AF	CBA9	RES 5, C
5C	LD E, H	C1	POP BC	CBAA	RES 5, D
5D	LD E, L	D1	POP DE	CBAB	RES 5, E
1E20	LD E, N	E1	POP HL	CBAC	RES 5, H
66	LD H, (HL)	DDE1	POP IX	CBAD	RES 5, L
DD6605	LD H, (IX + d)	FDE1	POP IY	CBB6	RES 6, (HL)
FD6606	LD H, (IY + d)	F5	PUSH AF	DDCB05B6	RES 6, (IX + d)
67	LD H, A	C5	PUSH BC	FDCB05B6	RES 6, (IY + d)
60	LD H, B	D5	PUSH DE	CBB7	RES 6, A
61	LD H, C	E5	PUSH HL	CBB0	RES 6, B
62	LD H, D	DDE5	PUSH IX	CBB1	RES 6, C
63	LD H, E	FDE5	PUSH IY	CBB2	RES 6, D
64	LD H, H	CB86	RES 0, (HL)	CBB3	RES 6, E
65	LD H, L	DDCB0586	RES 0, (IX + d)	CBB4	RES 6, H
2620	LD H, N	FDCB0586	RES 0, (IY + d)	CBB5	RES 6, L
2A8405	LD HL, (NN)	CB87	RES 0, A	CBBE	RES 7, (HL)
218405	LD HL, NN	CB80	RES 0, B	DDCB05BE	RES 7, (IX + d)
ED47	LD I, A	CB81	RES 0, C	FDCB05BE	RES 7, (IY + d)
DD2A8405	LD IX, (NN)	CB82	RES 0, D	CBBF	RES 7, A
DD218405	LD IX, NN	CB83	RES 0, E	CBB8	RES 7, B
FD2A8405	LD IY, (NN)	CB84	RES 0, H	CBB9	RES 7, C
FD218405	LD IY, NN	CB85	RES 0, L	CBBA	RES 7, D
6E	LD L, (HL)	CB8E	RES 1, (HL)	CBBB	RES 7, E
DD6E05	LD L, (IX + d)	DDCB058E	RES 1, (IX + d)	CBBC	RES 7, H
FD6E05	LD L, (IY + d)	FDCB058E	RES 1, (IY + d)	CBBD	RES 7, L
6F	LD L, A	CB8F	RES 1, A	C9	RET
68	LD L, B	CB88	RES 1, B	D8	RET C
69	LD L, C	CB89	RES 1, C	F8	RET M
6A	LD L, D	CB8A	RES 1, D	D0	RET NC
6B	LD L, E	CB8B	RES 1, E	C0	RET NZ
6C	LD L, H	CB8C	RES 1, H	F0	RET P
6D	LD L, L	CB8D	RES 1, L	E8	RET PE
2E20	LD L, N	CB96	RES 2 (HL)	E0	RET PO
ED7B8405	LD SP, (NN)	DDCB0596	RES 2, (IX + d)	C8	RET Z
F9	LD SP, HL	FDCB0596	RES 2, (IY + d)	ED4D	RETI
DDF9	LD SP, IX	CB97	RES 2, A	ED45	RETN
FDF9	LD SP, IY	CB90	RES 2, B	CB16	RL (HL)
318405	LD SP, NN	CB91	RES 2, C	DDCB0516	RL (IX + d)
EDA8	LDD	CB92	RES 2, D	FDCB0516	RL (IY + d)
EDB8	LDDR	CB93	RES 2, E	CB17	RL A
EDA0	LDI	CB94	RES 2, H	CB10	RL B
EDB0	LDIR	CB95	RES 2, L	CB11	RL C
ED44	NEG	CB9E	RES 3, (HL)	CB12	RL D
00	NOP	DDCB059E	RES 3, (IX + d)	CB13	RL E
B6	OR (HL)	FDCB059E	RES 3, (IY + d)		

Courtesy Zilog, Inc.

OBJ CODE	SOURCE STATEMENT	OBJ CODE	SOURCE STATEMENT	OBJ CODE	SOURCE STATEMENT
CB14	RL H	CBC0	SET 0, B	CBFE	SET 7, (HL)
CB15	RL L	CBC1	SET 0, C	DDCB05FE	SET 7, (IX + d)
17	RLA	CBC2	SET 0, D	FDCB05FE	SET 7, (IY + d)
CB06	RLC (HL)	CBC3	SET 0, E	CBFF	SET 7, A
DDCB0506	RLC (IX + d)	CBC4	SET 0, H	CBF8	SET 7, B
FDCB0506	RLC (IY + d)	CBC5	SET 0, L	CBF9	SET 7, C
CB07	RLC A	CBCE	SET 1, (HL)	CBFA	SET 7, D
CB00	RLC B	DDCB05CE	SET 1, (IX + d)	CBFB	SET 7, E
CB01	RLC C	FDCB05CE	SET 1, (IY + d)	CBFC	SET 7, H
CB02	RLC D	CBCF	SET 1, A	CBFD	SET 7, L
CB03	RLC E	CBC8	SET 1, B	CB26	SLA (HL)
CB04	RLC H	CBC9	SET 1, C	DDCB0526	SLA (IX + d)
CB05	RLC L	CBCA	SET 1, D	FDCB0526	SLA (IY + d)
07	RLCA	CBCB	SET 1, E	CB27	SLA A
ED6F	RLD	CBCC	SET 1, H	CB20	SLA B
CB1E	RR (HL)	CBCD	SET 1, L	CB21	SLA C
DDCB051E	RR (IX + d)	CBD6	SET 2, (HL)	CB22	SLA D
FDCB051E	RR (IY + d)	DDCB05D6	SET 2, (IX + d)	CB23	SLA E
CB1F	RR A	FDCB05D6	SET 2, (IY + d)	CB24	SLA H
CB18	RR B	CBD7	SET 2, A	CB25	SLA L
CB19	RR C	CBD0	SET 2, B	CB2E	SRA (HL)
CB1A	RR D	CBD1	SET 2, C	DDCB052E	SRA (IX + d)
CB1B	RR E	CBD2	SET 2, D	FDCB052E	SRA (IY + d)
CB1C	RR H	CBD3	SET 2, E	CB2F	SRA A
CB1D	RR L	CBD4	SET 2, H	CB28	SRA B
1F	RRA	CBD5	SET 2, L	CB29	SRA C
CB0E	RRC (HL)	CBD8	SET 3, B	CB2A	SRA D
DDCB050E	RRC (IX + d)	CBDE	SET 3, (HL)	CB2B	SRA E
FDCB050E	RRC (IY + d)	DDCB05DE	SET 3, (IX + d)	CB2C	SRA H
CB0F	RRC A	FDCB05DE	SET 3, (IY + d)	CB2D	SRA L
CB08	RRC B	CBDF	SET 3, A	CB3E	SRL (HL)
CB09	RRC C	CBD9	SET 3, C	DDCB053E	SRL (IX + d)
CB0A	RRC D	CBDA	SET 3, D	FDCB053E	SRL (IY + d)
CB0B	RRC E	CBDB	SET 3, E	CB3F	SRL A
CB0C	RRC H	CBDC	SET 3, H	CB38	SRL B
CB0D	RRC L	CBDD	SET 3, L	CB39	SRL C
0F	RRCA	CBE6	SET 4, (HL)	CB3A	SRL D
ED67	RRD	DDCB05E6	SET 4, (IX + d)	CB3B	SRL E
C7	RST 0	FDCB05E6	SET 4, (IY + d)	CB3C	SRL H
D7	RST 10H	CBE7	SET 4, A	CB3D	SRL L
DF	RST 18H	CBE0	SET 4, B	96	SUB (HL)
E7	RST 20H	CBE1	SET 4, C	DD9605	SUB (IX + d)
EF	RST 28H	CBE2	SET 4, D	FD9605	SUB (IY + d)
F7	RST 30H	CBE3	SET 4, E	97	SUB A
FF	RST 38H	CBE4	SET 4, H	90	SUB B
CF	RST 8	CBE5	SET 4, L	91	SUB C
9E	SBC A, (HL)	CBEE	SET 5, (HL)	92	SUB D
DD9E05	SBC A, (IX + d)	DDCB05EE	SET 5, (IX + d)	93	SUB E
FD9E05	SBC A, (IY + d)	FDCB05EE	SET 5, (IY + d)	94	SUB H
9F	SBC A, A	CBEF	SET 5, A	95	SUB L
98	SBC A, B	CBE8	SET 5, B	D620	SUB N
99	SBC A, C	CBE9	SET 5, C	AE	XOR (HL)
9A	SBC A, D	CBEA	SET 5, D	DDAE05	XOR (IX + d)
9B	SBC A, E	CBEB	SET 5, E	FDAE05	XOR (IY + d)
9C	SBC A, H	CBEC	SET 5, H	AF	XOR A
9D	SBC A, L	CBED	SET 5, L	A8	XOR B
DE20	SBC A, N	CBF6	SET 6, (HL)	A9	XOR C
ED42	SBC HL, BC	DDCB05F6	SET 6, (IX + d)	AA	XOR D
ED52	SBC HL, DE	FDCB05F6	SET 6, (IY + d)	AB	XOR E
ED62	SBC HL, HL	CBF7	SET 6, A	AC	XOR H
ED72	SBC HL, SP	CBF0	SET 6, B	AD	XOR L
37	SCF	CBF1	SET 6, C	EE20	XOR N
CBC6	SET 0, (HL)	CBF2	SET 6, D		
DDCB05C5	SET 0, (IX + d)	CBF3	SET 6, E		
FDCB05C6	SET 0, (IY + d)	CBF4	SET 6, H		
CBC7	SET 0, A	CBF5	SET 6, L		

Courtesy Zilog, Inc.

Computation of Execution Times

The following information addresses the question of how to compute execution times for sequences of Z-80 instructions. Execution time is usually an important attribute of a program which must be considered when selecting alternative methods of implementation.

Consider the following sequence of instructions:

```
LD    A, 36H
LD    B, 49H
OR    B
AND   99H
RL    A
```

How much time will it take your Nanocomputer to execute these instructions? To determine the answer to this question you must know the clock rate of the external clock of the Nanocomputer. It is 2.5 MHz or 2.5 Megahertz or 2,500,000 cycles per second. That is, each cycle lasts for

$$\frac{1}{2.5 \times 10^6} \text{ second } = .0000004 \text{ second}$$

Since 1 sec. $= 10^3$ milliseconds (msec) $= 10^6$ microseconds (μsec) $= 10^9$ nanoseconds (nsec), the cycle time of your Nanocomputer is 0.0004 msec or 0.4 μsec or 400 nsec. Specially selected Z-80 CPU chips can run at 4 MHz, or a cycle time of 250 nsec. The tables in Appendix A give the number of T-states, or external clock cycles, required to execute each Z-80 instruction. Thus, using these tables, we may make the following computation.

Instruction	No. T-states	No. Times Executed	Total Execution Time (μsec)
LD A,36H	7	1	7 T-states = 2.8
LD B,49H	7	1	2.8
OR B	4	1	1.6
AND 99H	7	1	2.8
RL A	4	1	1.6

Thus, the execution time for the instruction sequence is 11.6 μsec.

For the above example, the number of times each instruction is executed is uniformly 1. Let us look at a delay loop for our next example.

```
        LD    A,06H
        LD    B,08H
LOOP:   INC   A
        DEC   B
        JP    NZ,LOOP
```

The timing computation for this instruction sequence is as follows:

Instruction	No. T-states	No. Times Executed	Total Execution Time (μsec)
LD A,06H	7	1	2.8
LD B,08H	7	1	2.8
INC A	4	9	14.4
DEC B	4	9	14.4
JP NZ,LOOP	12 (condition met)	1	4.8
	7 (condition not met)	8	22.4
			Total: 61.6 μsec

If the above delay loop were set up as a subroutine, the delay caused by the routine would also include the time required to execute both the initial CALL statement and the final RET statement:

CALL	17	1	6.8
RET	10	1	4.0
			New Total: 72.4 μsec

Let us now look at one final example which utilizes the LDIR instruction:

```
        LD    HL,0100H
        LD    DE,0200H
        LD    BC,0010H
        LDIR
```

Instruction	No. T-states	No. Times Executed	Execution Time (μsec)
LD HL,0100H	10	1	4.0
LD DE,0200H	10	1	4.0
LD BC,0010H	10	1	4.0
LDIR	21 (If BC $\neq$ 0)	15	126.0
	16 (If BC = 0)	1	6.4

Total: 144.4 μsec

Precautions While Handling MOS Devices

MOS devices are extremely sensitive and can be damaged by:

- Static electricity and
- Incorrect insertion into socket on the Nanocomputer board.

The following precautions should be observed when handling MOS devices:

1. Ensure that you are statically discharged immediately before touching the device. This can be accomplished by rubbing your hands on conductive material.
2. Avoid touching the pins.
3. Avoid pin contact with any material likely to hold a static charge, e.g., a nylon carpet.
4. If it is necessary to transport an MOS device outside of its normal operating environment, the device should be mounted on conductive foam to effectively prevent the pins from being subjected to different static potentials.
5. Ensure replacement parts are mounted properly, e.g., pin 1 oriented correctly.

Master Symbol Table

Label	Address
BAUDRT	0FAE
CONTST	FB43
INMODE	0FAB
METUT	FADC

References

1. *The Compact Edition of the Oxford English Dictionary,* Oxford Univ. Press, 1971.

2. Rudolf F. Graf, *Modern Dictionary of Electronics,* Howard W. Sams & Co., Inc., Indianapolis, Indiana, 1977.

3. James Martin, *Telecommunications and the Computer,* Prentice-Hall, Inc., Englewood Cliffs, New Jersey, 1969.

4. Abraham Marcus and John D. Lenk, *Computers for Technicians,* Prentice-Hall, Inc., Englewood Cliffs, New Jersey, 1973.

5. Microdata Corporation, *Microprogramming Handbook,* Santa Ana, California, 1971.

6. J. Blukis and M. Baker, *Practical Digital Electronics,* Hewlett-Packard Company, Santa Clara, California, 1974.

7. Donald E. Lancaster, *TTL Cookbook,* Howard W. Sams & Co., Inc., Indianapolis, Indiana, 1974.

8. H. V. Malmstadt, C. G. Enke, and S. R. Crouch, *Instrumentation for Scientists Series, Module 3. Digital and Analog Data Conversions,* W. A. Benjamin, Inc., Menlo Park, California, 1973-4.

9. H. V. Malmstadt and C. G. Enke, *Digital Electronics for Scientists,* W. A. Benjamin, Inc., New York, 1969.

10. J. D. Lenk, *Handbook of Logic Circuits,* Reston Publishing Company, Inc., Reston, Virginia, 1972.

11. A. James Diefenderfer, *Principles of Electronic Instrumentation,* W. B. Saunders Company, Philadelphia, Pennsylvania, 1972.

12. P. R. Rony and D. G. Larsen, *Logic & Memory Experiments Using TTL Integrated Circuits, Book 2*, Howard W. Sams & Co., Inc., Indianapolis, Indiana, 1979.

13. Robert L. Morris and John R. Miller, Editors, *Designing with TTL Integrated Circuits*, McGraw-Hill Book Company, New York, 1971.

14. Charles J. Sippl, *Microcomputer Dictionary and Guide*, Matrix Publishers, Inc., Champaign, Illinois, 1976.

15. Donald Eadie, *Introduction to the Basic Computer*, Prentice-Hall, Inc., Englewood Cliffs, New Jersey, 1973.

16. Texas Instruments Incorporated, *Microprocessor Handbook*, Dallas, Texas, 1975.

For information about the Nano-computer, contact:

SGS-Ates Corporation
240 Bear Hill Road
Waltham, MA 02154

SGS-Ates Corporation
13784 Via Alto Court
Saratoga, CA 95070

SGS-Ates Corporation
2340 Des Plaines Ave.
Suite 309
Des Plaines, IL 60018

Index

A

Absolute jump, 178-180
Accumulator, 40, 207
Add, 243
  -with-carry, 243, 247
Address
  byte
    hi, 29
    lo, 29
  display, 30
  memory, 28
Addressing mode, 99, 111-112, 139-173
ALGOL, 84
Alternate Register Set (ARS), 39
  key, 53
Analog computer, 22
AND, 205, 209, 212-213
Arithmetic instructions, 243-265
ASCII code, 11
Assembly
  code, 79
  language, 82
    programming, 84-85
    pseudo-up code, 202

B

Base, 12
BASIC, 84
Baudot code, 12
Baud rate generator, 49
BAUDRT, 58-59

Binary
  code, 9, 12-14, 79-81
  coded decimal (BCD) code, 12, 182
  coding, 11
  information, 22-23
Bit, 9, 11
  addressing, 149-150
  manipulation, 223-241
    instructions, 225
  process, 224
  set, reset, and test group, 275
"bit bucket," 187
Bits per second, 10
Block
  transfer instructions, 99, 140, 158-160, 270
    LDD, 118
    LDDR, 118
    LDI, 117
    LDIR, 117-118
  search instructions, 243-245
    group, 245
Boolean
  algebra, 207
  statements, 208
  symbols, 207-208
Branch instruction, 44
Breadboard description, 61-62
BREAK ("panic button") key, 59-60
Breakpoint (BRK) key, 55-56
Buffers, three-state, 65
Bus drivers, 49
Byte, 21
  data, 26-27

C

Call group, 277
Calls, 175, 183-188
Carry flag, 175, 180
Case analysis, 202-203
CASS switch, 56-57
CB instructions, 110
Central Processing Unit (CPU), 60-62
C flag, 252
Character, 23
Chip
  integrated-circuit, 22-23
  microprocessor, 22
Clock, 49, 60
COBOL, 84
Code(s)
  ASCII, 11
  assembly, 79
  Baudot, 12
  binary, 9, 79-81
    coded decimal (bcd), 12
  digital, 9-21
  EBCDIC, 12
  gray, 12
  hexadecimal, 9, 79-81
  instruction, 12
    two-digit, 9
  mnemonic, 80, 81-83
  object, 82-83
  relocatable, 152
  source, 82-83
Coding
  binary, 11
  off-on, 11
  two-state, 11
Communication, 9-11
Compare-decrement (CPD), 253
  -repeat (CPDR), 253
Compare-increment (CPI), 252
  -repeat (CPIR), 253
Compiler, 84
Computation of execution times,
        287-289
Computer
  analog, 22
  digital, 21-22
  fluidic, 22
  mechanical, 22
  program, 23, 33-34

Conditional
  branch instruction, 117
  jumps, 180, 182-183
  relative jump instructions (DJNZ),
        183
Counting systems
  binary, 9, 12
  decimal, 9
  hexadecimal, 9, 14-17
CP instruction, 244
CPL instruction, 205, 212
CP s instructions, 252-253
CPU instructions, 33-45, 279-286
Criterion
  efficiency, 193-194
  functional, 193

D

DAA instruction, 249-251
Data "D", 26
  byte, 26, 36, 38
  transfer, 99-137
DD instructions, 111
Decimal adjust accumulator (DAA),
        182, 243
  instruction, 249-251
Decoding, 101
Decrement register, 99, 116-117
DeMorgan's theorem, 205, 210-211
Device
  code, 36, 38
  select pulse, 38
Digital
  code(s), 9-21
  computer, 21-23
Displacement byte, 36, 38-39
Divide, 243
Don't care, X, 187
DP operations, 57
Dual-in-line package (DIP) chip, 60
Dump (DP) key, 56

E

EBCDIC code, 12
ED instructions, 111
Efficiency criterion, 193-194

8-bit
  arithmetic and logic groups, 206,
    244-249, 271
  binary number, 14
  load(s), 139
    group, 268
EPROM memory, 49
Even parity, 181
Exchange
  group, 270
  instructions, 139
Execution times, 267-278
  computation of, 287-289
Extended addressing, 99, 115-116, 148
External device monitoring, 214-215

F

FAST FORWARD (>>) key, 58
FD instructions, 111
Flag, 39
  C, 252
  carry, 175, 180
    half-, 182
  parity/overflow, 175, 181
  register, 146
  sign, 175, 181
  subtract, 182
  zero, 175, 181
Flexibility, 169
Fluidic computer, 22
FORTRAN, 84
Four-byte instructions, 36
Functional criterion, 193

G

General-purpose
  AF operations, 206, 244
  arithmetic and CPU control group,
    272
  register, 33, 39-40
Go key, 53-54
Gray code, 12

H

Half
  bytes, 235
  -carry (H) flag, 182

Halt: HALT, 42
Hexadecimal code, 9, 14-17, 79, 81
  two-digit, 9
H flag, 243, 246
HI
  byte, 186
  memory addresses, 29
High level language, 79, 83-84

I

Immediate addressing, 99, 113, 147
  mode, 34
Immediate extended addressing,
    99, 115, 147
Implied addressing, 149
Increment
  accumulator: INC A, 43
  (INC) key, 54
  register, 99, 116
Index register, 38, 39
  IX, 111
  IY, 111
Indexed addressing, 38, 150-151
Initialize, 117
Input group, 278
Instruction, 23-24
  code, 12
  cycle, 177
  decoding, 99
  group tables, 152-154
Instructions, 33, 34-35
  arithmetic, 243-265
  block search, 243-265
  CB, 110
  DD, 111
  ED, 111
  FD, 111
  logical, 205-222
  multibyte, 35-36
  single byte, 35-36
  unconditional jump, 177-180
  Z-80 microprocessor CPU, 33-45
Integrated-circuit chip, 22-23
Interfacing, 21
INTERPRETER, 84
Interrupt page address, 39
I/O ports, 61

J

JOVIAL, 84
JP instruction, 41
JR instruction, 179
Jump
  group, 276
  if not zero, 117
  table, 203
Jumps, 175-183
  absolute, 178-180
  conditional, 180, 182-183
  relative, 178-180

K

"K," 28
Keyboard, 48-49
"Key byte," 252

L

Language(s), 9-11
  high level, 79, 83-84
Last in, first out (LIFO), 156
LD
  instruction, 41
  operation, 58-59
LEFT ARROW key, 51
Libraries, 183-184
LO
  byte, 186
  Memory address, 29
Load
  Address (LA) key, 52-53
  accumulator direct: LD (addr), A, 43
  immediate to accumulator: LD A, data, 43
  (LD) key, 56
Load-decrement (LDD), 118
  -repeat (LDDR), 118
Load-increment (LDI), 117
  -repeat, (LDIR), 117-118
Logic
  1 state, 12
  symbols, 211
  0 state, 12

Logical
  instructions, 205-222
    Z-80 group, 211
  symplicity, 169
Loops, 44
  time delay, 99
LSB (least significant bit), 26

M

Machine language, 21, 24-25
Masking, 205, 213
Master symbol table, 293
Mechanical computer, 22
Memory, 22, 27-28, 60, 99-137
  address, 28
    hi, 29
    lo, 29
  locations, range of, 28-29
  read-only, 22, 27-28
  read/write, 22, 27-28
  refresh, 39
Microcomputer, 21
  programming, 21-32
Microprocessor
  chip, 22
Minicomputer, 27
Mnemonic
  code, 24, 80, 81-83
  language, 21, 24
  operation, 24
Modified page zero addressing, 148-149
MOS devices, precautions, 291
MSB (most significant bit), 26
Multibit operations, 209
Multibyte instructions, 35-36
Multiple precision addition, 248
Multiply, 243

N

NAND gate, 211
Nanocomputer NBZ80, 47-77
  p-c board layout, 50
N flag, 243, 246
Nibbles, 235
No-operation: NOP, 42

NOT, 205, 210
Notation, 16
NUM-byte, 257-261

O

Object code, 82
Odd parity, 181
Off-on coding, 11
One-byte operation codes, 102-103
One-time-cost technique, 200
Op codes, 267-278
Operation, 33, 34-36
  code(s), 36, 37
    one-byte, 102-103
    three-byte, 108
    two-byte, 104-107, 109
OR, 205, 210, 214
O through F keys, 50
Output group, 278
Overflow, 146

P

"Panic button" BREAK key, 59-60
Parallel I/O ports, 49
Parentheses, 41
Parity, 181
  even, 181
  odd, 181
  /overflow flag, 175, 181
PASCAL, 84
Pheromones, 10
Pin configurations for IC chips, 63
PL/1, 84
POP, 139, 156
Portability, 84
Power requirements, 50
Precautions (MOS), 291
Program
  control transfer, 175-177
  counter (PC) register, 39, 175
Programming
  language(s), 21, 80
  microcomputer, 21-32
Protocol, 224
Pseudo-ops, 202
PUSH, 139, 156
  and POP the stack, 155

P/V flag, 246

Q

Q, logic variable, 209

R

Radix, 12
RAM memory, 49
Range of memory locations, 28-29
Read-only memory, 22, 27-28
Read/write memory, 22, 27-28
Register, 33, 39-40
  addressing, 99, 112-113, 146-147
  general-purpose, 33
  special-purpose, 33
Register indirect addressing, 99, 114-
    115, 147-148
Registers, 99-137
Relative
  addressing, 151-152
  jump, 178-180
Relocatable code, 152
Relocating, 152
Reset, 223
  key, 60
  process, 224
Restart
  instruction, 148-149
    (RST N), 188
  group, 188
Return group, 277
Returns, 175, 183-188
REWIND (<<) key, 58
RIGHT ARROW key, 51
RL (rotate left), 230
RLD instructions, 223, 228
ROM memory, 49
Rotate
  digit
    left (RLD), 234-235
    right (RRD), 235-236
  group, 274
  instructions, 223, 227
  left circular (RLC), 229
  right circular (RRC), 229
RR (rotate right), 230
RRD instructions, 223, 228

S

Schottky TTL chips, 63
Search group, 270
2ND key, 53
"Self-documenting," 192
Self-modifying, 169
Serial I/O ports, 49
Set, 223
  process, 224
Seven-segment display numbering
      scheme, 77
Shift
  group, 274
  instructions, 223, 227, 232
  left arithmetic (SLA), 232-233
  right arithmetic (SRA), 233-234
Sign flag, 175, 181, 246
Single
  byte instructions, 35-36
  Step (SS), 53-54
16-bit
  arithmetic
    group, 273
    instructions, 251-252
  load group, 155, 269
  loads, 139
"Slow motion," 53
SNOBOL, 84
Solderless breadboard, 61-62
Source code, 82-83
Space, 169
Special-purpose register, 33
Stack, 139, 155-156
  pointer (SP), 39, 155, 175
STORE (ST) key, 51-52
Subtract (N) flag, 182, 243
Subtract-with-carry, 243, 247
Super Nanocomputer NBZ80S, 47-77
"Swaps," 159-160
Symbols, 23

T

Test process, 224
"the address specified by," 41
Three-byte
  instructions, 36
  operation codes, 108
Three-state buffers, 65

Time, 169
  delay loops, 99
Transfer of program control, 175-177
TTY/CASS switch, 56-57, 60
Two-byte
  instructions, 36
  operation codes, 104-107, 109
Two-digit hexadecimal code, 9
Two's complement, 139-146
  number, 38-39
Two-state coding, 11

U

"Upward compatibility," 35
Unconditional jump: JP addr, 44
  instructions, 177-180

V

Value byte, 203

W

Word, 27
  of caution, 64-65

X

X, don't care, 187
XNUM, 257-261
XOR, 205, 210, 213-214

Y

YNUM, 257-261

Z

Z-80
  CPU, 48-49
  instruction set, 100-110
  microcomputer programs, 79-96
  microprocessor CPU instructions,
      33-45
Zero (Z) flag, 117, 175, 181, 246
ZNUM, 257-261